D1477133

THERMAL ANALYSIS
OF MINERALS

Dumitru N. Todor

UNIVERSITY OF NOTTINGHAM
WITHDRAWN
FROM THE LIBRARY

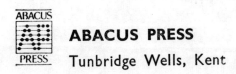
ABACUS PRESS
Tunbridge Wells, Kent

THERMAL ANALYSIS OF MINERALS

© ABACUS PRESS 1976
Abacus House, Speldhurst Road, Tunbridge Wells, Kent, England
ISBN 0 85626 101 7

Authorized translation from the Romanian language edition of ANALIZA TERMICĂ A MINERALELOR first published by Editura tehnică, Bucharest, 1972. Revised English edition first published in 1976 by Abacus Press

Translated by SERGIU MARCUS
Translation editor JOHN HAMMEL Ph.D.

No part of this publications may be reproduced,
stored in a retrieval system, or transmitted,
in any form or by any means, electronic, mechanical,
photocopying, recording, or otherwise, without the
prior permission of Abacus Press

Printed in Romania

UNIVERSITY OF NOTTINGHAM
61 0043864 3
TELEPEN
£12.50

WITHDRAWN
FROM THE LIBRARY

THERMAL ANALYSIS
OF MINERALS

Preface

Geological activities involve both assiduous field-work and thorough laboratory investigations. The methods of thermal analysis rank among the most useful tools for carrying out inquiries into the nature of minerals. Although these methods have been known for a long time, it was only in the last thirty years or so that they have acquired a wider applicability, considerably enlarging their field of usefulness. Today, a complete analysis of solid mineral substances, whether natural or artificial, can hardly be conceived without the contribution of thermal analysis.

The methods of thermal analysis are based on a group of related instrumental techniques by means of which the physical or chemical modifications occurring in a sample subjected to temperature variations are measured. The modifications appearing as a function of temperature and time are closely connected with the chemical nature and the structure of the substance analysed. Being specific to every compound, these modifications, recorded in the form of thermal curves, serve to determine the composition of the compounds present in the sample. The benefits of the methods of thermal analysis are manifold, but foremost among them is their large area of investigation, the rapidity with which the determinations are carried out, and the low cost of the analyses.

The present work has been conceived to serve as a guide-line for those who carry out thermal analyses and for those who are to interpret their results, helping them to understand thoroughly the processes which arise when solid compounds are heated. It is therefore hoped that this text will not only meet the needs of geologists and chemists practising in the fields of geology, mineralogy, ore dressing, solid state physics and chemistry, building materials, ceramics, and even metallurgy, but will also be directly useful to students of chemistry and geology.

The book describes the theoretical and practical principles of thermal analysis methods. It discusses the experimental factors underlying these methods and the data interpretation procedures. It considers the detectable physical phenomena and chemical processes, and provides detailed accounts of the thermal behaviour of a great number of minerals. In each separate case, the description of the behaviour of native compounds is accompanied by the thermal curves which I have obtained on simple minerals. With few exceptions, the descriptions provided illustrate my own viewpoint. They are the result of many years of experience in this field and the processing of much data I have gathered in the course of time. There also appear some discrepancies between data from the literature, which have generally been obtained by single techniques, and my own data, which have been obtained by multiple techniques. However, these discrepancies are discussed critically.

N. D. Todor

Contents

Contents

Classification and Principles
of Thermal Analysis Methods

The methods of thermal analysis are based on the relationship between substances and temperature, that is, on a study of the thermal state of substances and of the changes that take place in a substance depending on temperature.

Temperature is one of the magnitudes which define the state equilibrium, and kinetics of material systems; it affects almost all physical and chemical constants of substances. The thermodynamical states of substances are determined by two closely connected processes: The mechanism of heat transfer considered as a whole at a given moment, and the thermokinetic processes which determine the variations of the physical and chemical properties of the substance investigated. These two thermal processes and the physical or chemical phenomena which arise on heating a substance determine all the aspects of the methods of thermal analysis.

The evolution of thermal processes, whether physical or chemical in nature, in a well-defined material system which constitutes the object of thermo-analytical investigations is determined by the way in which thermal energy is fed to the instrumental analytic system.

A material system can be raised or lowered to the desired temperature by heating or cooling, respectively. The aggregate phenomena attending the propagation of heat within the same body or in different bodies is called *heat transmission*. The process by which heat is transferred depends on a difference of temperature existing between one part and another of the body or between different bodies. Heat spontaneously passes from the warmer to the colder body. Thermal energy generally propagates in bodies in three ways: by conduction, convection, and radiation.

By thermal conduction heat is transferred gradually from one molecule to the next within a body or between bodies in contact, without any apparent displacement of substance. Warmer molecules performing faster motions hit against contiguous colder molecules the motions of which are slower, yielding some of their kinetic energy, whereby colder molecules become warmer, and warmer molecules colder.

By thermal convection, heat is transferred in a way similar to the macroscopic displacement of warm fluids, that is, this transfer takes place with a transportation of substance within the same phase or between different but adjoining phases.

By thermal radiation, heat is transferred as radiant energy, in the form of electromagnetic waves which are partly or wholly changed into heat on meeting a body in their path.

One, two or even all three mechanisms may operate in any heat transfer, depending on the nature and state of aggregation of the substance subjected to a change of temperature by heating. In solid substances, heat transfer by conduction is predominant. This transfer may easily be described on the basis of the theory of thermal conductivity. Thus, within a body in which heat is transferred by conduction a difference of temperature must exist at any moment between two near points. The temperature at a point whatsoever of a material system depends on the co-ordinates x, y, and z of the related point, and on the time t:

$$T = f(x, y, z, t) \tag{1}$$

The temperature distribution at a certain moment in all points of the system considered is called the *range of temperature*. According to whether the range of temperature is independent of time or varies with it, heat is transferred in a *steady* or in an *unsteady state*, respectively. In the steady state, heat remains constant at any point of the system. Heat entering a portion of the body or all of it comes out wholly through the surface bounding the portion considered or the whole body. In the unsteady state, heat is accumulated in the system; this accumulation may also be negative when the system gets colder.

In a range of temperatures whatsoever, the points of equal temperature form isothermal surfaces. The closer two isothermal surfaces are, the more sudden will be the temperature variation. The limit of the ratio between the difference ΔT the temperatures and the distance Δn between two surfaces, when Δn tends towards zero, is called *the temperature gradient*. This gradient is given by the relation:

$$T \text{ grad.} = \lim_{\Delta n \to 0} \left[\frac{\Delta T}{\Delta n} \right] = \frac{dT}{dn} \tag{2}$$

When the temperature is given by Equation (1), the gradient at the moment T is:

$$[T \text{ grad.}]_t = \left[\frac{\partial T}{\partial x} + \frac{\partial T}{\partial y} + \frac{\partial T}{\partial z} \right]_t \tag{3}$$

The temperature gradient is expressed by a temperature difference per unit volume.

The heating or cooling of solid bodies in the unsteady state takes place with a time variation of the range of temperatures. When a solid body with a uniform temperature T_1 is brought into a medium with a temperature T_2, it will grow warmer if $T_1 < T_2$ or colder if $T_1 > T_2$, which means that the temperature of the body T_1 tends towards the temperature of the body T_2. As a rule, a body gets hot progressively from the outside towards the inside, which means that the temperature varies more quickly in points nearer to the surfaces than in points placed deeper inside the body. This fact greatly affects the kind and intensity of the recorded thermal effects, because a certain time (depending on the size of the body) will be necessary for thermal processes to take place within the whole mass of the body.

Most generally, the problem of heat transfer through solid bodies in the unsteady state is stated as follows: Knowing the temperature range of a system at a moment whatsoever and the variation law of the temperature in the exterior medium, it is required to determine the temperature range and the enthalpy *) of the system at another moment. The problem is treated theoretically on the basis of Fourier's equation:

$$\frac{\partial T}{\partial t} = a \left[\frac{\partial^2 T}{\partial x^2} + \frac{\partial^2 T}{\partial y^2} + \frac{\partial^2 T}{\partial z^2} \right], \tag{4}$$

which expresses the relation between the temperature T, the time t, and the thermal diffusibility a, in a point of coordinates x, y, z.

When integrating this equation, the shape of the solid and the initial conditions have to be taken into account; complex relations arrived at in the end are presented as diagrams for use.

In complex methods of analyses such as thermal analysis, in which several types of surfaces of separation exist (for example, gas-solid or solid-liquid), or in systems involving powdered solid aggregates in which thermal processes take place in an open system, the heat transfer is very complicated, and implies several mechanisms. The description of the transfer process of thermal energy on the basis of a simple mechanism does not agree with reality in the case of these systems. Nevertheless, in the case of most substances subjected to thermal analysis the process of heat transfer can most adequately be described by a simplified theory of thermal conductivity, a procedure adopted by M. G. Lukasszewski (1965).

Thermal energy transfer and Mass transfer are generally treated together. Thus, the thermokinetic aspect of a sample is determined not only by the rate of thermal transfer, but also by the mechanism of diffusion. The diffusive processes in solid substances are governed by the laws of mass action and of thermodynamic

---

*) Enthalpy is a magnitude of state formally defined by the relation $H = E + pV$ (where H is the enthalpy of one mol of substance, E the internal energy, p the pressure, and V the volume of the system). Hence, enthalpy is the sum of the internal energy of a substance and of the mechanical work pV. Enthalpy and internal energy are extensive properties of substances, i.e., properties proportional to the amount of substance, like weight, volume, and heat capacity, unlike the intensive properties, which are independent of the amount of substance, like temperature, density, and specific heat.

equilibrium. In thermal analyses there are frequent cases when volatile or gaseous products are given off as a result of a thermal process, and these products generate a supplementary pressure in the furnace which inhibits some chemical reactions or affects the physical phenomena. For this reason it is absolutely necessary to eliminate such a pressure from the analytical system. Since the transfer of heat and of mass as well as the rate at which such a transfer takes place, play a decisive part in obtaining real and reproducible thermal effects, they will again be considered in Chapter 2.

1.1   CLASSIFICATION OF THERMAL ANALYSIS METHODS

Quite a number of methods of thermal analysis have been developed in the course of time to investigate thermal processes occurring when a solid products heated or cooled. In order to classify these methods one must first of all start from the nature of the thermal processes which take place and are recorded as a function of the temperature T or of the time t. A first classification has been made ever since they were worked out as analytical methods, when they were grouped in two classes:

(i)   Methods of thermal analysis for determining the variation of the temperature.

(ii)   Methods of thermal analysis for determining the variation of the mass.

In the course of time, with the theoretical and practical development of these methods, other classification criteria have appeared. One of these takes into account the kind of coordinates in which the heat curves are recorded. According to this criterion, thermal methods are also divided into two main groups.
    The first group includes methods recording the temperature of the sample point T_s; they are conventionally called *methods of temperature curves*.
    The second group includes all the methods recording a function whatsoever of the temperature of the sample point; they are called *methods of functional heat curves* (Pilojan, 1964).
    The first group includes only two methods:

(A)   The method recording the temperature of the sample point depending on time or, briefly, the method of time-temperature curves:

$$T_s = f(t). \tag{5}$$

(B)   The method of recording the temperature of the sample point as a function of the point temperature of the medium (*i.e.*, of the point in which the temperature is measured in the furnace):

$$T_s = f(T_m). \tag{6}$$

The second group, also called the group of functional heat curves, includes all the other thermal methods. This group may in turn be subdivided into several subgroups:

(a) The method of recording diferential thermal curves or differential thermal analysis (DTA). This subgroup includes all the methods of thermal analysis which record the difference between the temperature of the sample point T_s and the temperature of the point of a thermally inert substance T_i, as a function of the time t or of the temperature T. In order to be able at any desired moment to determine the temperature T of the heating programme, modern instrumental analytical equipment permit the temperature to be measured either in the furnace or in the thermally inert substance or in the sample to be analysed. When the temperature is measured in the furnace or in the thermally inert substance, it increases or decreases linearily in unit time. If the temperature is measured in the sample, this linearity is maintained constant only in the temperature range in which thermal processes do not take place. Mathematically, this method is expressed by the following two equations:

$$\Delta T = f(t); \quad \Delta T = f(T). \tag{7}$$

(b) The method of recording derivative thermal curves or derivative thermal analysis. This subgroup includes all methods of thermal analysis recording the temperature derivative between the temperature of the sample point T_s and the temperature of the point of a thermally inert substance (T_i). In other words the methods in this subgroup permit to record the rate of change of T_s or the ΔT as a function of t or T. Expressed in the form of mathematical relations, this subgroup includes the following methods of recording thermal curves:

$$(1) \quad \frac{dT_s}{dt} = f(t) \quad ; \quad (2) \quad \frac{dT_s}{dt} = f(T_i);$$

$$(3) \quad \frac{d\Delta T}{dt} = f(t) \quad ; \quad (4) \quad \frac{d\Delta T}{dt} = f(T);$$

$$(5) \quad \frac{dT_s}{dT_i} = f(t) \quad ; \quad (6) \quad \frac{dT_s}{dT_i} = f(T_i); \tag{8}$$

$$(7) \quad \frac{d\Delta T}{dT} = f(t) \quad ; \quad (8) \quad \frac{d\Delta T}{dT} = f(T).$$

It also includes methods recording the reciprocal derivatives of the previously listed magnitudes, that is:

$$(9) \quad \frac{dt}{dT_s} = f(t) \quad ; \quad (10) \quad \frac{dt_i}{dT_s} = f(T_i);$$

$$(11) \quad \frac{dt}{d\Delta T} = f(t) \quad ; \quad (12) \quad \frac{dt}{d\Delta T} = f(T);$$

$$(13) \quad \frac{dT_i}{dT_s} = f(t) \quad ; \quad (14) \quad \frac{dT_i}{dT_s} = f(T_i); \tag{9}$$

$$(15) \quad \frac{dT}{d\Delta T} = f(t) \quad ; \quad (16) \quad \frac{dT}{d\Delta T} = f(T).$$

(c) The method of recording integrated thermal curves or integrated thermal analysis (ITA). This subgroup includes methods recording the integrated average temperature of the sample related to the volume or to the area. By area we understand not only the external area of the sample, but also that of any internal section of it. Expressed mathematically, in this subgroup we distinguish the following methods of recording thermal curves:

$$(1) \quad \bar{T}_s = f(t) \qquad\qquad ; \qquad (2) \ \bar{T}_s = f(T_i);$$

$$(3) \quad \overline{\Delta T} = \bar{T}_s - T_i = f(t) \ ; \qquad (4) \ \overline{\Delta T} = \bar{T}_s - T_i = f(T); \qquad (10)$$

$$(5) \quad \overline{\Delta T'} = \bar{T}_s - \bar{T}_i = f(t) \ ; \qquad (6) \ \overline{\Delta T'} = T_s - T_i = f(T)$$

where:

$\bar{T}_s$ is the integrated average temperature recorded on the surface or in the volume of the sample;

$\bar{T}_i$ is the integrated average temperature recorded on the surface or in the volume of a portion whatsoever of the thermally inert substance.

(d) The method of recording mixed thermal curves or mixed thermal analysis (MTA). This subgroup includes methods recording the derivatives of the curves of the previous subgroup, ITA, whose mathematical expressions are:

$$(1) \quad \frac{d\bar{T}_s}{dt} = f(t) \ ; \qquad (2) \qquad \frac{d\bar{T}_s}{dT_i} = f(T_i);$$

$$(3) \quad \frac{d\overline{\Delta T}}{dt} = f(t) \ ; \qquad (4) \qquad \frac{d\overline{\Delta T}}{dT} = f(T); \qquad (11)$$

$$(5) \quad \frac{d\overline{\Delta T'}}{dt} = f(t); \qquad (6) \qquad \frac{d\overline{\Delta T'}}{dT} = f(T).$$

(e)   The method of recording thermogravimetric curves or thermogravimetry (TG). This subgroup includes the methods of thermal analysis by means of which the mass variation m of the sample is recorded depending on the temperature T or on the time t, and whose mathematical expressions are:

$$(1) \quad m = f(T); \qquad\qquad (2) \quad m = f(t). \qquad (12)$$

(f)   Methods of recording derivative thermogravimetric curves or derivative thermogravimetry (DTG). This subgroup includes all methods of thermal analysis for recording the derivative of the mass variation of the sample as a function of the time t or the temperature T, and which have the following mathematical expressions:

$$(1) \quad \frac{dm}{dt} = f(t) \ ; \qquad (2) \quad \frac{dm}{dt} = f(T);$$

$$(13)$$

$$(3) \quad \frac{dm}{dt} = f(T); \qquad (4) \quad \frac{dm}{dT} = f(t).$$

Since in the course of time a certain vacillation has been observed in respect of the classification and nomenclature of thermal methods, the need was felt for this matter to be regulated by the International Confederation of Thermal Analysis (I.C.T.A.). Thus, at the Third Congress of Thermal Analysis (Davos, Switzerland, 23—27 August 1971) the following classification and nomenclature has been suggested:

THERMAL ANALYSIS

This is a general notion which covers a group of mutually related instrumental techniques for measuring the parameters of any physical property or chemical stability depending on temperature.

METHODS ASSOCIATED WITH A CHANGE IN MASS

(1) Static methods

Isobaric determination of the change in mass. This group includes instrumental techniques by means of which the mass of a substance is recorded as a function of the temperature T, at a partially constant pressure of the process or of the volatile products. The recording of the process is the curve of the isobaric change in mass. As a rule, this curve is represented graphically with the variation of the mass on the y-axis, negative variations downward, and the temperature on the x-axis, increasing from left to right.

Isothermal determination of the change in mass. This group includes instrumental techniques by means of which the mass of a substance is recorded in the time t at a constant temperature. The recording of the process is the isothermal curve of the change in mass. As a rule, this curve is represented graphically in a similar way to the previous one with mass variations as ordinates and the time as abscissae increasing from left to right.

(2) Dynamic methods

Thermogravimetry (TG). This group includes instrumental techniques by means of which the mass of a substance in given surroundings, heated or cooled under controlled conditions at a constant rate, is recorded as a function of time or of temperature $m = f(t$ or $T)$. The recording is the thermogravimetric curve (TG). The mass is plotted as ordinate, with negative mass variations downward, *vs.* time or temperature as abscissae, increasing from left to right.

Derivative thermogravimetry (DTG). This group includes instrumental techniques which indicate the first derivative of the experimentally determined thermogravimetric curve as a function of time or temperature, $dm/dT = f(t \text{ or } T)$. The recording is that of the derivative thermogravimetric curve (DTG). The derivative of mass variations is plotted as ordinate, with negative variation downward, *vs.* the time or temperature as abscissae, increasing from left to right.

METHODS ASSOCIATED WITH CHANGE OF ENERGY

Differential thermal analysis. This group includes instrumental techniques for recording the differences in temperature which appear between a substance and a thermally inert material, when both the substance and the inert material are subjected to identical amounts of temperature, in surroundings heated or cooled at controlled rates. The recording is that of the curve of differential thermal analysis (DTA), in which the temperature difference ΔT is plotted as ordinate with endothermal processes downward and exothermal ones upward, *vs.* time or temperature as abscissae, increasing from left to right.

Differential enthalpic analysis (DEA). This group includes instrumental techniques for recording the energy required to study the difference of temperature between a substance and a material related either to time or to temperature, while both substances are subjected to identical temperature conditions in surroundings heated or cooled at controlled rates. The recording is the differential enthalpic analysis *(DEA)*; it represents the absorbed heat applied per unit time or temperature as ordinate *vs.* the time or temperature as abscissae increasing from left to right.

METHODS ASSOCIATED WITH THE EVOLUTION
OF VOLATILE PRODUCTS

These methods include instrumental techniques for determining the nature of the source of volatile products formed during the thermal process.

METHODS ASSOCIATED WITH DIMENSIONAL CHANGES

Dilatometry and differential dilatometry. These methods include instrumental techniques for measuring the changes in size of a substance depending on temperature. The recording is the simple or differential dilatometric curve.

Multiple techniques

These include a collection of the above-mentioned methods combined in a single instrumental aggregate for simultaneously measuring on the same sample, in the same unit time and under the same temperature conditions the processes appearing as a result of the action of thermal energy on a substance. As a rule, such a unitary aggregate in most cases includes the instrumental equipment for obtaining the TG, DTG and DTA curves.

Table 1 gives the nomenclature adopted by the I.C.T.A. as well as the names which have been abandoned.

Table 1 **Terminology accepted and rejected by the ICTA at the Third Congress of Thermal Analysis, Davos — Switzerland, 23—28 August 1971** *after Duval (1972)*

Accepted name	Accepted Abbreviations	Rejected name
General term: Thermal Analysis	—	Thermography. Thermoanalysis

Methods associated with change of weight:
1. Static
  Isobaric detn. of wt. change
  Isothermal detn. of wt. change
		Isothermal thermogravimetric analysis

2. Dynamic Thermogravimetry	TG	Thermogravimetric analysis. Dynamic thermogravimetric analysis
Derivative thermogravimetry	DTG	Derivative thermogravimetric analysis
Methods associated with change of energy: Differential thermal analysis	DTA	Thermal analysis. Derivative thermal analysis
Differential enthalpic analysis	DEA	Dynamic differential calorimetry
Methods associated with evolution of volatil products: Differential gas analysis	DGA	Thermovaporimetric analysis
Methods associated with changes in size. Dilatometry. Differential dilatometry		
Multiple techniques; simultaneous TG, DTG, DTA, etc.		Derivatography. Differential thermal and thermogravimetric analysis

Of all these methods, the most convincing results in the investigation of solid compounds, especially in mineralogy, have been obtained by means of differential thermal analysis, thermogravimetry, and derivative thermogravimetry. At the present stage, these methods are used either separately or by grouping the three methods in a single instrumental unit which records the four thermal curves, that is, the DTA curve, the DTG curve, the TG curve, and the temperature curve T, in the same time, on the same sample, and at the same temperature. Nevertheless, the other methods also have their advantages as well as specific fields of application. The analyst may select the most advantageous method of recording the thermal curves. In the following a description will be given only of such methods which have great applications in thermo-analytical laboratories.

1.2 DIFFERENTIAL THERMAL ANALYSIS (DTA)

The method of differential thermal analysis originates in the improvement of thermocouples as accurate temperature measuring instruments. Le Châtelier (1887) was the first to use the system of thermocouples and photographic recording to investigate the modifications occurring in argillaceous minerals when they are heated. To this end, he employed the simple and direct method of recording the heating and cooling curves. Le Châtelier's method has then been improved by Robert-Austin (1899) whe introduced differential thermocouples and a thermally inert substance. This fact enabled him substantially to reduce the variations which appear on heating or cooling the furnace. In 1903, Saladen suggested another equipment for recording the DTA curve as a function of temperature. This equipment was later improved by Le Châtelier and is known by the name of the Saladen-Châtelier apparatus. Wallach (1913) and Fenner (1913) were the first to use differential thermal analysis in the investigation of argillaceous minerals and of silicates. Fenner's technique is essentially that in use today, but with some improvements. In the course of time, particularly the apparatus underwent rather important modifications. De Keyser (1938—1939), Norton (1939), Hendriks, and Alexander's (1939) papers have resulted in rapid development and generalization of these methods for the study of minerals. Since 1940 the technique has been improved appreciably and the fields of use have been extended.

Differential thermal analysis essentially represents an instrumental modernization of the conventional method of investigating phase transformations by means of time and temperature recordings obtained during the uniform heating of a solid substance. Experimentally the method consists of heating under identical conditions a sample and a thermally inert reference material while continually recording the temperature T existing in the furnace and the temperature difference ΔT resulting between the sample and the reference material. Under ideal conditions, the temperature difference ΔT which results in the course of heating or cooling should be recorded at a uniform rate proportional to the temperature of the sample or of the inert reference material or of the surrounding medium, depending on the type of instrument used.

These investigations are carried out with various types of instruments or differential calorimeters of furnace design whose rate of heating in time is constant. As a rule the temperature difference between the sample and the inert material is recorded with a differential thermocouple device having one thermocouple placed in the sample and the other in the reference material, both being simultaneously heated at a constant rate (Figure 1.1).

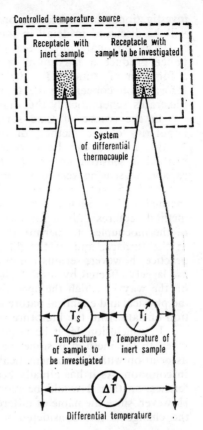

Figure 1.1 Schematic diagram of an apparatus for differential thermal analysis:

ΔT is the temperature difference between sample and inert thermal substance; T_s is the temperature of the sample; T_i is the temperature of the substance.

Assuming the temperature flow to be equivalent in the furnace, in the sample, and in the inert substance, hence a temperature difference between them equal to zero, the instrument would then record the so-called *base line* as a function of time and temperature $\Delta T = 0$. If one phase is modified or if a decomposition reaction takes place in the sample with heat absorption or evolution, the temperature gradient against the reference material will then be modified and the temperature variation will be recorded by the instrument as an electromotive force deviating from the initial base line. The sense of the deviation against the zero line is determined by the temperature gradient between the sample and the reference material, showing at the same time the nature of the thermal process taking place. Hence, since the conversions occurring in the sample investigation involve endothermal or exothermal processes, they may produce negative or positive deviations of the temperature difference ΔT against the arbitrary zero line ($\Delta T \neq 0$).

Such variations depend not only on the nature of the thermal process which takes place, but also on some physical properties of the material under investigation, on the heating or cooling rate, and on some basic factors which will be discussed in detail in the next chapter.

Any physical conversions or chemical reactions generated by temperature hence produce a maximum in the recording of the temperature difference as a function of time $\Delta T = f(t)$; from this maximum it is possible to obtain information concerning the temperature and the conversion rate. Figure 1.2 illustrates schematically the diagram of a differential thermal curve.

In the course of time some advantages have contributed towards a greater popularity of the method of differential thermal analysis. The curves obtained by this method can be recorded with conventional automated apparatus. The method is sensitive enough to determine very small temperature variations; it is capable of sensing very slow conversions occurring over wide temperature ranges.

At first sight, owing to its simplicity and rapidity, the method of differential thermal analysis seems to be excellent for the investigation of the solid state. The method requires only a furnace, a support for the samples, and an arrangement of thermocouples to permit the determination of the surrounding temperature in the furnace, and of the differential temperature in the analytical system. In practice, however, serious complications appear owing to the fact that the results are largely affected by some factors depending on the construction of the apparatus, on the way in which the operating technique is conducted practically, as well as on the physical and chemical nature of the material under investigation. An interpretation of data from the literature requires all these factors to be taken into account.

In conclusion, let it be noticed that the name of *differential thermal analysis* given to the method is somewhat of a misnomer, because it frequently causes an association with the mathematical notion of a differential, with which it has nothing in common. As it has already been shown, this method records a temperature difference, so that it would be more correct to call it *thermal difference analysis*. However, since the name of differential thermal analysis has generally been accepted the change is not considered to be necessary.

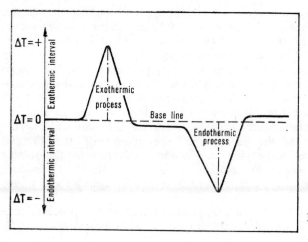

Figure 1.2 Idealized diagram of a DTA curve.

1.3 THERMOGRAVIMETRY (TG)

Thermogravimetry is an instrumental technique by means of which a sample
subjected to analysis is weighed continuously as it is heated at a constant rate of
temperature rise with time in the furnace. In fact, the method is a development
of the conventional method of heating and weighing a solid product by stages.
When a substance is heated at various temperatures it undergoes a series of
transformations, some of which are attended by changes in mass. By following
up the variation of the mass as a function of the temperature, $m = f(T)$, we may
draw conclusions concerning the transformations which have occurred in the sample
under investigation. By graphically plotting these weight variations in mass and
temperature coordinates one obtains the thermogravimetric curve. This procedure
is rather inconvenient and not very accurate. It is nevertheless used even today
in some laboratories for orientating determinations. However, more accurate
and rapid determinations are obtained by using a thermobalance in conjunction
with the simultaneous graphical or photo recording of the mass variations produced
as a function of temperature in the sample.

The operating principle of a thermobalance is the following: The sample to
be investigated is heated in a receptacle fixed to the beam of a balance inside an
electric furnace with adjustable temperature and uniform temperature rise per unit
time (Figure 1.3). The temperature of the furnace is measured by means of a
thermocouple placed inside the furnace. If the outfit is not provided with an automatic recording system, the mass of the sample is then read off the scale of
the balance by stages of 5 or 10 °C and a graph is plotted to illustrate the mass
variation as a function of temperature. If mass variations are recorded automatically,
the TG curve is obtained as a function of time instead of temperature, $m = f(t)$.
The TG curve obtained by automatic recording is equally valid only when the
temperature rise in the furnace is rigorously constant.

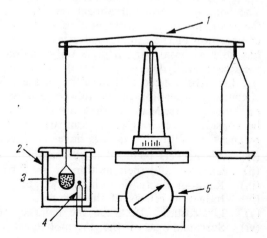

Figure 1.3   Fundamental   scheme   of
thermal   balance:

1, balance; *2*, oven; *3*, sample support; *4*, thermocouple; *5*, millivoltmetre.

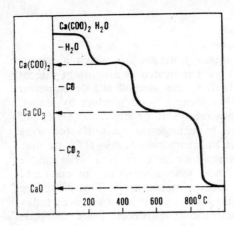

Figure 1.4   TG curve of calcium oxalate monohydrate.

On the basis of TG curves it is possible to establish how the mass of the sample varies under the influence of thermal energy. For example, by observing the TG curve of calcium oxalate monohydrate we notice four distinct ranges of mass modifications (Figure 1.4).

The change in mass may be established with an accuracy of 0.5—0.1 per cent depending on the type of thermobalance used. On the basis of the results of determinations it is possible to carry out accurate stoichiometric or percentage calculations. Three parts may, generally, be distinguished in a thermogram:
(i)   A part indicating the decrease in mass;
(ii)   A part indicating the increase in mass;
(iii) A horizontal part indicating no change in mass.

For analytical practice, particularly with research to determine the thermal stability of a compound, the horizontal parts of the TG curve are the significant ones, and they give all indications required for an adequate thermal treatment. The optimum thermal treatment temperature of analytical precipitates is that of the midpoint of the horizontal part of the TG curve, provided a well-defined composition of the sample under investigation corresponds to it. If the TG curve has no horizontal part, it gives only qualitative information and cannot be used for quantitative determinations of the composition of a compound.

Let it be noticed that the form of the TG curve is not dependent only on the chemical composition of the substance under investigation, but also on a number of other factors. Many of these are closely connected to one another and cannot be considered separately. In comparative studies with various types of thermal balances the following factors have to be considered:
(i)   Air pockets included in the sample seat;
(ii)   Currents and their motion in the furnace;
(iii) Random fluctuations in the weighing and recording mechanisms;
(iv)   Induction effects of the furnace;
(v)   Electrostatic effects on the balance mechanism;
(vi)   Surroundings of the thermobalance;

(vii)   Condensation of the products on the support of the sample;
(viii)   Measurement and calibration of the temperature;
(ix)   Calibration of the weights of the balance;
(x)   Unfolding rate of the recording paper;
(xi)   Possible reactions of the sample with the material of construction of the
         sample seat.

With time, thermogravimetry has been developed and improved in various ways. The trends in equipment design and the fields of use will be reviewed briefly.

Two trends have been recorded in the design of thermobalances as instruments for analytical determinations: the construction of thermobalances with means proper to each laboratory by conveniently converting an ordinary analytical balance, and the construction of thermobalances as self-contained special equipment. We do not intend to describe thermobalances constructed in the course of time. We only wish to mention that they are wholly similar in principle to the analytical balances encountered in chemical laboratories.

In spite of the limits and sources of error, the field of use is very large. If analytical data obtained on different balances are not identical in respect of the form of the TG curve, nevertheless, data obtained under rigorously preserved experimental conditions on the same balance are reproducible and sufficiently adequate for the investigation of the following phenomena due to temperature:

(i)   Thermal decomposition of natural and artificial compounds;
(ii)   Corrosion of metals in various atmospheres at high temperatures;
(iii)   Chemical reactions of solid substances;
(iv)   Roasting and calcination of ores;
(v)   Distillation and evaporation of liquids;
(vi)   Pyrolysis of coal, oil, wood, etc.;
(vii)   Conditions of evaporation and sublimation;
(viii)   Dehydration and hydration studies;
(ix)   Thermo-oxidative degradation of polymers;
(x)   Thermal decomposition of explosives;
(xi)   Investigation of analytical precipitates;
(xii)   Research on reaction kinetics;
(xiii)   Discovery of new chemical compounds.

Inconvenient cases may also occur when using this analytical method, for instance when two reactions develop close together, overlapping in the same range of temperature, or when the reaction rate is different. In this case the method becomes uncertain, and the interpretation of the curves obtained is involved and inaccurate. To obviate this shortcoming some authors, Eytod (1954), Hooley (1957), Szabo and Kiraly (1957), Peters and Wiedemann (1959) among others, have carried out analytical determinations in a vacuum. Their results have been on the whole satisfactory because in a vacuum thermal decompositions develop as a rule more rapidly, between close temperature limits; thus, reactions which under ordinary conditions would develop simultaneously, in this case could be distinguished from each other better (Duval, 1963).

1.4 DIFFERENTIAL THERMOGRAVIMETRY

It has been shown that thermogravimetric curves can be used for quantitative calculations of the composition of a compound only if they present a horizontal part, corresponding to a compound with a well-defined and constant composition over a wider temperature range. In order to extend the field of use to include also compounds whose TG curve has no horizontality, an attempt was made to read this simple curve by obtaining differential curves. It was also shown that the simple TG curve recorded in coordinates of temperature T vs. mass variation m, is determined by the relation $m = f(T)$. Mathematically, the differential curve of the mass variation is a graphical expression of the temperature derivative against the function of mass change of the compound under investigation:

$$f(T) = \frac{dm}{dT} \tag{14}$$

The shape of such a curve is different from the simple curve of mass variations. The two curves are illustrated for comparison in Figure 1.5.

In practice, differential thermal curves may be constructed by mathematical calculations on the basis of data obtained as a result of the previously recorded TG curves of the samples investigated. Thus, in order to pass from a TG curve to the construction of a differential curve it is necessary at first to calculate the differential between the two mass values, that is, dm for well-defined temperature ranges, for example by steps of 50 °C. In order to do this, on the graphical or photo recording of the TG curve produced by the thermobalance we measure the height H of the mass variation by means of a graduated ruler at intervals of 50° C.

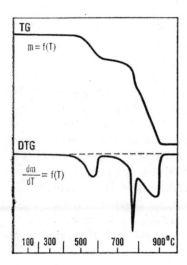

Figure 1.5 Graphical comparison between the TG curve and the differential curve.

We then calculate the difference ΔH between the magnitudes obtained. These data are listed in a table such as the following:

$T/°C$	H/mm	$\Delta H/mm$
0	85	0
50	79	6
100	52	27
150	48	4
200	47	1

From points ΔH plotted on ruled paper we construct the differential curve of the mass variation with ΔH plotted as ordinate *vs.* the temperature T as abscissa.

By comparing a differential curve thus constructed with a curve obtained on the same sample by means of differential thermal analysis, the thermal effects in both curves will overlap; this, however, refers only to such thermal effects that have occurred with change in mass.

The construction of a differential curve of the change in mass on the basis of the TG curve is somewhat difficult and the results obtained are not very accurate.

Keyser (1953) has attempted to forestall the inconveniencies connected with an interpretation of the TG curve by graphical differentiation. For this he fastened to each end of a thermobalance a crucible for processing the samples (Figure 1.6). The same amount of the sample under investigation was weighed in both crucibles, which were then heated in two furnaces adjusted so that the temperature of one should constantly show a difference of 4 °C against that of the other, and this temperature difference must be kept up over the whole heating duration. In this way the change in mass depending on temperature will take place in both crucibles over constant time intervals, causing the beam of the balance to oscillate. The change in mass is automatically recorded in the form of a differential curve on a rotating cylinder provided with photographic paper by means of an optical device and of a special mirror fastened to the oscillating beam of the balance. For example,

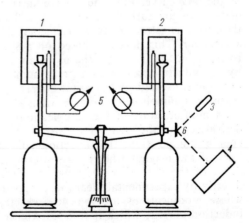

Figure 1.6 Fundamental scheme of Keyser's differential balance (1953):

1, hotter oven; *2*, cooler oven; *3*, lamp; *4*, photo recording drum; *5*, millivoltmeter; *6*, mirror.

if at a given temperature the mass of the sample in the hottest furnace begins to decrease, the balance will then show an inclination corresponding to the change in mass.

From this moment on the equilibrium of the balance has been upset by the resultant of two reaction moments acting one against the other. This resultant further changes in magnitude. As soon as the decomposition rate of the sample in the hotter furnace slows down, the inclination of the balance beam becomes smaller. If a second decomposition reaction begins in the sample under investigation even before the primary decomposition has come to an end, the beam of the balance will then tilt back and so on. The curve recorded by this experimental procedure is approximately the first derivative of the change in mass depending on temperature. The instrumental technique of differential thermogravimetry has proved very useful owing to the fact that the curve obtained is the first derivative of the change in mass, that is, $dm/dt = f(t)$, hence the derivative of the curve $m = f(T)$ in relation to time. The application possibilities of this method are, however, somewhat limited, owing to the fact that the instrumental equipment designed for such determinations cannot also provide the simple TG curve of the change in mass.

1.5 DERIVATIVE THERMOGRAVIMETRY (DTG)

Starting from the premise that the use for analytical purposes of the two curves obtained simultaneously on the same sample and in the same unit time would be more advantageous, a number of researchers have been looking for other experimental procedures. Thus, Erdey, F. and J. Paulik (1954) on the one hand, and Waters (1956) on the other hand have tried to obtain the experimental curve by a new experimental method. This was also based on the principle of the differential method set out above. At first these authors have attempted a graphical derivation of the TG curve, but they have arrived at the conclusion that graphical derivations are rather inconvenient and inaccurate. To remove this disadvantage they have constructed an experimental derivation device of the TG curve called a *derivator*. This device is based on a system of magnetic induction implemented by replacing the arm of the thermobalance opposite to the sample under investigation by an induction coil with a great number of turns. The coil is placed in the homogeneous field of horseshoe-shaped magnets; it is also connected to a very sensitive millivoltmeter (Figure 1.7). With this simple device, in addition to the mass modifications of the sample, it is also possible exactly to determine their derivative and the oscillation rate of the balance. When the balance leaves the equilibrium position, the induction coil also moves, and its turns cut the force lines of the magnet whereby an electric induction current arises in the coil. The curve of the derivative thermogravimetry, or DTG curve can thus be recorded directly by experimental means in proportion to the oscillation rate of the balance whose modifications are indicated exactly by the millivoltmeter owing to the induction current which it receives. Hence, this experimental arrangement permits

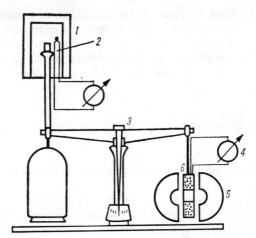

Figure 1.7 Fundamental scheme of Erdey, Paulik and Paulik's derivation balance (1954):

1, oven; *2*, thermocouple; *3*, thermal balance; *4*, galvanometer; *5*, permanent magnet; *6*, induction coil.

the recording of both curves, and gives a clear image of the way in which mass modifications occur depending on temperature.

It has already been shown that differential or derivative curves of mass modifications resemble the curves obtained by differential thermal analysis, but they express only thermal processes caused by a change in mass. This gives the possibility to distinguish thermal processes caused by mass variations from those due to phase transformations or other reactions which do not involve changes in mass. In comparing the curves obtained by the two methods, a series of advantages will become apparent, namely:

(i) DTA and DTG curves may easily be obtained with the same instrumental device.

(ii) Thermal effects recorded by the DTA curve extend over a wide temperature range owing to continued heating of the material after the thermal process has taken place. Thermal effects recorded by the DTG curve exactly indicate the temperatures of the beginning and end of the thermal process as well as the temperature at which the alteration in mass has its maximum velocity, that is, the temperature at which the thermal effect reaches its highest vertex.

(iii) Thermal processes which take place in very narrow temperature ranges are not distinguishable on the DTA curve, on which they appear as if generated by a single phenomenon. On the DTG curve these effects are separated by sharp maxima, thus indicating how many thermal processes have participated in the alteration in mass.

(iv) As the DTG curve is the exact derivative of the TG curve, the area enclosed by the recorded thermal effects faithfully represents the change in mass which has taken place. On the basis of these areas it is possible to carry out much more accurate quantitative determinations than by measuring mass variations at various temperature intervals expressed by the TG curve.

(v) The method of derivative thermogravimetry can be used also to investigate compounds which cannot be examined by differential thermal analysis. For example, some organic compounds decompose during heating, and thereby greatly change their volume which causes a total failure of the DTA curve, whereas mass variations are accurately recorded.

1.6 MULTIPLE TECHNIQUES (THERMAL DERIVATOGRAPHY)

Thermal derivatography represents a combination in a single instrumental aggregate of the three experimental techniques discussed above. As can be seen, differential thermal analysis permits one to establish readily the way in which thermal processes develop. By means of thermogravimetry, and of derivative or differential thermogravimetry it is possible to establish exactly what alteration in mass occurs in the sample during heating. From these three possibilities, the idea has arisen that the simultaneous application on the same sample of the three instrumental techniques ensures fully identical operating conditions, and also reduces the time required for an analysis as compared to the time required if each method would be applied separately.

The first instrumental apparatus of this kind has been created by F. and J. Paulik, and Erdey (1958); it was named by them a *derivatograph*. We have already shown that this name has not been agreed by the ICTA on the ground that it would lead to confusions with other instrumental techniques from other fields; the name *multiple techniques* was suggested instead. Derivatography, however , is an acceptable term, and to avoid certain confusions we shall call it *thermal derivatography*, based on the fact that the device which yields the DTG curve is generally accepted by the name of *derivator* the world over.

This instrumental device simultaneously measures: the temperature of the sample, the temperature of the thermally inert substance, the temperature of the furnace, the temperature difference between the sample and the thermally inert substance at the moment when thermal processes take place (DTA curve), the change in mass of the sample depending on temperature (TG curve), and the rate of change in mass (DTG curve) of the same sample, and in the same unit time. Figure 8 illustrates the schematic diagram of the derivatograph designed by the above-mentioned authors.

Operation of the device is fully automatic; it records the four curves on a light-sensitive paper fastened to a rotary cylinder which turns at constant speed. The sample under investigation is placed in the crucible *3*, which is heated in the furnace *1*, whose temperature rise in unit time is uniform. Two sources of light *7* and *8* are located on the beam of the balance; light signals from these sources are transmitted to the photographic paper *12* through the lens *6*, recording the TG curve. On the beam of the balance opposite to the sample under investigation there is an induction coil *10* in the homogeneous field of the permanent magnet *9*. The field of force of the magnet raises an induction current in the coil, whose voltage

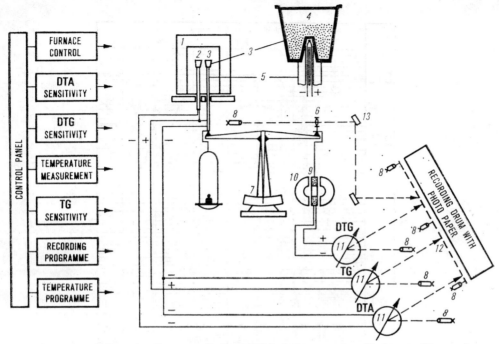

Figure 1.8   Schematic   diagram   of   the   MOM   derivatograph — Budapest   (Hungary).

is proportional to the rate of motion of the balance beam. The light signal of the galvanometer *11* connected to the coil poles traces the DGT curve on the same photographic paper.

In addition, the instrument simultaneously measures processes of chemical and physical conversion which develop under the action of thermal energy, like the equipment for differential thermal analysis. The crucible *3* which holds the sample is designed so that the welded point of the thermocouple should lie within the sample, in contact with the bottom. This thermocouple is connected to a second thermocouple whose weld is placed in a second crucible, identical to the first and filled with thermally inert material. The light signal transmitted by the mirror of the galvanometer records the DTA curve on the photographic paper, since the galvanometer itself is differentially connected to the poles of the thermocouples.

Considering that the experimental aim is to determine the temperature at which the processes take place in the sample, a third galvanometer has been introduced between the poles of the thermocouples whose light signal traces the temperature curve *T*. This temperature curve can be interpreted only if the recording paper is provided with a calibrated temperature scale. The temperature scale is calibrated on the photographic paper by means of a special device *13*, either before or after the determination. The graph obtained is the so-called *thermal derivatogram*, an example of which is provided by Figure 1.9.

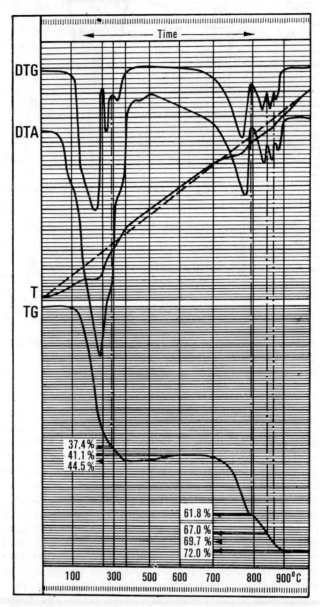

Figure 1.9   Thermal   derivatogram   of   an   isomorphous
crystalline   association   of $CuSO_4$ and $FeSO_4$ with nH_2O.

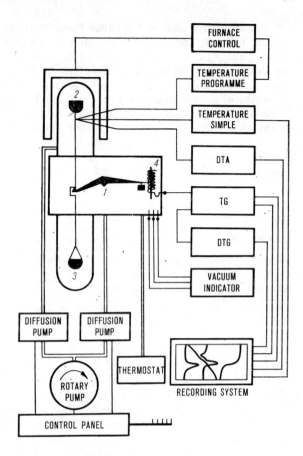

Figure 1.10 Schematic diagram of the thermo-analytical equipment by Mettler (Switzerland).

The operating principle of the derivatograph illustrated in Figure 1.8 is to a certain extent similar to that of all types of complex thermal analysis instruments. There are at present a great number of complex instruments for thermal analyses designed by specialized firms or built by local means in each laboratory. The number of complex instruments based on the operating principle of the derivatograph is rather large; a few types have, however, gained an almost unanimous appreciation. Figure 1.10 illustrates the schematic diagram of the instrument produced by Mettler whose obvious advantage lies in that it permits determinations to be carried out at lower pressures than the atmospheric, as well as in various controlled atmospheres.

Another instrument, built by the French firm Setaram, is based on the same principle, but has the advantage of being coupled to a gas chromatography apparatus. This on the one hand permits to determine weight variations in two ways, that is, also by interpretation of the TG and DTG curves by gas chromatography, and on the other hand to study the nature of the gases evolved during heating, and at the same time to determine the percentage composition. Among the other types mention shall be made of the instrumental equipment made by Perkin-Elmer whose great advantage is that it very accurately renders thermal effects and mass variations when operating with very small samples, of the order of tenths of a milligram and even less. Obviously, there are at present very many types of thermal analysis instruments in the world market, but the principles underlying their operation are in the main the same.

Experimental Factors in the Methods of Thermal Analysis

The previous chapter shows that the methods of thermal analysis seek to determine the temperature differences between the unknown sample and a thermally inert substance, the mass modifications which occur as a function of temperature, and the rate at which these changes in mass take place. For results to be real and reproducible, it is first of all necessary to ensure that experimental conditions are identical.

    To obtain successfully reproducible thermal curves certain experimental factors which greatly affect the shape of the curves must be strictly observed. Temperatures that are characteristic of the thermal effects which appear in the sample during heating must also be strictly controlled. Temperatures at which physical modifications or chemical reactions occur, as well as the temperatures at which these modifications begin or end are not constant, with the exception of melting points which are always well defined temperatures. The inconstancy of the temperatures at which some thermal processes occur is most frequently caused on the one hand by the conditions under which the determinations are carried out, and on the other by the nature of the materials investigated.

Arens (1951) suggested a number of experimental factors which must be considered in differential thermal analysis, dividing them into primary and secondary factors. The primary factors include the rate of temperature increase in the furnace, the height and radius of the sample groove, the nature of the sample, the position of temperature and of differential temperature measurement in the furnace, the nature and properties of the thermocouples, the density and degree of settling of the sample, the size of sample particles after grinding in the mortar, and the effect of covering the sample with a lid. As secondary factors Arens mentions the size of natural particles, the degree of crystallization, the presence of associations in the sample under investigation, etc.

Obviously, only the primary factors are common to all the types of solid associations, and the secondary factors are specific to each separate sample. The influence of these factors is discussed at length in the specialized literature, e.g. for differential thermal analysis by Mackenzie (1957), and for thermogravimetry by Duval (1963). In both cases, the authors discuss these factors separately, without comparing the two methods; there is few data in the literature concerning the case of a unitary aggregate for complex analyses. The following sections will be concerned with the way in which thermal curves are affected by these factors.

2.1 RATE OF TEMPERATURE INCREASE IN THE FURNACE

All apparatus for thermal analysis used at present are generally provided with devices which permit linear and constant heating with time. The heating rate of the apparatus is from 0.5 to 50 °C, and in some cases it is even higher. Selection of the heating programme is particularly important because the rate at which the temperature is raised in the furnace affects determinations quantitatively, having a large influence on the results obtained. Two considerations are involved in selecting the heating programme of the furnace, both closely connected with the nature of the sample investigated. Thus a heating rate below 10 °C min^{-1} satisfies the cases in which two thermal conversions overlap wholly or partly. In this case, the slower the heating rate, the larger the intervals at which these conversions appear in the recording. However, it is not possible to decrease the heating rate below a certain limit because the thermal effects recorded are large and without well-defined starting and end points. When the heating rate is greater than 15—20 °C min^{-1}, the recording of the thermal effects taking place is narrow, with very sharp points, and close thermal effects overlap, giving rise in most cases to false effects which are hard to construe.

The above are best illustrated in the following example. In the case of gypsum heated at a rate of 5 °C min⁻¹, the water of crystallization is removed in three well defined stages. When the heating rate is of 10 °C min⁻¹, only two dehydration stages appear on the thermal curves, that is, the passage of gypsum into plaster, and then into anhydrite. Finally, at a heating rate of 20 °C min⁻¹, the intermediate dehydration stages disappear almost completely (Figure 2.1).

The influence of the heating rate on thermal curves can be accounted for by the fact that with increasing heating rate the amount of gaseous products evolved within the sample also increases, giving rise to a temperature difference between the sample and the furnace. This discrepancy can be greater or smaller, while gases are in their turn removed faster at higher heating rates. It follows from the example given that the temperatures at which thermal effects occur in the three cases vary with the heating rate. At a low heating rate, thermal effects occur at lower temperatures than at higher heating rates. At the Algiers 1952 International Geology Congress, Mackenzie and Farquharson suggested a heating rate of 10 °C min⁻¹ with a variation of ±1 °C as stardard heating rate for differential thermal analysis. This recommendation, adopted by most mineralogical laboratories, fails however to become a standard heating rate because the highly varied chemical composition of the materials investigated has shown that other heating rates have to be used in each case on its own merits. The heating rate of 10 °C min⁻¹ has been preserved as a standard rate for the investigation of minerals only, and especially for argillaceous ones.

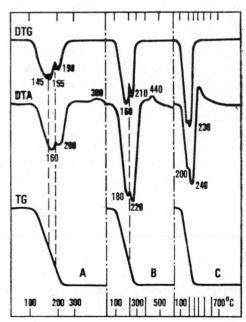

Figure 2.1 Comparative thermal curves of gypsum, obtained at three heating rates, while preserving the same recording rate: A, 5 °C min⁻¹; B, 10 °C min⁻¹; C, 20 °C min⁻¹. The values on the curves indicate the temperature of the maximum of the thermal effect.

In conclusion, the heating rate affects the height and width of thermal effects recorded by DTA and DTG curves, while the TG curve is substantially changed at various heating rates. Low heating rates produce broad superficial thermal effects, whilst high rates produce narrow thermal effects, with sharp points, with contiguous effects tending to merge, and overlapping totally or partially. Likewise, more sensitive measuring instruments are required at low than at high heating rates, because the electric thermocurrent produced is very feeble. For this reason, the optimum heating rate in any investigation must be a compromise depending on the nature of the sample under investigation, on the technical potentialities of the analytical instrumental device, on the thermally inert material used, and on the furnace. The heating rates so far used by various investigators vary within wide limits, from 0.5 to 200 °C min^{-1} and this large variation depends on the maximum temperature to which the sample is heated and on the nature of the investigation.

2.2 THE POSITION OF TEMPERATURE MEASUREMENT

The main role of thermal analyses is to accurately determine the temperature at which thermal processes take place so as to permit the results of an unknown sample to be compared on the basis of this temperature with those of a standard sample. The apparatus used to carry out the determinations are provided with three possibilities for measuring the temperature: (i) in the sample under investigation; (ii) in the thermally inert substance; and (iii) in the furnace. Experimental data have shown that it is much more correct to measure the temperature in the sample under investigation. If the temperature is measured in the furnace, the heating programme of the furnace will not take place at a completely uniform rate in unit time. Assuming, however, that this should happen, a special instrumental device would be necessary to indicate the temperature of the furnace over the duration of heating compared to that of the sample under investigation, because the temperature variations of the sample are independent of the furnace temperature. The above observations are fully valid also when the temperature is measured in the thermally inert substance. The thermally inert substance will have the same temperature as the sample under investigation only in the range in which chemical reactions or physical conversions take place. For example, if a reaction or a thermal phenomenon attended by evolution of heat appears in the sample, the temperature of the sample then rises above the temperature of the furnace and of the thermally inert substance (in the case of exothermal effects); conversely, if the reactions or thermal processes occur with heat absorption (the case of endothermal effects) the temperature of the sample will stay below that of the furnace and of the thermally inert substance. Hence the real temperature of any thermal process is determined accurately only when it is measured in the sample under investigation.

2.3 ROLE OF SHAPE AND MATERIAL OF CONSTRUCTION OF THE GROOVE FOR TEST SAMPLE

The groove for test samples is the name given to the space in which the sample and the thermally inert substance are placed in the instrumental analytical system. Various groove shapes for samples were used in the course of time both in self-made apparatus and in those produced by commercial firms. The design of these grooves is aimed at obtaining, with an infinitesimal amount of sample, the largest possible deviation on the thermal curves at the moment when the thermal process takes place. Although this is not easily feasible, it is nevertheless desirable to use the smallest possible sample; for this reason it is recommended that the groove should take a sufficient amount of material to give the highest thermal effects that are at the same time reproducible and easily interpreted.

The materials used in the construction of these grooves are of two kinds: metals or ceramics. Metals most frequently used in the construction of grooves include nickel, high temperature stainless steel, noble and half-noble (plain or alloyed) metals. Ceramic materials used in the construction of grooves include alumina with silica admixtures, burnt clays, high temperature resistant glass, and frequently graphite. No systematic tests have been made concerning the advantages and disadvantages of the materials from which these grooves are made. It could, however, be established that there is a difference both as to the field of use and the reproduction of thermal effects. The advantages and disadvantages of the two types of materials may be summed up as follows.

Metallic grooves, which are in widespread use, can much more easily be processed; they are not porous, and give only small deviations of the heat flux, and hence of the basic line of the DTA curve. Their disadvantage, however, is that the intensity of the thermal effects tends to be small because the heat transfer takes place rapidly through their walls, and between these walls and the sample mass.

Ceramic grooves, on the other hand, yield thermal effects of large intensities for the same amount of reacting material as in metallic grooves, because the heat transfer proceeds slowly through their walls. Ceramic grooves, however, also have certain disadvantages. For example, placing them in the furnace is more difficult because they must be very well centred on account of their low thermal conductivity rate. Another disadvantage is that, owing to their porous structures, they may affect the shape of the thermal effects or they may get contaminated in the case when the sample contains a compound which melts. Generally, in such sample grooves the base line of the DTA curve is very difficult to obtain, because of the low and non-uniform heat transfer rate from the exterior towards the interior of the groove. This is due to the low thermal conductivity of the materials used to make these grooves.

As to the *shape* of the sample grooves, two trends have compelled recognition in the course of time: the use of block-shaped grooves (Figure 2.2, sketch number 1 to 5), and the use of crucible-shaped grooves (Figure 2.2, sketch number 6-11). Block-shaped grooves, regardless of whether they are made of ceramics or metals, are provided with two or three orifices, one for the substance to be analysed, one

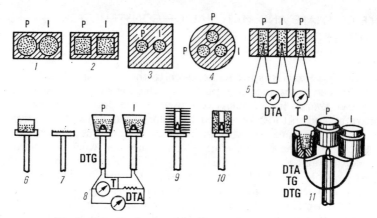

Figure 2.2 Various types of grooves for samples:
1, 5 block type grooves; *6, 11* crucible type grooves; *P*, sample to be analysed; *I*, thermally
inert substance.

for the thermally inert substance, and another (if there are three) for measuring
the temperature; the latter is filled, as preferred, with the sample to be investigated
or with thermally inert substance. Block-shaped grooves are the most indicated
for investigating the heat exchange, that is, for differential thermal analysis, but
they cannot be used under good conditions for thermogravimetry, and for
derivative thermogravimetry. As a rule, crucible-shaped grooves are made of metals.
These grooves have found a much wider field of use in complex thermal analyses,
satisfying the requirements imposed both upon heat exchange and mass exchange
measurements.

The most usual geometrical shapes of sample grooves are the cylindrical ones
but other geometrical shapes were used in the course of time. It appears that the
relation between shape and volume of the groove is not very important from the
view point of differential thermal analysis. In this sense, however, it is advisable
to show that the shape and height of the groove which is used depends on the
reaction undergone by the sample under investigation. For example, if the shape
of the groove is a cylinder of small diameter and high walls, and the material of
which it is made is watertight, the oxidation reactions tend to be inhibited, the
decomposition reactions to yield less marked thermal maxima, and the slopes
and levelness of the mass variations to be inconclusive. If the groove is shaped as
a cylinder, its increase in length beyond a certain limit does not affect so much the
magnitude of the thermal effects recorded on the DTA curve as on the TG and
DTG curves which it affects appreciably. It was found in practice that cylindrical
grooves whose length is one and a half times their diameter yield satisfactory results
in most cases both for differential thermal analysis and for plain or derivative
thermogravimetry, regardless of whether they are in the form of blocks or of
crucibles.

Grooves in the form of the frustum of a cone, whose cross-section illustrates
the description of the derivatograph, have been increasingly generalized world-

wide over the last ten-year period. These grooves, made of metals or ceramics, fully meet the requirements of heat exchange measurements as well as those in connection with mass variations.

A comparative study of the problems dealt with in this paragraph can be found in a paper by Erdey, Paulik and Paulik, (1966).

2.4   THE IMPORTANCE OF COVERING THE SAMPLE

It is, in general, difficult to state precisely when the experiments should be carried out with the samples covered or uncovered. Assuming that all experimental parameters are kept constant, there is a great difference between the curves which are obtained with the sample covered and those with the sample uncovered. Covering of the sample exerts a considerable influence on the beginning of the reactions, particularly when there exists a change of mass. Reactions which take place with a change of mass, involving dehydrations and decompositions, may also develop when the sample is covered, but show a temperature discrepancy of the thermal effect and particularly of the maximum peak of this effect. Reactions which are accompanied by an increase of mass, such as oxidations, may be completely inhibited or may proceed incompletely when the sample is covered, because the access of the oxygen required for oxidation is very difficult (Popa and Todor, 1970).

Figure 2.3 depicts two series of thermal curves of a sample of siderite: one series was obtained with an uncovered sample during analysis (case *I*), and the other with a covered sample (case *II*). It can be noticed that the decomposition temperature is about 20 °C lower in case *I* than in case *II*. It can also be noticed that the oxidation process takes place over an interval of about 100 °C in case *I*, whereas in case *II* this oxidation process extends over an interval of about 200 °C. This low oxidation rate of the substance entails a faint marking of the recorded thermal effect.

It can be said, in conclusion, that by covering the sample a straight base line of the DTA curve can be obtained in certain cases. In other cases, however, when vigorous reactions take place, attended by boiling or decomposition which would cause some of the sample to be forced out of the groove, this would be prevented from occurring during the thermal process. It is, nevertheless, better to operate as far as possible with uncovered samples. This precaution of operating with the uncovered sample is taken to permit the free admission and evolution of gasses and water vapours which attend thermal reactions, and which, in a closed system, would lead to the suppression of certain reactions, a fact causing an appreciable distortion of thermal curves.

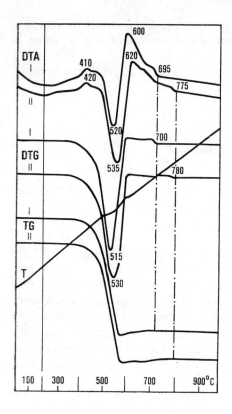

Figure 2.3   Thermal curves of siderite:
I, uncovered sample; *II*, covered sample.

2.5   INFLUENCE OF DEGREE OF GRINDING OF THE SAMPLE

In selecting the degree of grinding of the sample, two factors have to be considered: the size of the native sample grains and the size to which these must be reduced by comminution.

Carthew (1955) has found that by taking the equivalent spherical diameter as basis, when the particle size decreases below 2 mμ the thermal effects will increase asymmetrically and the temperature of the dehydration maximum of kaolinite will decrease below 550 °C. This observation confirms Berg's (1953) deductions and are wholly in accord with Scherer's (1949) theoretical considerations. Scherer suggested that particle sizes close to the colloidal size would have little effect on the heat of reaction.

Practical experiments, however, have proved that the curves obtained on certain samples may be largely dependent on particle size, whereas for other samples they do not seem to be largely affected. No reason has been found so far to explain this, but the process is believed to be closely connected with the structural factors of the sample. It is well, nevertheless, to establish the order of magnitude of the particles within close enough limits for the results to be reproducible. When comparing one's own thermal curves with those from the literature one has to admit that certain thermal effects of an unusual and different shape are possible also because of the differences in particle size.

In order to establish the extent to which particle size affects the characteristic shapes and temperatures of the thermal effects in the three types of thermal curves I have conducted experiments (Todor, 1971) with three different fractions of a siderite sample, namely, a finely ground sample, a coarsely ground sample, and a cube with sides of about 1 cm in length. Figure 2.4 illustrates the three thermal curves obtained.

It was experimentally proved that the decomposition temperature is all the lower the finer the degree of grinding of the sample. In the case of oxidation, the larger the granulation of the aggregate, the closer the temperature interval in which oxidation takes place, because the spaces filled with air which remain between the granules are bigger at a larger granulation, enhancing oxidation and promoting the exchange of gasses within the sample.

It can be stated, in conclusion, that the smaller the granulation of the sample the smaller will be the decomposition temperatures, and the smaller will be the

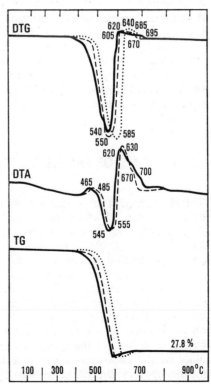

Figure 2.4   Variation of the thermal curves depending on the granulation of a siderite sample:
— — — — coarsely ground sample (above 2 mµ)
—————— finely ground sample (below 2 mµ)
. . . . block sample.

surfaces of the thermal effects. These observations are valid for the whole range of physical conversions or chemical reactions, excepting oxidations, and this fact can be referred to the smaller forces required for changes taking place inside the crystals in proportion as particle dimensions grow smaller. For the best possible correlation of results both in one's own laboratory as well as between various laboratories the most useful diameter sizes to which sample grains should be reduced are from 0.01 to 0.02 mm. This particle size can readily be achieved by using two screens with these sizes of opening, and collecting the sample for analysis on the 0.01 mm screen.

2.6 DENSITY OR DEGREE OF SETTLING OF SAMPLE

Differences in the density or degree of settling of the sample in the groove are the most common causes of deviations from the base line of the DTA curve. A marked settling is to be recommended in most cases with a view to obtaining a pronounced thermal effect with a straight zero line. A low density or settling degree, that is, a loosening up of the sample in the reaction groove promotes feeble reaction development which affects thermal processes by distorting their recording on the thermal curves. Let it be reminded that when determining organometallic compounds, whose molecules are large, the samples must be settled very well and even pressed, otherwise they will come out of the reaction groove on heating. This is due to the fact that on decomposing as a result of rapid oxidation by means of the oxygen included in the voids between particles, the volume of the molecules expands very much.

2.7 AMOUNT OF SAMPLE TESTED

The ideal amount of sample required for a thermal analysis should be a little sphere covering the weld of the thermocouple and producing perceptible thermal effects. This is not quite so easy in practice since, on the one hand, highly sensitive thermocouples would be required, and on the other, a very sensitive thermal balance and a very fine temperature measuring, amplifying and recording technique.

Considering the results obtained by Mackenzie and Farquharson (1952), in the scheme suggested for standardizing the differential thermal analysis, and considering all other factors to be kept constant, the weight of the sample examined may vary from 0.2 to 1 g without this variation having any appreciable influence on the results. As a rule, the amount of sample to be taken in hand is determined by the sensitivity of the apparatus any by the intensity of thermal processes taking place in the substance under investigation. At first sight it would seem that by increasing very much the sensitivity of the instrumental equipment the amount of sample required for analysis could be greatly reduced. In these cases, however, the control of experimental conditions must be very exacting in order to avoid large deviations from the base line.

Naturally, the weight and volume of the sample affect the temperatures characteristic for the beginning and ending of chemical reactions. This influence, however, is smaller in the case of physical phenomena. Systematic work on the role of the amount of sample for analysis was carried out by Richer and Vallet (1953), with a view to establishing the best decomposition temperature in the case of artificial and natural calcium carbonate using an atmosphere of dry air or carbon dioxide. Duval (1963) also reports the influence of the amount of sample in hand in the case of chelates and of calcium oxalat monohydrate.

2.8 THERMALLY INERT SUBSTANCE — EFFECT OF DILUTING SAMPLE WITH THERMALLY INERT SUBSTANCE

It has already been shown that in differential thermal analysis a thermally inert substance is heated simultaneously with the sample to be investigated. Thermal phenomena which appear during heating or cooling are recorded against this substance. To obtain correct results by this method, while expressing only temperature anomalies due to physical processes or chemical reactions which occur in the mass of the sample, the selection of the thermally inert substance is very important. Most frequently, however, this fact is considered of minor importance.

The first condition required from a thermally inert material is that it should not produce thermal effects in the temperature range in which the determinations are made. This property of the thermally inert substance is checked experimentally by heating it in both grooves, that is, both in that reserved for the sample and in that reserved for the thermally inert substance. The recording obtained in this case should be as close as possible to a straight line. Aluminium oxide, previously calcinated at temperatures above 1400 °C, is the most frequently used thermally inert substance. The thermal characteristics of aluminium oxide are not always similar to those of the sample under investigation. This leads to a deviation from the base line of the DTA curve, and false thermal effects are therefore obtained.

Arens (1951), using kaolinite calcinated at 1200 °C, has shown that the specific heat and the thermal conductibility of calcinated kaolinite are very different from those of ordinary kaolinite; he, nevertheless, obtained very good base lines, assuming that this difference in thermal conductibility was due only to the size of the particles.

However, the use of the precalcinated sample as thermally inert material is not generally advisable because reversible conversion processes such as the polymorphic transformation of β-quartz into α-quartz at a temperature of 573 °C cannot be observed owing to their annihilation as a result of the transformations taking place both in the sample under investigation and in the thermally inert substance. In this case, a temperature difference will no longer appear between the sample and the thermally inert substance, because both thermocouples will have the same temperature.

In the course of time, various metallic oxides or other inorganic combinations were used as thermally inert materials without, however, yielding the best results. In general, deviations from the base line of the DTA curve are caused by the different thermal conductivity of the inert material against that of the sample under investigation.

Notoriously, from the viewpoint of thermal conductivity, crystals may be described by the specific coefficient of thermal conductivity K, representing the amount of heat transmitted in unit time perpendicular to the face of a cube with sides of 1 cm. The temperature difference between two opposite faces of the cube may be expressed by the equation:

$$\frac{dQ}{dt} = -KF\frac{dT}{ds}$$

where F is the surface through which heat is transmitted, s is the density, and T is the temperature.

The coefficient K is measured in cal cm^{-1} s^{-1} $°C^{-1}$.

There is a close connection between thermal conductivity, and the reticular structure of the crystals. From this viewpoint, crystals may be good heat conductors, such as native metals and minerals with metallic glitter, or bad heat conductors, such as non-metalliferous minerals in general.

Hence the best inert materials are those which have the same thermal conductivity as the material under investigation; but, whatever might be the material used, it must have the same grading and its weight must be equal to that of the sample to be analysed. In practice, however, the conclusion was unanimously reached that aluminium oxide is the most adequate inert material, after being first calcinated at 1400 °C.

When the sample amount is too small to fill the groove or when exceedingly intense thermal effects are produced, which the recording system fails to sense, then the sample may be diluted with the thermally inert substance. When the sample is diluted with the thermally inert substance it is necessary for the diluent to have approximately the same grading as the sample to be analysed. It is also required that the mixture of sample and thermally inert substance be perfectly homogeneous. This can be achieved by lightly grinding in an agate mortar the sample together with the thermally inert material in presence of a liquid having no influence on the sample and which is highly volatile, for example, acetone.

2.9 INFLUENCE OF FURNACE ATMOSPHERE ON THE DEVELOPMENT OF REACTIONS

Furnace atmosphere is understood to mean the free space within the furnace holding the gases which result from the heat promoted chemical processes. As a matter of fact, the atmosphere in this free space of the furnace is continually changing.

In the beginning this atmosphere is either that of the surroundings or, in some cases, that which it is desired to create. However, as heating goes on it will change its composition. This is the result of chemical reactions taking place in the sample, whereby volatile products are given off in gaseous form. Whereas the atmosphere initially present in the furnace can be kept under control in respect of its composition and pressure, this is much more difficult with the atmosphere produced as a result of chemical processes during heating. Variations in the composition and pressure of the furnace atmosphere directly affects the determination by methods of thermal analysis.

The thermal decomposition process of a natural or artificial product proceeds slowly; at a given temperature the gases given off as a result of the related process have a certain pressure termed *the decomposition pressure*. For example, when calcium carbonate is decomposed, the following relation exists between temperature and carbon dioxide formed as decomposition proceeds:

T	500	600	700	800	900 °C
p	0.2	2.4	25	180	760 mmHg

The equilibrium between both phases, that is, between the amount of carbon dioxide which results and the content of non-decomposed calcium carbonate, is determined directly at the temperatures given by the pressure of the gas:

$$p_{CO_2} = k = \text{const.}$$

It follows that the decomposition of calcium carbonate is accelerated when the total or partial pressure of carbon dioxide surrounding the calcium carbonate is smaller. This fact explains why the decomposition temperature is lower and decomposition takes place in a more restricted temperature range when the analysis is carried out in a vacuum than in air or in a carbon dioxide atmosphere (Figure 2.5). Hence a change in the composition of the furnace atmosphere calls for a modification of decomposition temperatures; therefore, the atmosphere within the furnace has to be kept carefully under control (Erdey and Paulik, 1955).

The relations between decomposition temperatures of the analysed substances, the pressure created in the furnace, and the nature of the gases resulting from decomposition were studied by many research workers. Determinations were carried out in various atmospheres, such as H_2, N_2, O_2, SO_2, air, and inert gases.

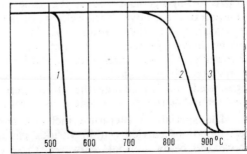

Figure 2.5 Heat decomposition of a calcite sample in various atmospheres *(according to Erdey, Paulik and Paulik, 1966)*:
1, vacuum; *2*, air; *3*, carbon dioxide.

Experiments have shown that if there is a gas in the atmosphere of the furnace similar to that released by thermal decomposition of the substance, an increase of the initial and final temperatures of the thermal effect produced by decomposition is to be expected. This phenomenon was first observed by Vallet (1937), who heated copper pentahydrate in a metal crucible and in wet and in dry air.

The gases formed within the sample as a result of some thermal process caused by dehydration, combustion, decomposition, etc., also have an appreciable influence on thermal effects. This influence can be referred to the formation velocity of the gaseous product within the sample as a result of a thermal decomposition process by which the pressure will increase with increasing temperature. If more gas is produced within the sample than the amount of air eliminated through its pores, an accumulation of gases will take place in the sample, causing the inner pressure to increase; this slows down the reaction velocity and practically brings decomposition to a halt.

An accumulation of gases within the sample is also promoted by some of the experimental factors such as covering the sample with a lid, the density and compactness of the sample in the reaction groove, an increased amount of sample worked, and a quick temperature rise in the furnace. All these, moreover, make for slowing down the decomposition reactions and for the overall decomposition to take place at higher temperatures.

Gases resulting from decomposition as heating proceeds accumulate not only in the free spaces between particles, but to a much larger extent inside the particles themselves. In this case volatile products in the form of gases have to pass through a bed of solid material; it therefore stands to reason that the development of thermal decompositions is in the first place affected by particle size.

In some cases thermal determinations are conducted in the presence of special gas streams which are introduced into the furnace for the purpose of removing the atmosphere created as a result of the thermal process. Particular attention should be paid in such cases to the rate at which these streams are introduced, because the composition of the furnace atmosphere changes in relation to the velocity of the gas stream introduced and if the velocity is not constant essential modifications of the thermal curves will be produced.

Instruments are not all built to permit determinations in the presence of gas streams. There are instruments whose furnace is open at the upper part to enable the gas to circulate readily by convection, and in this way to subject the reaction groove to impingement and at the same time to shocks, producing a continuous vibration of the groove. If the velocity of the gas stream is too high, these vibrations are transmitted to the recording system, causing distortion of thermal curves which become unreliable and hard to understand. Other furnace types have at the upper or lower part two or three orifices which can be opened or closed by the operator as required. It is possible in this way to control the velocity of the gas stream introduced, and to change the atmosphere in the furnace more or less quickly, thus removing the gases released as a result of a thermal process.

The specialised literature includes numerous experimental data concerning determinations carried out in various gas atmospheres and at various pressures, above and below normal. However, these data are widely scattered and difficult to compare with each other because not all experimental parameters were kept constant. It is an apparently logical assumption that by removing the gases released as a result of a thermal decomposition process, the pressure in the furnace might be kept constant. A pressure difference will nevertheless be created within the sample whose influence on thermal effects will not be too large. It is also a well-known fact that the influence of convection currents is moderate when operating at pressures below normal, but if the pressures are too low a number of frequently unknown error sources will crop up. This fact was confirmed by Eyrant and Cotton (1955), who have shown that at pressures below 1 mm Hg the recorded thermal effects are highly erroneous.

It can be stated, in conclusion, that whatever might be the experimental pressure adjusting procedure in the furnace, the pressure is to be kept constant during the determinations.

2.10   THE NATURE AND PROPERTIES OF THERMOCOUPLES

Thermocouples are used for temperature measurement in the instrumental equipment for thermal analysis.

A thermocouple consists of two wires of different composition, welded together at one end, and which have the property when heated at the welding spot to give rise to an electric current proportional to the amount of heat applied.

In selecting the thermocouple, various factors have to be taken into consideration. Thus, the thermocouples used must not be affected chemically by the material to be investigated in case it is in direct contact with it, nor by the volatile products resulted from thermal decomposition. At a minimum temperature rise the thermocouples used must produce an electromotive force sufficiently large to be sensed by the galvanometer with which the thermocurrent is measured.

Ideal thermocouples are those built of noble metals; they are unaffected by thermal attack and they have a long lifetime as compared to those built of common metals. The value of the electromotive force of a thermocouple depends on the composition of the metals welded together; hence these metals are selected according to the highest temperature at which investigations are conducted.

The electromotive force of a thermocouple is expressed in microvolts or in millivolts for a temperature difference of one degree. But in most cases the electromotive force of a thermocouple fails to vary linearly with temperature; thus which thermocouple is best fitted for the case under investigation can be decided only with approximation.

In a wide temperature range from 100 to 2200 °C the thermocouple consisting of two wires of which one is platinum and the other a platinum and rhodium alloy is used successfully. In most cases this alloy has the following composition: Pt 80 per cent and Rh 20 per cent. The electromotive force of such a thermocouple is small, but it will give perfect indications respecting the temperature range and reproducibility of the electromotive force.

For temperatures from 100 to 800 °C it is proper to use thermocouples made from special nickel and chromium alloys which are cheaper and more readily procured. The electromotive force of these thermocouples is four to six times larger than that of platinum/platinum-rhodium thermocouples and they stand well up to a temperature of 800 °C.

For still lower temperatures, thermocouples made from constantan-copper or constantan-iron wires can be used. In this case, however, one has to take into account that at temperatures of about 500 °C copper and iron oxidise vigorously, and therefore thin wires which are quickly destroyed should be avoided. To prevent premature oxidation of iron or of copper a number of precautions have to be taken either by protecting the wires in a ceramic casing or by carrying out determinations in a vacuum or in an atmosphere of inert gases, thus greatly reducing their corrosion.

As already stated, the electromotive force of the various thermocouples is far from being constant over the whole temperature range in which they are used, that is, it does not increase proportionally to the temperature rise.

To obtain accurate results with the thermocouple selected it must meet several special requirements. The wires of which they are made must be structurally homogeneous over their whole length since otherwise local currents would be formed which might distort the results obtained. In order to annihilate local mechanical stresses in wires these are previously annealed by passing an electric current through them strong enough to make them glow. The test for homogenity is carried out as follows: The wires, which are welded together at one end, are connected to a sensitive galvanometer at the other end and the flame of a gas burner is passed along their whole length. If the wire is homogeneous, the galvanometer needle should stand still. The lack of chemical homogeneity of the wires cannot be removed by annealing, and should this be the case they must be replaced.

Since in the previously discussed method of differential thermoanalysis, the temperature and the temperature difference are measured by means of a differential thermocouple system, it is required that both welding points of the conductors leading to the galvanometer should have the same temperature in case they are not introduced into the sample and into the thermally inert substance.

A rather important problem raised when thermocouples are used is their calibration. With many types of apparatus the calibration of the temperature scale for the thermocouple in question is already carried out by the manufacturer, but in most cases thermocouples must be calibrated or at least checked from time to time.

Calibration is carried out with various pure substances whose thermal effects amount as a rule to phase changes and always take place at a well-defined temperature.

After the 1956 Thermoanalysis Conference at Aberdeen a Standards Committee was set up under the chairmanship of McAdie (Canada) to carry out in the first place the investigation and selection of the substance types which will permit us to define the characteristics of each apparatus with a view to systematically comparing the results obtained by various experimenters. These temperature standards were broadly speaking selected from a number of about 200 proposed substances, the selection being performed on the following grounds:

(i)   Chemical stability of the substance; no change to occur during storage however prolonged.
(ii) Chemical inertness of the substances; they are not to react with crucibles or the sample grooves of apparatus in the temperature range used.
(iii) Temperature of thermal conversion effect to be specified by thermodynamic equilibrium methods.
(iv) Substances used should not require previous mechanical or thermal treatments.
(v)   Substances used should be capable of being heated both in the surrounding atmosphere and in an inert one without yielding secondary thermal effects.
(vi) If the substances used also produce other thermal effects which cannot be looked upon as the effect needed for standardizing, these effects should take place at distinctly different temperatures.
(vii) Substances used as standards should be inexpensive and readily obtainable in a high degree of chemical purity.

Table 2 **Temperature values of substances proposed as temperature standards as compared to the temperature standards indicated by IBS**

Substance	Cohversion temperature	Heating rate	n	Heating temperature measured in points		
				A	B	D
KNO_3	127.7	a	36	128±4	128±4	134±5
		b	62	127±5	129±4	137±6
$KClO_4$	299.5	a	41	297±6	299±6	304±6
		b	62	298±5	300±5	309±6
Ag_2SO_4	412.0	a	40	425±6	426±7	433±7
		b	67	424±8	429±6	438±6
SiO_2	573.0	a	39	567±7	572±5	575±5
		b	71	543±38	569±6	575±4
K_2SO_4	583.0	a	38	576±11	584±4	588±4
		b	66	558±29	583±4	589±5
K_2CrO_4	665.0	a	37	663±12	668±5	671±4
		b	59	657±14	668±5	671±5
$BaCO_3$	810.0	a	72	802±8	807±6	815±7
		b	41	800±7	809±4	819±8
$SrCO_3$	925.0	a	37	922±7	928±6	934±6
		b	57	921±10	928±6	938±7

Values of conversion temperatures gives by the National Bureau of Standards, Washington D.C. 20234.
According to results recorded by ICTA it appears that the real temperature of Ag_2SO_4 is 430± 2 °C and that given by the IBS is erroneous.

n is the number of analyses carried out by all laboratories participating in the first programme launched by the ICTA; a is data obtained at heating rates below 4.9 °C min⁻¹: b is data obtained at heating rates above 5.0 °C min⁻¹.

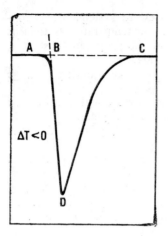

Figure 2.6 Determination of the three temperature points of a thermal effect on a DTA curve.

Considering these criteria, only eight out of the initially proposed substances were selected and distributed to twenty five laboratories for testing in view of correlating the conversion temperature of thermal effects. Returned data indicate for every substance three temperatures, *A*, *B*, *D*, measured in three different points of the thermal effects, corresponding to points *A*, *B*, *D*, from Figure 2.6, whose values are listed in Table 2.

Research workers from the laboratories participating in this programme have tried also to correlate the temperatures of thermal effects when substances are cooled after having undergone the respective thermal phenomenon; on the basis of experimental data, however, the conclusion was reached that standardizing should be carried out only on heating, because some substances when cooled exhibit metastability phenomena.

It follows from the experimental data listed in Table 2 that scattering of the temperature values obtained is greater for the temperature measured at point *A*, that is, for the initial temperature of the thermal phenomenon, than at points *B* or *D*.

Although the thermal phenomena selected were generally clear-cut and determinations were carried out in laboratories with a vast experience in this field, the scattering of results is nevertheless high enough. Values listed in Table 2 refer to the first programme launched by the ICTA. A second programme was subsequently launched, with two more substances added: indium whose effect lies at 157.0 °C and tin whose effect lies at 231.9 °C; unfortunately data obtained are not known.

Since the nature of thermocouple composition affects only the aspect of the rendering of thermal effects recorded by the method of differential thermoanalysis, it is necessary that papers and publications illustrated by such curves should also show the thermocouple used.

2.11 CHARACTERISTIC TEMPERATURES OF THERMAL EFFECTS AND CAUSES OF THEIR VARIATION

It was found experimentally that the only correct procedure in establishing the temperatures of thermal effects is by reporting the time function of the curves obtained *vs.* the temperature of the sample investigated. These temperatures of the thermal effects are most frequently characterized in published papers by the peak temperature of the thermal effect in the case of endothermal phenomena, and by the initial temperature of the effect in the case of exothermal phenomena.

Characteristic temperatures of thermal effects are not absolute values; they depend, as already stated, both on a number of experimental factors, and on the nature and structure of the material under investigation. Causes affecting these temperatures will briefly be enumerated in the following.

The characteristic temperatures at which the thermal effects of a substance to be analysed occur are in the first place affected by the presence of alien ions in the sample. Take, for instance, a sample of calcite in which calcium ions were partly replaced with manganese; at first sight it would appear that, as a result of this substitution, thermal analyses would make obvious two temperature ranges in which thermal decomposition takes place, one caused by the decomposition of calcium carbonate and the other by that of manganese carbonate. In fact, however, only one endothermal effect is obtained caused by the decomposition of calcium carbonate with the only difference that the larger the amount of manganese ions in admixture with calcium the lower is the decomposition temperature.

Alien substances present in a product may also cause a marked depression of the melting point. The influence of melting point variation in the system KCl-NaCl was studied by Nguyen-Ba-Chanh and Bastide (1968), whose graphical reproduction is depicted in Figure 2.7. Fodvarine and Koblenez (1955) found that decomposition temperatures have different values in presence of alien ions.

Another element on which the characteristic temperature depends is the crystallization degree of the substance investigated. According to Grimshaw (1945), Grim (1947), and Murray (1954), the endothermal reaction and the exothermal reaction of faintly crystallized kaolinite develop in a wider temperature range, and the temperature of thermal maximums has lower values than those corresponding to well-crystallized kaolinite. Caillers and Henins (1948) ascribe the temperature differences of thermal effects in the case of two argillaceous minerals also to the different degree of crystallization of the two minerals. Likewise, when a natural product and its synthetic equivalent are analysed one obtains differences of the temperature of thermal effects; these differences are also caused by the different crystallization degree of the two compounds.

When a product is being heated, chemical reactions may take place among its components which may appreciably modify the characteristic temperatures at which thermal effects take place and even the shape of these effects on the curves

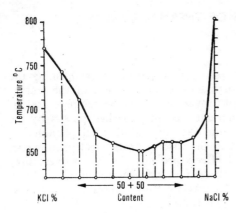

Figure 2.7 Lowering of the melting point
of the system KCl-NaCl *(Nguyen-Ba-Chanh
and Bastide, 1968)*.

It was thus noticed that if an intimate mixture of dolomite and calcium hydroxide is heated, the endothermal effect at about 700 °C, caused by the decomposition of magnesium carbonate from the dolomite lattice is hardly perceptible on the thermal curves. This annihilation of the endothermal decomposition effect of dolomite is due to the exothermal reaction which instantaneously sets in as carbon dioxide is being formed by decomposition of magnesium carbonate, and calcium oxide by the previous decomposition of calcium hydroxide. Consequently, the first endothermal decomposition effect of dolomite is almost annihilated, while the second endothermal decomposition effect of dolomite is amplified owing to the decomposition reaction of calcium carbonate additionally formed as a result of the reaction of carbon dioxide with calcium oxide. Reactions of this kind are numerous enough. Investigations were conducted in this direction by Berg (1943, 1945), Schwab (1950), and Graf (1952), who found that a mixture of NaCl, KCl, Na_2CO_3, and Na_2SO_4 with calcite causes the endothermal decomposition of calcite completely to disappear, allowing other reactions to take place.

Volume modifications which appear in the sample during heating also have a large enough influence on the shape of the DTA curve. Volume contractions, agglomeration or melting of the material by heating affect the behaviour on heating of the initial sample, and consequently the shape and amplitude of the thermal effects recorded on the curves. For example, magnesium and calcite lose on heating 52 per cent and 44 per cent, respectively, of their weight at the decomposition temperature, and a modification of the thermal conductivity will hence take place because the residue is different from the initial sample, resulting in a modification of the base line of the DTA curve. The influence of the thermal conductivity on the DTA curve may be mitigated in most cases by first diluting the sample with a thermally inert substance.

It follows from previous considerations that a knowledge of all processes and reactions taking place in the compounds subjected to analysis is somewhat difficult but not impossible, because good results are obtained after not too long an experimental time and by investigation of synthetically prepared standard samples.

2.12 GENERAL CONCLUSIONS ON EXPERIMENTAL FACTORS

In carrying out thermal analyses and interpreting the curves in view of establishing the composition of a sample one must never forget that the development of reactions taking place in the sample as a result of thermal energy are largely connected with experimental operating conditions. The thermal curves obtained are always the result of several thermal effects which, in their turn, are closely connected with the factors bearing upon the development of chemical reactions and physical conversions going on in the sample. For example, if the recording of thermal curves of the same sample is repeated in other experimental conditions, then these curves may differ from one another so much that it is frequently difficult to compare them.

Development of the changes taking place under the action of thermal energy also depends on the structure of the material to be analysed, which determines the thermal conductivity of the compound, its thermal capacity , and the equilibrium of the chemical reactions.

Chemical reactions caused by rising temperatures must in principle develop at a certain temperature the same as physical processes. Unlike chemical reactions, melting points are processes which always take place at well-defined and exact temperatures. Chemical reactions, for example, decomposition reactions, must be completed theoretically as soon as the sample has reached the decomposition temperature; these are, however, ideal theoretical cases because thermal effects recorded on the curves instead of being drawn together, appear extended over large temperature ranges.

Likewise, if thermal modifications due to physical processes would take place with a large heat consumption or a vigorous heat release, these modifications should appear on the DTA curves as effects with large peaks and small width. As a rule, analysed substances are, however, bad heat conductors; they are in command of a considerable heat storage capacity, and for this reason they require a longer time for the transmission of heat from the external layers of the sample to its central point where the thermocouple is located. Thus a temperature gradient arises inside the sample, and this has to be taken into consideration in studying thermal effects.

Development of conversions caused by a linear increase of the temperature is also influenced by the emergence of new phases which arise during heating. In this sense, mention should also be made of the reactions developing between solid components and gases resulted from thermal decomposition processes. From the partial or total pressure created by the gaseous product evolved in the decomposition one could determine mathematically the magnitude of decomposition in a closed system. Reactions taking place simultaneously with evolution of the gaseous product as a rule develop slowly, and are completed only when the temperature is appreciably increased. Gaseous components arising as a result of a decomposition process reach the pressure in the furnace progressively and as a rule only at higher temperatures. On the recorded thermal curves these reactions yield large loop-shaped thermal effects without well-defined peaks.

Also analogous to the previous ones are recorded those reactions and equilibria which take place between various phases, for example, between solid and liquid or between solid and gaseous phases. Equilibria between solid and liquid phases, as well as the reaction rate between these two phases is similarly affected. These reactions are featured by the diffusion rate or by the rate at which the products resulted from the reactions of the liquid are transported on the surface of the solid material.

At first sight it would seem that, owing to the shortcomings already shown, the thermal curves obtained cannot be used successfully for analytical purposes. Nevertheless, these curves can be used for establishing the composition of a compound accurately enough.

To this end, in carrying out thermal analyses the following conditions must be met:

(i)   The temperature scale of the instrument should be standardized with high purity standard reagents.

(ii) The same groove should be used for samples; on changing this groove, the zero line has to be standardized again.

(iii) Standard curves should be obtained on monominerals or on pure single substances, and on mixtures of known composition for the purpose of comparing them with curves obtained on unknown samples.

(iv) The same system of thermocouples should be used.

(v)   The groove should be filled with the sample to be analysed under rigorously standardized conditions, so that the charges should be mutually comparable.

(vi) The increase rate of the temperature in the furnace should be kept constant over the whole temperature range in which the determination is carried out.

Since the dimensions of particles, the degree of crystallization; the kind and amount of substituted ions, as well as the admixture of foreign matter greatly affects not only the heat of transformation, hence the DTA curve, the application of differential thermoanalysis for quantitative purposes will be limited. Therefore, the DTA curve will be used only to establish the nature of thermal conversions, and this implicitly will help in qualitative identifications for establishing the compounds present in the sample investigated. For quantitative interpretations, data furnished by thermogravimetry and by derivative thermogravimetry is in most cases sufficient.

3

Interpretation of Thermal Curves

Curves obtained by the methods of thermal analysis may be interpreted from several viewpoints specific to each investigation, but all of them have as a starting point an analytical, qualitative or quantitative interpretation.

Thus, by means of the DTA curve it is possible, in the first place, to establish the temperature difference between the sample investigated and the thermally inert substance which shows whether the thermal process occurred with consumption or release of heat; in the second place, the DTA curve can be used to find the characteristic temperature of the thermal process. In addition, DTA curves are also used for analytical interpretation of TG and DTG curves, to specify thermal effects and the cases in which it is necessary to find the absolute value of the modification of the heat content. Calculation of the absolute value of the temperature difference ΔT between the sample and the thermally inert substance can be carried out by means of the area of the thermal effect between its two sides and the base line of the DTA curve.

By an analytical interpretation of the TG and DTG curves it is possible to determine the mass variation produced as a result of a chemical process. This also permits one to establish the reaction rate, and the temperature range in which the reaction proceeded; it finally leads to a quantitative determination of the compounds which have generated these reactions.

3.1 ANALYTICAL INTERPRETATION OF THERMAL CURVES

Quite a number of methods for the analytical interpretation of thermal curves are described in specialized works. These interpretations are highly varied from the viewpoint of the operating procedure. In the following discussion I will present only the basic features of the main interpretation procedures.

3.1.1 Qualitative interpretation of the DTA curve

As shown above, curves recorded by the methods of differential thermal analysis indicate not only the thermal effects of chemical reactions related to changes in mass, but also the physical changes which a compound undergoes as an effect of thermal energy. Differential thermal analysis thereby provides more cues for the identification of an unknown product than derivative thermogravimetry.

Before proceeding with a quantitative interpretation of the DTA curve, it is first necessary to establish the sign of the thermal effect, that is, whether the effect is endo-thermic or exo-thermic.

Secondly, one must determine the specific temperatures of each separate thermal effect. Three values are considered, as a rule, when establishing the specific temperatures of a thermal effect, namely the peak temperature of the effect and the temperatures of the two bases. The values are compared with data obtained on standard samples or, failing such samples, with existing data from the literature. It should be mentioned that only the temperatures specific to the peak of the thermal effect can be determined accurately on DTA curves, whilst the temperatures of the beginning and end of the thermal effect may be determined only with an approximation because of the uncertainty of the base line.

Over the whole temperature range used in differential thermal analysis the base line ought to be an horizontal straight line; in practice, however, it always deviates more or less from this linearity. These deviations are due to the fact that it is not always possible to achieve thermal symmetry of the heating installation. One of the most frequent causes leading to line deviation is that thermal energy reaches the sample crucible or groove first by heat conduction from the furnace to the sample, and then by reaction.

The atmosphere in the furnace absorbs readily enough the heat of the furnace walls, owing to its reduced capacity to keep the heat. The space in the furnace, holding this atmosphere, may be considered homogeneous with respect to heat distribution. The amount of heat transmitted by radiation depends on the distance between the radiation surfaces and the absorbent or the sample. To avoid base line deviation, it is frequently necessary to modify the distance between the furnace wall and the groove in which the sample is seated. In other words, the groove holding the sample is moved closer to or farther from the furnace wall then the groove filled with thermally inert material.

Likewise, if the winding of the surface causes an irregular distribution of the electrical heating resistance, overheating of the wall surface may occur in certain spots, resulting in a temperature difference between the sample and the thermally inert material. As a rule, this fact may cause shifting of the base line from the horizontal in one direction or another. In both cases, the deviation may be removed by moving and turning either the furnace or the sample groove around. Good results were obtained also by interposing between the furnace and the sample a protecting wall consisting of a good heat conductor, for instance, a quartz tube.

Deviation of the base line may also be produced in case the heat conductivity and the specific heat of the sample fail to agree with those of the thermally inert material. In these cases, the galvanometer used to record the DTA curve shows a temperature difference between the thermally inert material and the sample. This temperature difference can be diminished by applying a low heating rate. Likewise, in order to remove this temperature difference, it is advisable to use as a thermally inert material a substance whose thermal conductivity is equal to that of the sample about to be analysed, which is generally very hard to achieve.

As heating progresses, a modification of the specific heat conductivity of the sample may also be brought about, and this in turn also leads to modifications of the base line. As a rule, after a thermal effect has taken place, the DTA curve fails to return to the same level as before this effect, remaining below or rising above the original level. The deviation of the linearity of the DTA curve occurs as a result of a change in the physical properties of the sample due to the physical or chemical process which has taken place.

Modification of the heat conductivity, and hence also deviation of the DTA curve from the base line, is caused by the formation of conglomerates which appear in the sample as heating proceeds. In industrial research it is very important to establish the temperature and the nature of those conglomerates which appear while a product is being heated. When the conglomerate appears at higher temperatures, the deviation of the base line occurs as a break.

Shifting of the base line of the DTA curve may also be due to other causes than those already enumerated. In such cases particular attention has to be paid to the analytical interpretation of those processes. The fact must not be overlooked that on heating standard mixtures prepared artificially do not always behave analogously to native compounds, and different thermal curves are therefore recorded.

3.1.2 Quantitative interpretation of the DTA curve

In the course of time, many researchers have tried to set up a method of interpretation enabling one to determine quantitatively the temperature difference between the sample and the thermally inert substance by means of the thermal effects recorded on the DTA curve. The indirect aim of this method is to make it possible to establish the amounts of the components present in the sample about to be investigated.

A direct connection between the peak height of the thermal effect recorded on the curve and the amount of the component which has produced this thermal effect was originally postulated. At present, interpretation is generally based on the well-known relation which exists between the surface of the thermal effect S and the amount of heat Q absorbed or evolved by the substance about to be investigated. Mathematically, this is expressed by a simple relation:

$$S = kQ \qquad (16)$$

where k is a proportionality factor.

Since the factor k largely depends on many experimental conditions, it has not yet been possible to give it a rigorous mathematical interpretation. Practical observations have shown that this factor depends on the thermal conductivity, on the calorific capacity, on the form and dispersion degree of the sample, on the ratio of heat exchange between the sample and the ambient medium in the furnace, on the characteristics of the instrumental equipments, etc.

Speil (1944) showed that the surface of thermal effects depends on four experimental parameters, namely:

(i)   The heat of reaction Q per unit mass, expressed in cal g^{-1};
(ii) The mass of the sample m, expressed in grammes;
(iii) The thermal conductivity λ (expressed in cal K^{-1} cm^{-1} s^{-1}) of the sample when a metal crucible is used;
(iv) The shape coefficient g of the sample groove.

The following relation holds between these parameters:

$$S = g\,\frac{Qm}{\lambda} \qquad (17)$$

Let it be assumed that some thermal effect is taking place in the time interval t_1 and t_2 or in the temperature interval T_1 and T_2. Considering this fact, the surface may be expressed by means of the following equation:

$$S = \int_{t_1}^{t_2} \Delta T\, dt \ [\text{in K s}^{-1}] \qquad (18)$$

The amount of heat absorbed by the thermally inert material in a given time interval is determined from the temperature increase from T_{i_1} to T_{i_2} depending on the mass of the thermally inert material m_i and on its specific heat c_i. This amount of heat is conveyed to the thermally inert material by heat conductivity and it will be proportional to the heat conductivity k_i of the thermally inert material, and to the difference between the temperature T_i of the thermally inert material and the temperature T_f of the furnace:

$$m_i c_i [T_{i_1} - T_{i_2}] = k_i [T_f - T_i] \qquad (19)$$

Modification of the amount of heat m_s of the sample as a result of a thermal process is affected by a modification of the active substance m which gives this process through the thermal energy $\pm m \dfrac{dH}{dt}$ released or absorbed in unit time t. Here H is the total amount of heat absorbed or released on modification of the active substance in the sample as a result of some thermal process.

The following relation holds for expressing the modification of the amount of heat absorbed or evolved by the sample in a given time interval:

$$m \frac{dH}{dt} + k_p [T_c - T_s] = m_s c_s [T_{s_1} - T_{s_2}] \tag{20}$$

where:

m = Mass of active sample;
m_s = Total mass of sample;
c_s = Specific heat of sample;
k_s = Thermal conductivity of sample;
T_f = Temperature of furnace;
T_s = Temperature of sample;
T_i = Temperature of thermally inert material.

If the mass of the sample and of the thermally inert material are approximately equal, that is, $m_i = m_s$, then also in practice $T_{i_1} - T_{i_2} = T_{s_1} - T_{s_2}$. In this case even the specific heat of the sample c_s does not, as a rule, deviate from the specific heat of the thermally inert material c_i. For this reason no great error is made if the above equation is put in the following form:

$$m_i c_i [T_{i_1} - T_{i_2}] = m_s c_s [T_{s_1} - T_{s_2}] \tag{21}$$

In this case equations (20) and (21) may be expressed together in the form:

$$m \frac{dH}{dt} = k_i [T_c - T_i] - k_s [T_c - T_s] \tag{22}$$

If the thermal conductivity of the sample and that of the thermally inert material are considered to be practically equal, that is, $k_s = k_i$, then equation (22) may be written thus:

$$m \frac{dH}{dt} = k [T_s - T_i] = k\Delta T \tag{23}$$

whence it follows that:

$$T = \frac{m}{k} \cdot \frac{dH}{dt} \tag{24}$$

This means that the temperature difference ΔT between the sample and the thermally inert material at a given moment is all the greater as the amount of active substance m is larger, as the heat conductivity k of the sample is lower, and as the amount of heat dH/dt evolved or absorbed in unit time by the sample is larger.

If it is intended to calculate the modifications of the temperature difference between the sample and the thermally inert material with time during the development of a thermal process, then equation (22) will be integrated over the time interval $t_1 - t_2$, that is:

$$m \int_{t_1}^{t_2} \frac{\mathrm{d}H}{\mathrm{d}t} \, \mathrm{d}t = k \int_{t_1}^{t_2} T \, \mathrm{d}t, \tag{25}$$

whence

$$m \Delta H = \int_{t_1}^{t_2} \Delta T \, \mathrm{d}t. \tag{26}$$

Since H is a constant, for a given modification of the equation it will become:

$$m = \frac{k}{\Delta H} \int_{t_1}^{t_2} \Delta T \, \mathrm{d}t. \tag{27}$$

It follows from the mathematical considerations set out above that the amount of active component of the sample or the amount of thermal energy evolved or absorbed is proportional to the surface of the thermal effect. This means that it is possible to determine quantitatively the active components which produce the thermal effect of a sample on the basis of the surface of this thermal effect, because, as it was seen, there exists a direct proportionality between the surface of the thermal effects recorded on the curves and the mass of the active sample.

At first sight, these quantitative determinations on the basis of the surface of the thermal effects recorded on the curves require only a simple measurement of the surface of the thermal effects with a planimeter. But in order to determine with any precision the surface of the effect it is necessary first to define the basis of the thermal effect. In most cases this is determined by joining the two bases of the thermal effect with a straight line, which is not always possible, especially when the thermal effects are due to decomposition. In this case it is possible to use an artifice. Let us assume, for example, that the recording of the DTA curve is repeated with the sample previously heated to a temperature higher than that at which the thermal effect considered for calculation had taken place. In this way an horizontal DTA curve is obtained, which by definition becomes the basis of the thermal effect.

In order to specify the degree of reproducibility of the method for the determination of the active component on the basis of the surface of the thermal effects, experimental analyses were made by a number of researchers who sought to deduce an accurate relation between the surface of the thermal effects on the experimental curves and different amounts of sample, using the same volume which was achieved by dilution of the sample with thermally inert material. This operating method of diluting the sample with thermally inert material is the most indicated one because it changes only the amount of active sample m, leaving the other experimental factors unaltered.

To this end, Saule (1952) and Barshab (1952) tried to obtain thermal curves whose thermal effects should be as close as possible and higher by settling the undiluted sample around the thermocouple and then outside of it, adding then the thermally inert substance until the groove is filled. But results obtained with mixtures in different proportions were not very conclusive owing to the lack of uniformity of the sample within the groove in spite of the fact that the coefficient of shape g was maintained rigorously constant.

It follows from what was said with respect to the quantitative interpretation of the DTA curve that in order to make quantitative determinations it is necessary to operate with an invariable heating programme, and at the same time to make a previous standardization with standard mixtures of various concentrations, consisting of high purity components identical with those of the sample about to be analysed. This was necessary because it was found that the coefficient of thermal conductivity varies from one body to another, which is due to the variation of thermal diffusivity. Hence, if this condition is observed, it will be possible to use the experimental curves $\Delta T = f(T, t)$ even without transformation of the coordinates. This is a rapid method for the quantitative determination of the curves obtained by the method of differential thermal analysis (Ray and Kostomaroff, 1959).

A number of authors (e. g. Mackenzie (1952), Grimshaw and Roberts (1958)), sought to establish other relations between the amount of active component in the sample subjected to analysis and the surface of the thermal effect. But these have not proved to be sufficiently accurate and were generally abandoned.

More recent studies in this field were made by Berg and Egunov (1969). The starting point of these studies were two DTA curves obtained with the same sample, one diluted in various proportions and the other undiluted. To dilute the sample a thermally inert material was used which does not react with the sample and whose specific heat is known. The surface of the thermal effect, the dilution ratio, the deviation from the base line, and the heating rate were considered for computation.

3.1.3 Practical performance of quantitative interpretations

The most adequate method for the quantitative determination of the ratio between the surface of the thermal effect and the amount of active component in a sample is the method of *standard curves*. This method, of long standing in thermal analysis, gives good results only when some experimental factors are kept constant for a long time. The principle of the method is as follows: A number of standard samples are prepared from a known simple mineral sample (primary standard) by dilution with aluminium oxide over a range of concentrations in which the component of the unknown sample is also included. The DTA curve obtained by means of these standard samples are used to measure the surface of the thermal effect. The experimental points obtained, or the surface in square millimeters of the thermal effect, are plotted on a graph with the surface S of the thermal effect as ordinate vs. the concentration of the standard samples as abscissa. A straight or almost straight line is obtained by joining these experimental points.

There are several procedures for measuring the surface of the thermal effect, but the following three are used most frequently:

(i)   Measure the thermal effect very accurately by means of a planimeter.
(ii) Copy the thermal effect on ruled paper or on tracing paper, cut out the resulting surface and weigh it on an analytical balance.
(iii) Use special diagrams which are applied over the area of the thermal effect which is taken in calculation so that the concentration of the active component is determined directly by adding up the length of the segments included in the area of the thermal effect.

After analyses with standard mixtures are carried out, the unknown sample is analysed and the surface of the thermal effect is determined exactly in the same way as in standardizing. To the end, this surface of the thermal effect of the unknown sample is read off the standard graph and the concentration of the active component is thus determined. It is very difficult to determine the surface of a thermal effect when this partially overlaps the surface of another thermal effect which has taken place almost simultaneously as a result of another chemical or physical modification. In these cases other thermal effects given by the component sought must be taken for analysis or, failing a specific thermal effect, the quantitative determination of the compound by means of the method of differential thermal analysis must be abandoned.

It may be stated in conclusion that in the quantitative determination of a thermally active component on the basis of the surface of thermal effects on DTA curves errors are comparatively large and in most cases these interpretations provide only orientative quantitative data. If the differential thermal analysis is part of a complex of thermal analyses providing all three thermal curves (DTA, TG, and DTG), the interpretations which are made on DTA curves are only of a quantitative nature. Nevertheless, if the sample subjected to analysis contains only compounds which on heating give processes without mass modifications, then the thermal effects resulting from these physical modifications may be interpreted also from a quantitative point of view.

The specialised literature includes a large number of examples in which the authors have used DTA standard curves to determine some minerals on the basis of the surfaces of thermal effects. From these mention should be made of the work carried out by Grim and Rouland (1942), Schafer and Rossel (1942), Speil (1944), Grim (1947), Grimshaw and Roberts (1953), Sargordskii (1953).

3.1.4 Quantitative interpretation of TG and DTG curves

Interpretation of the TG curve is at first sight simple enough, requiring only to weigh the sample before and after carrying out the determination, when it has cooled down to the temperature of the surroundings. The difference between the two weighings gives the mass variation of the sample. By linearly measuring the total height of the mass variation, and distributing this measured height to various temperature ranges in which the chemical processes are taking place it is possible to calculate the mass variation specific to each separate reaction. But this calculation can be made only in the case of compounds whose mass is constant between the various reactions which give modifications, and this constancy must appear on the curve as a perfectly horizontal straight line, proving that various compounds of stable mass have resulted from the substance under investigation.

Analytical practice has shown that only a very small number of compounds, either native or artificial, fulfil the requirement of mass stability. For this reason, the simultaneous interpretation of the TG and DTG curves will be presented, and with a view to a most complex interpretation of thermal curves, some remarks will be made in connection with the DTA curve as compared to the TG and DTG curves.

The DTA, DTG, and TG curves are generally said to be functions of temperature, even when the reaction is stated to have started at X °C. It is almost paradoxical to speak about the mass modification rate or about the DTG curve as a function of temperature. It must, therefore, be shown if the experimental derivation system, that is, the system with magnetic induction coil which records the DTG curve, is capable of reproducing exactly the mass modification rate $(dm/dt = g/t)$ as a function of time, and how close must this be considered as a function of temperature. This was proved mathematically in 1958 by F. and J. Paulik, and Erdey.

It can be noticed readily that the velocity of motion of the balance during a thermal process which takes place with mass variation, that is, the oscillation rate (ds/dt) of the balance beam from which the induction coil is suspended, is proportional to the mass modification rate (dm/dt) of the sample about to be analysed, owing to the mechanical impulse which the induction coil receives from the oscillation of the balance. Hence, it may be assumed that the two values are approximately equal, that is:

$$\frac{dm}{dt} \approx \frac{ds}{dt} \tag{28}$$

By means of Neumann's law it is possible to calculate the e.m.f. of the induction current which arises in a coil rotating in a homogeneous field of force. For this we have to take into consideration the force of the homogeneous field H, the rotation velocity of the induction coil ds/dt, and the total length h of the induction coil winding wire, which are related as follows:

$$E = H \cdot h \frac{ds}{dt} \tag{29}$$

In practice, the permanent magnetic field between the poles of the magnet in which the induction coil oscillates is homogeneous. In this case, the value of the product $H.h$ from equation (29) is also constant and the equation may therefore be written:

$$E = \frac{ds}{dt} \text{const.} \tag{30}$$

Let us admit that this constant is in fact the resistance of the current circuit indicated by the galvanometer as the e.m.f. of the induction current. Hence, it may be stated that the run of the induction coil, if not too long, is proportional to the intensity of the induction current which has arisen in the coil. Therefore, the deviation g/t of the galvanometer renders truly the derivative of the mass variations:

$$\frac{g}{t} \approx 1 \approx E \approx \frac{ds}{dt}.$$

(31)

It is also known that the temperature of the furnace is a function of time, that is, $T = u/t$. This function is determined by the heating rate of the furnace. For uniform heating, the heating programme of the furnace is represented by a linear relation:

$$T = A\,t + t_0.$$

(32)

Coefficient A indicates the temperature growth rate per unit time. This heating rate notably affects the shape and intensity of thermal effects recorded on the curves. It is, therefore, absolutely necessary that the value A or the heating rate should remain constant over the range of the whole heating programme. For a linear heating programme, assuming that the temperature of the sample increases uniformly with that of the furnace, the temperature function and the time function of the galvanometer run are proportional to the differential quotients of the TG curve:

$$\frac{dm}{dt} = g(t) = g'(T).$$

(33)

If the mass variation function becomes $m = f(T)$, that is, if this mass variation is taken as a function of temperature, then the following relation obtains:

$$\frac{dm}{dt} = \frac{dm}{dT} \cdot \frac{dT}{dt}.$$

(34)

But, as shown above, the derivative of Equation (32) is a constant value:

$$A = \frac{dT}{dt},$$

(35)

and by introducing this value into equation (34) one obtains the following relation:

$$\frac{dm}{dt} = A \cdot \frac{dm}{dT}.$$

(36)

Substituting the value dm/dt from equation (33) into this relation we get:

$$A \cdot \frac{dm}{dt} \approx g(t) \approx g'(T).$$

(37)

It follows from these considerations that when heating is uniform, the DTG curve may be taken into account not only as a function of time but also a function of temperature. However. as mentioned before, the temperature of the sample is modified at the same time as the heating of the furnace, but somehow independently of the temperature of the furnace, according to the known function $T = v(t)$. The mathematical formula of this function is not known, and as a matter of fact it need not be, since this function is recorded by means of a galvanometer which is connected in parallel to the differential thermocouple, and thus the temperature of the sample is observed at any moment, also permitting an interpretation of thermal curves as a function of temperature (F. and J. Paulik, and Erdey, 1964).

Three important conclusions may be drawn for practical purposes from what was stated above, namely:

(1) Earlier interpretations made by the conventional method of differential thermal analysis, and in which the results were expressed as a function of the temperature of the thermally inert material or of the furnace were not correct, because the temperature of the furnace or of the thermally inert material may at a given moment be different from that of the sample. By measuring the temperature in the sample about to be analysed a number or errors are removed and the thermal curves interpreted as a function of temperature are analogous to those interpreted as a function of time.

(2) In the restricted sense of the word, DTA, DTG, and TG curves are functions of time, but with certain reservations they may also be considered as a function of temperature. One has, therefore, either to speak only about the function of time $dm/dt = g(t)$ or only about the function of temperature $dm'/dt = g'(T)$ of the sample about to be investigated, since the modification of the temperature in the sample $T = f(t)$ is subjected to them.

(3) For the reproducibility of DTA, DTG, and TG curves to be constant with time it is necessary that the furnace should be heated linearily. At an unchanged heating rate, that is, when the heating programme is linear, the temperature will remain unchanged for every sample.

From what was said above it follows that the recording of the DTG curve renders turning to account of the TG curve considerably easier. This results conclusively from the following:

(i)   Since in a sample with several components, thermal reactions are closely connected or partly overlapping, the TG curve presents a continuous mass variation mobility which will appear on the DTG curve separated in the form of cusps, enabling the related reactions to be clearly distinguished. Instrumental devices which record the DTG curve on the basis of magnetic induction will sense the slightest change in the mass modification rate, and these determinations are therefore the most adequate for reactions of this kind which cannot be determined by means of ordinary thermal gravimetry.

(ii) Temperature ranges in which chemical reactions take place can be established much better and more exactly by means of the DTG curve than by means of the TG curve. TG curves can, at most, show the temperature intervals which indicate the beginning and the end of the reaction; but in conjunction with DTG curves, they indicate the development of thermal processes and the temperatures at which changes occur in them.

3.1.5 Simultaneous interpretation of DTA, DTG, and TG curves

Simultaneous interpretation of the three types of thermal curves may be carried out from two points of view: that of the mass modification on one hand, and that of the modification of the heat content on the other.

According as the development of the DTA curve is identical with or different from that of the DTG and TG curves, there are several possibilities of interpretation of thermal processes. Three cases may be distinguished in the interpretation of thermal curves:

(1) When, as a result of heating a product, it is found that thermal modifications are recorded on the DTA curve only, while the DTG and TG curves indicate no change in mass, then the conclusion may be drawn that the sample has undergone only physical transformations or chemical reactions without any mass modification.

(2) When all three thermal curves show a chemical modification taking place at a well-defined temperature, that is, they appear as an horizontal line, then the product newly formed as a result of a thermal reaction is stable.

(3) When the DTA curve, on one hand, and the DTG and TG curves, on the other, differ as to shape and development, indicating, therefore, different thermal modifications, it means that these have arisen as a result of thermal effects of two or more chemical reactions or of chemical reactions combined with physical modifications. In this case, TG and DTG curves record either one or several of these reactions but only such that take place with weight modification, while the DTA curve records the sum total of chemical reactions and physical transformations.

The method of calculating the dolomite content in a sample of native kaolinitic clay will be presented as a practical example of the simultaneous interpretation of the DTA, DTG, and TG curves.

Under the action of thermal energy, dolomite decomposes at 700 to 950 °C in two stages, recorded by thermal curves as endothermal effects. The first reaction of thermal decomposition occurs as a rule from 700 to 800 °C, and is caused by the decomposition of magnesium carbonate from the dolomitic lattice, according to the following reaction:

$$(Mg,Ca)\,(CO_3)_2 \rightarrow CaCO_3 + MgO + CO_2.$$

The second reaction, recorded on the curve as a larger effect, is the thermal decomposition of calcium carbonate: $CaCO_3 \rightarrow CaO + CO_2$. In this case, the quantitative calculation of the carbonate content is carried out as follows:

Straight lines are drawn perpendicular to the TG curve from the upper cusps of each thermal effect recorded on the DTG curve (Figure 3.1). The perpendiculars divide the TG curve into segments proportional to each separate thermal effect, corresponding to each loss of mass caused by the related reaction. The ratio between the total height (in mm) from A to E, corresponding to the total loss of mass, and each separate segment ($A-B$, $B-C$, $C-D$, and $D-E$) gives the total loss of mass due to each thermal effect or to each chemical reaction.

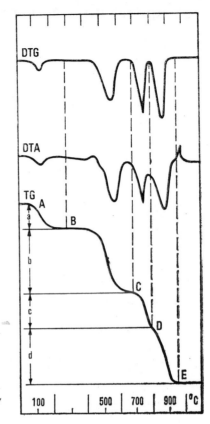

Figure 3.1 Thermal curves of kaolinitic clay associated with dolomite.

Figure 3.1 illustrates this process, and reveals the following stages of loss of mass:

(i) The total loss of mass in the interval $A - E$ is:

$a + b + c + d$ [mm] $= Q$ [per cent].

(ii) The loss of mass due to argillaceous minerals in the interval $A-B-C$ is:

$a + b$ [mm] $= X$ [per cent].

(iii) The loss of mass due to the decomposition of magnesium carbonate in the interval $C-D$ is: c [mm] $= Y$ [per cent].

(iv) The loss of mass due to the decomposition of calcium carbonate in the interval $D-E$ is: d [mm] $= Z$ [per cent].

Two exothermic effects are noticeable on the DTA curve which, as can be seen, are not attended by changes in mass. The first exothermal effect situated at about 460 °C is due to the presence of iron oxides which have suffered a polymorphous transformation; the second exothermal effect, situated at about 960 °C, is due to a structural reorganization of dehydrated kaolinite present in the sample.

3.2 KINETIC INTERPRETATION OF THERMAL CURVES

Not only the DTA curve but also the TG and DTG curves are susceptible to quantitative interpretation from a kinetic point of view, especially when the recorded thermal effects are consequences of heterogeneous reactions which have taken place in the sample under the action of thermal energy.

In general, heterogeneous reactions which can be investigated by thermal analyses may be integrated with the following fundamental scheme:

$A_{(s)} \to A_{(g)}$: Endothermal effect with negative mass variations;

$A_{(s)} \to B_{(s)} + C_{(g)}$: Endothermal effect with negative mass variations;

$A_{(s)} + B_{(s)} \to C_{(s)}$: Endothermal or exothermic effect without mass variations;

$A_{(s)} + B_{(s)} \to C_{(s)} + D_{(g)}$: Endothermal or exothermal effect with negative mass variations;

$A_{(s)} + B_{(g)} \to C_{(s)}$: Endothermal or exothermal effect with positive mass variations;

$A_{(s)} + B_{(g)} \to C_{(s)} + D_{(g)}$: Endothermal or exothermal effect with positive or negative mass variations;

where: s = solid; g = gaseous; A, B, C, and D = compounds.

As follows from this scheme, heterogeneous reactions include a large variety of chemical processes whose study is of interest both from practical and theoretical points of view.

Some procedures for the kinetic interpretation of the DTA curve, on the one hand, and of the TG and DTG curves, on the other hand, will be presented in the following discussion.

3.2.1 Kinetic interpretation of the DTA curve

This quantitative interpretation of the DTA curve permits a measurement of the kinetic parameters of reactions, and was studied in detail by Rey and Kostomaroff (1959). Both researchers started from the Arrhenius equation, written in the following form:

$$k = A^{-\frac{E}{RT}} \tag{38}$$

where:

k = Kinetic constant of reversible reaction in homogeneous medium;

A = Frequency factor connected with reaction probability, hence with enthalpy variation;

R = Amount of heat, termed reaction energy or activation energy.

This relation, generally applicable to heterogeneous reactions, which is most frequently studied by means of thermal methods, requires a correction of the factor A

Figure 3.2 Graph of kinetic interpretation of DTA curves *(after Rey and Kostomaroff, 1959)*

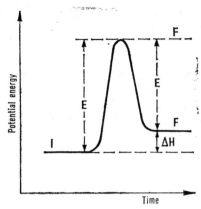

by a coefficient ν called the *factor of transformation* from one stage to another Hence, the Arrhenius equation modified by this factor takes the form:

$$k = \nu A^{-\frac{E}{RT}} \tag{39}$$

Before calculating the values of the factors ν, A, and E, it is necessary to know the thermodynamic representation of the *activity* concept, which may be rendered more concrete by assimilation with an energy barrier. To this end, a graph is made with potential energy plotted as the ordinate *vs.* time as the abscissa. Considering a system whose energy level is I, a curve will be obtained with the shape illustrated in Figure 3.2.

If the reaction caused by temperature takes place in the range of the system, then its final energy level F is different from I, and for the reaction to take place it is generally necessary to raise the energy level* up to a certain maximum. If time flows from right to left, we have to do with a reversible endothermal reaction whose activation energy is E_1. The reverse reaction is an exothermal one whose activation energy is E_2, and by definition these two reactions are equal to the enthalpy variation of the sample caused by these two reactions:

$$E_1 - E_2 = + \Delta H \text{ (endothermal effect)} \tag{40}$$

$$E_2 - E_1 = - \Delta H \text{ (exothermal effect)} \tag{41}$$

These relations are valid both for chemical reactions and for physical transformations. But, while a sample is being heated, a chemical reaction may take place concurrently with a continually rising temperature, and the products resulting from this reaction may be removed from the system in a gaseous form. In this case, if the instrumental system cools down, the reverse reaction becomes

---

* *Energy level* is the energy state of an atom or a molecule related to a certain state, considered to be the fundamental one.

unlikely and the term E_2 is not involved: hence equations (40) and (41) may be written as follows:

$$E_1 = \Delta H \tag{42}$$

Further, the Arrhenius coefficients E and A have to be calculated depending on the experimental factors. Kissinger (1956) has shown that E and A may be expressed as a function of v and T_m (where v is the heating rate of the furnace, and T_m is the experimental temperature of the peak thermal effect on the DTA curve), as follows:

$$-E = R \, \frac{d \ln \left[\dfrac{v}{T_m^2} \right]}{d \left[\dfrac{1}{T_m} \right]} \quad \text{[in cal mol}^{-1}\text{]} \tag{43}$$

and

$$\ln vA = \ln \frac{E}{R} + \ln \frac{v}{T_m^2} + \frac{E}{RT_m}. \tag{44}$$

In order to be able to calculate equation (43) a number of three determinations by the method of differential thermal analysis, each at a different heating rate, have to be carried out compulsorily, resulting in a variation of T_m. Kinetic energy may be calculated by plotting the values obtained, in a graph with the value $R \ln(v/T_m^2)$ as ordinate, and the value $1/T_m$ as abscissa. To obtain accurate results, particular care is advised because, when E is calculated for exothermal heterogeneous reactions, the values obtained are generally higher than ΔH.

3.2.2 Kinetic interpretation of TG and DTG curves

In the course of time, isothermal methods of kinetic calculation and a large number of interpretation methods based on thermal curves obtained by the method of ordinary thermogravimetry or of derivative thermogravimetry were developed. Such an interpretation was developed for the first time by van Krevelen and co-workers (1951); they starded from the fundamental equations of chemical kinetics:

$$\frac{du}{dt} = k(\mu_0 - \mu)^n \tag{45}$$

and

$$k = k_0 e^{-\frac{E}{RT}} \tag{46}$$

where μ represents the mass variation (expressed in gravimetric units) of the concentration or the transformation degree of the substance A at the moment t; μ_0 is the initial value of the magnitudes k, k_0, R, and n, representing the kinetic constant, the pre-exponential factor, the activation energy, and the order of reaction, respectively.

Further, the authors mentioned above have taken into account the relation which shows that, unlike isothermal methods, thermal analysis methods require a continual temperature increase; hence the temperature of the system subjected to analysis increases in unit time t in keeping with a linear law:

$$\frac{dT}{dt} = a \qquad (47)$$

Introducing equations (46) and (47) into the fundamental equations of kinetics (45) one obtains:

$$\frac{du}{(\mu_0 - \mu)^n} = \frac{k_0}{a} e^{-E/RT} dT \qquad (48)$$

To solve this case, one selects as variable the function F of undecomposed substance at moment t or at temperature T, and denoting the ratio E/R by A, equation (48) becomes:

$$-\frac{dF}{F^n} = \frac{k_0}{a} e^{-A/T} dT \qquad (49)$$

An approximate integration of this equation was carried with the assumption that the reaction proceeds in a temperature range in which absolute temperature meet the following condition:

$$0.9\, T_m < T < 1.1\, T_m \qquad (50)$$

where T_m is the temperature at which the maximum value of the reaction rate is recorded.

The equation obtained as a result of integration and which can be used as a working formula is:

$$\ln \int_F^1 \frac{dF}{F^n} = \ln \frac{k_0}{a} \cdot \frac{b^{-A/T_m}}{T_m} \cdot \frac{1}{\dfrac{A}{T_m} + 1} + \left(\frac{A}{T_m} + 1 \right) \ln T \qquad (51)$$

where b is a constant equal to 0.368.

The value of the integral $I = \int_F^i \frac{dF}{F^n}$ was listed in a table for different values of n.

For any decomposition reaction whatsoever the order of reaction may be found by graphically representing the expression $\ln I$ as a function of $\ln T$ (where T is the absolute temperature). From the slope of the straight line obtained by drawing perpendiculars to the ordinate it is possible to obtain the activation energy and the pre-exponential factor.

Studies concerning the kinetic interpretation of mass variations were also carried out by other research workers, including Freeman and Caroll (1958), Horowitz and Metzger (1963), Coats and Redfern (1964), Murgulescu and Segal (1967 and 1969).

In summing up considerations concerning the kinetic interpretation of thermal curves it must be specified that the values obtained in the case of kinetic determinations may also be affected by a number of experimental factors. Nevertheless, the determination of kinetic parameters from thermal curves has an ever increasing applicability, owing to certain advantages thermal methods present against conventional isothermal studies, e.g., much greater rapidity of determination, use of a single sample, possibility of considerably extending the temperature range.

3.3 THERMODYNAMIC INTERPRETATION OF THERMAL CURVES

Quantitative interpretation of thermal curves on the basis of thermodynamic principles were made only in respect of DTA curves. These quantitative interpretations start from the principle that, thermodynamically considered, the amount of heat Q absorbed or evolved by a substance is equal to the variation of the enthalpy ΔH of the thermal process which has taken place. Theoretically, it is, therefore, possible to calculate ΔH starting from the surface S of the thermal effect recorded on the DTA curve.

Several researchers have carried out such calculations and compared them with known thermodynamic data. Thus, Barshad (1952) and Sabatier (1954) have standardized the DTA curve graphically as in the usual procedure for graphical analytical determinations, carrying out differential thermal analyses on samples whose reactions have a known enthalpy. The value of thermal effects was thus determined in cal g^{-1} per unit surface.

As has been shown in connection with the analytic interpretation of DTA curves, the relation which gives the surface of the thermal effect is a function of four experimental parameters, equation (17). In the present case, the same relation is used to determine the surface of the thermal effect with the only condition that the coefficient g, representing the coefficient of shape of the reaction groove, should have the same experimental accuracy as in the case of quantitative analytical determinations of the DTA curve. From a thermodynamic viewpoint, the coefficient g was calculated by Saule (1952) and Boersma (1955), using the solution of Poisson's problem on the transmission of heat in a cylindrical body of radius r and volume V:

$$g = \frac{1}{4} \frac{r^2}{V} \quad \text{[in cm}^{-1}\text{]} \tag{52}$$

Replacing the terms by their values in equation (17) one obtains:

$$\Delta H = S \frac{4\lambda}{qr^2} \quad \text{[in cal g}^{-1}\text{]} \tag{53}$$

•

From this equation ΔH is then calculated, and the apparent specific mass q is determined. The latter is closely connected with the compactness of the sample in the groove, which in turn is an important factor to be considered in the calculation only when the analysis of the sample is carried out in a metal crucible. If a ceramic crucible is used, the thermal conductivity of the crucible is of the same order of magnitude as the conductivity of the sample, provided the determinations are carried out with non-metal samples. In this case this equation is much more complicated. Operating with metal crucibles, Rey and Fostomaroff (1959) have shown that the direct calculation of ΔH based on Equation (53) gives analogous results to those obtained by other methods.

In conclusion, it should be pointed out that whatever might be the procedure used for the analytical interpretation of thermal curves, good and accurate results can be obtained only by checking the degree of precision of the chosen method on a number of samples with known values, on the so-called standard samples. Consequently, it is better that each laboratory should have a sufficient supply of standard samples to be analysed also by other methods, and data obtained by these methods should be comparable with those obtained by thermal methods

3.4 RECOMMENDATIONS FOR THE COMMUNICATION OF ANALYTICAL DATA

Since thermal analysis includes dynamic methods, it is necessary to add all experimental data, to enable the results to be judged critically. Uniformity of research data and expression of results is absolutely necessary since many publications lack important experimental information. In this connection, the following recommendations should be observed in published papers so that authors and reviewers might be spared confusion in the communication of data. The way of communicating such details would naturally depend on the point of view and preferences of the authors and on the aim followed in publishing the paper. Since most published papers refer especially to the three methods, DTA, DTG, TG, only these will be considered in what follows. Thus, any rendering of the DTA, DTG, and TG curves must be attended by the following information:

(i) Indication of all substances, including the sample about to be analysed, the thermally inert substance and possibly if the sample about to be analysed was diluted with the thermally inert substance. These indications will be given with definite names with formulae or with appropriate data concerning the composition.

(ii) Data on the origin of the sample, data on the preliminary treatments, if any, and on the chemical purity as far as known.

(iii) Mean value of the recorded heating or cooling rate.

(iv) Description of the gaseous atmosphere surrounding the sample, related to the pressure, composition and purity of the ambient medium in the furnace. Indications as to whether the atmosphere is static or generated by the sample or if it is a dynamic atmosphere through the sample or over it. If necessary, the moisture content and pressure of the surrounding atmosphere should also be specified. When operating at pressures other than atmospheric indications must be given as to the methods of pressure control.

(v)   Data concerning the dimensions and geometrical shape of the sample groove and the material of which it is made, as well as the method of filling this groove with the sample.

(vi)   Scale of the abscissa for time or temperature must be given at an established place. Time or temperature must be recorded increasing from left to right.

(vii) Data as to the method selected for identifying intermediate and final products.

(viii) Perfect reproducibility of the original thermal curves as rendered by the instrumental equipment.

(ix)   Every thermal effect must be identified, if necessary , and additional proof must be supplied.

When papers are concerned primarily with the TG curve, the following supplementary data should be added:

(x)   Make and description of the thermal balance with indications as to its sensitivity as well as the location of the thermocouples for measuring the temperature.

(xi)   Data concerning the mass of the sample and the scale of mass variations on the ordinate. Other scales may also be used on the ordinate such as partial decompositions or variations of the molecular composition, in which case this has to be specified in detail.

When papers are concerned mainly with the DTG curve, the following supplementary data should be added:

(xii) Whether the derivation method is mathematical or whether the curves were obtained by way of instruments; the instrumental derivation system.

(xiii) Unit of measure on the ordinate.

When papers are concerned mainly with the DTA curve, the following supplementary data should be added:

(xiv) Mass of the sample and percentage of thermally inert material in mixture, if any.

(xv)   The scale on the ordinate must indicate deviations from the base line per degree centigrade, rendering in the graphical representation the linear magnitude of the unit degree, for example: 10 or 100 °C.

However, if these recommendations are not observed, reasons should be given for any deviations.

4.

Physical and Chemical Processes Detectable by Thermal Methods

Thermal processes of a physical or chemical nature which take place when an artificial or native solid product is heated or cooled are closely connected with the crystalline state of matter.

The property of an element or of a compound to assume the state of a solid body is purely mechanical in nature, and only of relative significance. A body is generally said to be solid when it has its own finite shape and opposes a considerable resistance to any forced modification of its shape.

The normal state of matter is crystalline. This state is an almost perfectly ordered aggregation of structural units, that is, of the component particles, atoms, ions or molecules. There are, however, numerous substances known to satisfy these properties without being truly crystalline or, if they are crystalline, to preserve permanent distortions as a result of very feeble mechanical action.

All solid products which are crystallized in a more or less geometrical form, macroscopically or microscopically visible or even invisible with the present means of investigation, generate on heating a series of processes that are physical or chemical in nature. In most cases these processes may be detected by thermal methods of analysis and are specific to the crystalline state.

For a better understanding of the changes which take place in crystals with temperature variations it is necessary to recall certain notions of thermodynamics.

Internal energy is defined as the amount of energy which a system has at a given moment. The variation of internal energy is taken to mean the total energy which the system gains or loses in the course of a process. This energy may be given to or taken from the system in any form as: heat, mechanical work, etc.

The variation of the internal energy dE during a transformation depends only on the initial and final states of the system and not on the specific change which the system has suffered in passing from one state to another. Therefore, the internal energy E is formally defined as a function of the state of the system having the property in any infinitesimal process whatsoever which takes place without change in composition to increase by an amount equal to the heat dQ absorbed by the system plus the mechanical work dW done on the system:

$$dE = dQ + dW.$$

Reversible and irreversible processes. A physical or chemical process is considered to be reversible when the system which generates it is in such a state of equilibrium that an infinitesimal variation of the conditions causes the process to develop in the opposite direction. But processes are reversible only when conditions differ infinitely little from the conditions of equilibrium and when the rate at which the process develops is extremely low. Almost all processes developing at higher rate are irreversible and take place only when the system is in a state somewhat far apart from that corresponding to the conditions of equilibrium.

Entropy. The notion of entropy is based on the fundamental difference between reversible and irreversible processes. Entropy is defined by two of its most important properties, namely:

(i)   In any reversible process, the variation in entropy of the system is measured by the amount of heat absorbed by that system divided by its absolute temperature:

$$S = \frac{Q}{T};\qquad(54)$$

(ii) In any irreversible process occurring spontaneously the change in entropy is greater than this amount.

The second law of thermodynamics states that the entropy S is a function of the state of the system, being independent of the way in which the system was brought in that state. For any variation in the course of which the amount of absolute heat is dQ, the following relations hold:

$$dS > \frac{dQ}{T}\quad\text{for any irreversible process;}\qquad(55)$$

$$dS = \frac{dQ}{T}\quad\text{for any reversible process.}\qquad(56)$$

If the pressure P and the volume variations dV are also taken into account, then the internal energy expressed by means of entropy will be given by the relation:

$$dE = T \cdot dS + P\,dV.\qquad(57)$$

The practical significance of entropy in problems of equilibrium consists in the fact that, according to equation (57), the entropy-temperature relation is similar to the volume-pressure relation. The entropy of a pure substance is a positive quantity which may be calculated at any temperature T if the specific heat C of this substance is known at all temperatures from absolute zero to the temperature T.

Specific heat. This value is defined as the ratio of the amount of heat dQ supplied (at constant pressure) and the corresponding temperature variation dT of a body per fundamental unit mass, that is:

$$C = \frac{dQ}{dT}\qquad(58)$$

As a rule, two specific heats are considered in practice, the mean specific heat C_m, and the real specific heat C_p. Summing up, the two specific heats are defined as follows:

(i) The mean specific heat is expressed by the folllowing ratio:

$$C_m = \frac{\Delta Q \int_{T_1}^{T_2}}{T_2 - T_1} \qquad (59)$$

where the term in the numerator is the amount of heat required to raise the temperature of one gramme of substance from T_1 to T_2, and it is expressed in cal g^{-1} K^{-1}. The mean specific heat of one and the same substance has different values depending on the temperature range studied. In mineralogical investigations, mean specific heats in the range of high temperatures are of particular interest.

(ii) The real specific heat is defined by the following expression:

$$C_p = \frac{dQ}{dT} \qquad (60)$$

where dQ is the infinitesimal amount of heat required to raise the temperature of one gramme of substance from T_0 to $T_0 + dT_0$. The real specific heat may be calculated from the mean specific heat by graphical differentiation as well as by analytical differentiation.

The relation between the mean specific heat and the real specific heat is given by the expression:

$$C_m = \frac{\int_{T_1}^{T_2} C_p \, dT}{T_2 - T_1} \qquad (61)$$

In thermo-analytical investigations two quantities are frequently used: the heat of formation and the heat of reaction. A knowledge of these quantities is required to fully understand the physical and chemical phenomena generated by temperature.

Heat of formation. The heat of formation is the amount of heat liberated or absorbed when a compound whatsoever is formed from its constituent elements; this amount is related to 1 g mol.

Heat of reaction. The fundamental law of thermochemistry shows that whatever the way in which a reaction takes place, the heat of reaction is equal to the difference between the sum of the heats of formation of the substances in the right hand side and the sum of the heats of formation of the substances in the left hand side of the reaction.

In this calculation one must take into account the physical nature of the compounds entering in reaction (the reactants) and of those which are formed (the products of the reaction), as well as of the other factors which affect the value of the internal energy of the reactions or of the products. The heat of reaction varies with the temperature, the pressure, the concentration, etc. at the moment when the reaction takes place. It is therefore necessary to know and to state precisely all factors which affect the heat of reaction.

4.1 PHYSICAL PROCESSES DETECTABLE BY THERMAL ANALYSIS

Melting. A characteristic property of the crystalline state is the passage from the solid to the liquid state and conversely; this passage takes place at a certain specific temperature called the *melting point.* Hence, every crystalline substance has a definite melting temperature at which the change of the state of aggregation of the substance takes place with an absorption of heat. This property of crystalline substances is set off by differential thermal analysis. But, owing to the present possibilities of the apparatus, in which pressure plays an important part, under current experimental conditions only a small number of substance melt by this method; most substances either decompose or remain unchanged as to the state of aggregation in the temperature range currently used in thermal analyses.

The melting process is briefly explained as follows: Thermal energy imparts to the molecules an energy of agitation called *thermal agitation.* The mean amplitude of the vibrations of atoms increases with rising temperature. When the temperature has reached values at which one may speak of a true collision between two neighbouring atoms, then the atoms generally fail to return to their initial positions of equilibrium; they mix instead, and the crystal lattice breaks down, the crystal melts. Hence, the melting process is nothing else but a breakdown of the crystal lattice.

According to the phase rule, the melting process invariably takes place at constant pressure; hence in this region tempe ature curves must show a horizontal line (Figure 4.1).

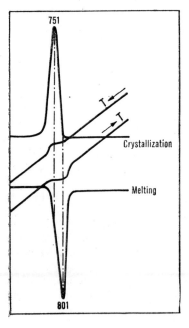

Figure 4.1 DTA curve of the melting-crystallizing process of a simple compound.

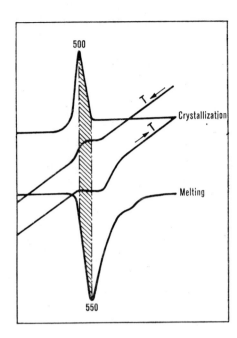

Figure 4.2 DTA curve of the melting-crystallizing process of a binary compound.

If binary mixtures are involved, the process becomes bivariable, and the straight line changes to a slope (Figure 4.2).

In the recording of melting processes by the method of differential thermal analysis, a marked endothermal effect appears on the DTA curve. In many cases, the endothermal effect caused by melting is preceded by a feeble exothermal effect, and only when this has taken place will the curve turn downwards. This exothermal effect appears only in the case of substances having a high coefficient of thermal expansion.

As it was shown before, the mean intensity of particle vibrations increases with rising temperature, and the repulsions appearing in these cases increase the average distance between particles, which leads to an expansion of the crystals. Naturally, such an expansion takes place only if the pressure exerted on the crystals from the outside is negligible in comparison with the internal forces. But, as it is known, the coefficient of thermal expansion of solids is generally very small, and increases very little with rising temperature, which explains the small number of substances giving this exothermal effect.

A relation between the melting points of simple substances and their characteristic melting temperatures was derived a long time ago on the basis of the fundamental melting process of solids (Gruz-Erdely and Schoy, 1957).

In the case of many crystallized substances with a large number of water molecules, belonging as rule to the group of salts, a false melting effect is noticed, consisting in a solution in its own water of crystallization. On the DTA curve, this thermal effect is always situated before the thermal effect due to the removal of water from the crystal lattice (Figure 4.3).

Crystallization. The reverse thermal process to that of melting is crystallization. Theoretically, the crystallization of a liquid homogeneous substance which was obtained by melting must take place at the same temperature as the melting of the solid body which has generated it; however, crystallization occurs as a rule after a certain undercooling of the molten liquid. This delay of crystallization is best observed from Figures 4.1 and 4.2 (hatched parts). There is no constant temperature difference between the highest point of the effect recorded on the DTA curve as a result of melting and that recorded as a result of crystallization. This temperature difference varies as a function of the amount of substance subjected to analysis and the heating or cooling rate. The crystallization process always begins at a temperature corresponding to the highest endothermal effect recorded on the DTA curve as a result of melting.

In the case of binary mixtures, ternary mixtures, etc., the crystallization effect of the melt recorded on the DTA curve is much smaller in surface than the effect of melting. This may be referred to the fact that, when mixed together, solid substances having different melting points affect one another in that the substances with the lowest melting point will depress the melting point of the other substances from the mixture. In this case the melting process of the mixture extends over a

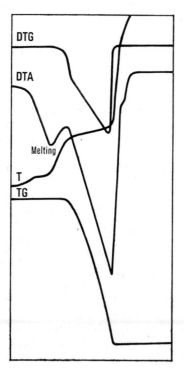

Figure 4.3   DTA curve of the pseudo-melting effect of $Na_2SO_4.10 H_2O$ in its own water of crystallization.

wider temperature range. On the other hand, crystallization or, more correctly, solidification of the melt will take place in the lump. These processes are illustrated diagrammatically very well in Figure 4.2 representing the case of the crystallization and melting of a binary mixture of potassium sulphate and sodium chloride which melts in the temperature range of about 170 °C (Todor, 1969), and crystallizes in the temperature range of about 50 °C. These temperature differences are determined by a number of experimental factors including the ratio in which the substances are mixed and the difference between their melting points in a pure state, the amount of sample processed, the heating and cooling rates of the sample, etc.

Crystallization, in the widest meaning of the word, may take place in three different forms: from liquids molten by cooling, from solutions saturated by dissolution of crystallization components at a higher temperature (and which will crystallize when the solution is cooled, in which case the solubility decreases with decreasing temperature), or by evaporation of the solvent. Of importance for thermal analyses are only those crystallizations which take place when the melts are cooled.

The melting-crystallization process may be studied only by the method of differential thermal analysis. The thermal effect recorded as a result of crystallization is the opposite of melting; it is therefore an exothermic effect, denoting that crystallization always takes place with evolution of heat.

Boiling is said to be the sudden passage of a liquid into the vapour state throughout its whole mass. This process takes place at a temperature at which the vapour pressure of the liquid becomes equal to the external pressure on the liquid, which is usually the atmospheric pressure. The temperature at which boiling takes place is called the *boiling point*.

Thermal analysis records this process by an endothermic effect appearing on the DTA curve, and by a loss of mass corresponding to the removal of the vapours evolved from the system. This loss is recorded by the TG and DTG curves. The boiling process was little studied by thermal methods on account of two shortcomings. In the first place, native compounds, even after they have suffered a number of transformations have very high boiling points, well over 1000 °C, and boiling occurs only after they have passed through the melting phase. In the second place, for this process to be analysed by thermal methods it is necessary to build special analytical apparatus capable of removing from the instrumental analytical system the products resulted in a state of vapours in order to prevent contamination of the instrumental equipment, since the resultant vapours will settle on the cooler parts of this apparatus.

Sublimation is the process of passage of a solid substance directly into the vapour state, without passing through the liquid state. The sublimation process is recorded on thermal curves analogously to boiling, and the same precautions must be taken as in the case of boiling.

Devitrification is taken to mean the spontaneous crystallization of solid bodies with a vitreous structure (synthetic glass, furnace slag, and volcanic glass) which are in an unstable state owing to the high content of accumulated energy, and which tend towards a more stable state. At the ambient temperature, this process sets in after a suffficiently long time. On raising the temperature, however, the devitrification process is accelerated, and it is recorded on the curve of differential thermal analysis as an exothermic effect.

In addition to the enumerated physical properties of crystalline substances, the crystalline state is further characterized by a series of properties connected with the crystalline structure. Some of these crystallographic properties may be studied by means of temperature variations or by the method of differential thermal analysis. They represent a substantial contribution towards an identification of the compound which generates them. The most representative crystallographic properties which may be studied by means of the methods of thermal analysis will be discussed in the following.

Polymorphism is said to be the property of certain substances to crystallize in two or more crystalline forms with different lattices. Hence, polymorphism may be defined as an automorphotropic change of structure of a chemical substance situated at the limit of two isomorphous series, caused by the influence of thermodynamic factors on the properties and mutual interactions of the constituent particles.

The property of a substance to crystallize in different forms capable of passing from one into the other under the action of thermal energy is an invaluable aid to identifying these substances.

The changes which take place at a certain temperature without a breakdown of the crystalline structure, consisting only in a regrouping of the material particles of wich the crystal is built up (hence, a reorganization of the lattice in a different crystallographic class) is called the *polymorphous transformation*. These transformations are generally denoted by the Greek letters α and β. The most currently used notation of these transformations is α for the high temperature transformation, and β for the low temperature transformation.

In the large range of the natural products exhibiting polymorphism it was possible to distinguish two kinds of transformations: *monotropic* and *enantiotropic*.

(1) Monotropic transformations are irreversible transformations which occur only when one of the crystalline forms is more stable than the others at any temperature situated below the melting point or the decomposition temperature of the product in question. Transformation of the unstable form, which is richer in energy, into a stable form is attended by an evolution of energy in the form of heat which is called *latent heat of polymorphous transformation*.

It frequently happens that the transformation rate of the unstable form should be very small, almost imperceptible. In this case the form is maintained unchanged for a very long time. For this reason it is also called the *metastable* form. This metastable form is determined by the structural units (atoms, ions or molecules) which are set in a certain type of lattice, and which is opposed by an inertia such that in order to pass into the type of lattice of the stable form it needs. a certain amount of initial energy called the *activation energy*. But, as it was shown, the transformation of the unstable form into the stable form is accelerated by an increase of the temperature. This kind of polymorphous transformation is studied by means of differential thermal analysis. DTA curves obtained over a crystallized substance with polymorphous properties of this type present an exothermic effect on heating, whereas no thermal effect will be recorded on cooling, hence the process is not reversible.

(2) Enantiotropic transformations are reversible transformations which become manifest with certain substances crystallizing in two or more crystalline forms, each form being stable only in a definite temperature range. Passage from one form into the other takes place at a well-defined temperature called the *polymorphous transformation point*. Transformation of the form stable at low temperature into the form stable at high temperature takes place with an absorption of heat; hence, an endothermic effect will be recorded on the DTA curve. On cooling the product, when the reverse transformation takes place, heat will be evolved; hence, an exothermic effect will be recorded on DTA curve, situated at the same temperature as the endothermic effect. This kind of polymorphous transformation is analogous to the melting and crystallization processes.

A peculiarity of polymorphism is the "paramorphosis" which denotes the process by which some crystals keep their external form even after its polymorphous transformation at high temperature. The best known example of paramorphosis is the passage of aragonite into calcite at temperatures above 450 °C.

The processes of polymorphism enumerated are illustrated in Figure 4.4 in which the three forms of polymorphous transformation recorded on the DTA curve are compared.

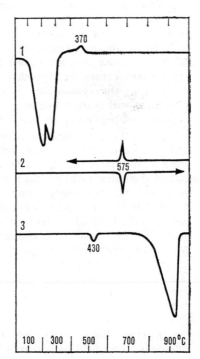

Figure 4.4 DTA curves of the three forms of polymorphous transformation:
(*1*) gypsum; (*2*) quartz; (*3*) aragonite-calcite.

Mention must also be made of the property of some crystallized compounds of appearing in various internal molecular modifications while keeping their chemical composition and the structure of their crystalline lattice. This property is called *polytropy*. Internal modifications of the molecule will take place at a certain temperature in this case also, mostly by rotation of some groups of atoms or radicals. In such cases, the configuration of the lattice is maintained constant. These modifications are called *molecular homeomeric transformations*. Very little is known about the polytropy of native compounds.

To sum up, the processes of polymorphism may be explained as follows. In the case of substances appearing in several modifications with a different symmetry, a change in symmetry relations may be assigned at least in part to the rotation of molecules against each other. For example, in the case of ammonium nitrate, NH_4NO_3, the modification with the highest symmetry in the cubic system is stable from a temperature of 125 °C to its melting point, 169.6 °C, while four more modifications are known at lower temperatures of which the thermal points of transformation are: -18; $+32.2$; $+84.2$; and $+125$ °C.

The higher symmetry of the stable modification at higher temperatures is generally characteristic only for rotation translations of the molecules. Moreover, structural relations and their modification with temperature depend on the lattice elements, on their size, as well as on the strength and orientation of the bonding forces mutually exerted between molecules. Polymorphous modifications are, therefore, processes due to a change of positions of the ions or atoms in the lattice.

Admitting that the solid state of matter is a state of rest, the ions and atoms in it are fixed at the nodes of the crystal lattice. On heating, ions and atoms are induced to vibrate, while still preserving their positions in the structure of the crystal lattice. Since ions are linked by forces of mutual attraction and repulsion, the crystal lattice may be considered as an oscillating system. With increasing temperature of the system the oscillating amplitude of some ions will also increase and these will entrain one after another the neighbouring ions causing the whole structure of the lattice to become an oscillating system.

By further increasing the temperature, the vibration of the ions becomes stronger and at a certain temperature, called the *polymorphous transformation temperature*, the equilibrium of the linking force field of the lattice gives way and the ions move out of their structural position in search of another position of equilibrium compatible with the new energy state. By changing their position, ions and atoms form a new lattice, the thermal agitation disappears, and a new state of rest is thus re-established, which is stable at higher temperatures. In the temperature range in which the old structure is changed into the new structure there is an intermediate moment of the two states when the thermal agitation and the motion for the change of position are very active, that is, the substances are in a "pseudogaseous state". This pseudogaseous state existing in a system at a given moment explains why substances with very similar polymorphous structures frequently exhibit a different behaviour on heating.

Isotypy and isomorphism. It was noticed that compounds presenting an analogous chemical composition are similar also from the point of view of the crystallographic forms; such compounds are said to be *isotypic*. According to the old conception over isotypy, it is assumed that the elements from the chemical formula of isotypic compounds have the same valency, for example, calcite, magnesite, rhodochrosite, siderite, etc. However, numerous examples of compounds are known which, although analogous in chemical composition, have different crystallographic forms. On the other hand, there are compounds with different chemical composition which exhibit similar crystallographic forms. This behaviour suggest the fact that the determining parameter of crystalline forms or of the reticular structure are not valencies but the ionic radii of the elements entering into the composition of the compounds in question. It was established experimentally that elements with close ionic radii lead to identical co-ordinating groups, presenting the same type of elementary polyhedron of the lattice. From this point of view, chemical compounds may crystallize either separately or in the form of mixed crystals, depending on the radius of the ions of which they are formed, thus leading to *isomorphism*.

Isotypic compounds. Two or more chemical compounds are isotypic when the ions forming their structures have a ratio between the radius of the cation and the radius of the anion close to unity, and polarization is analogous. It was proved crystallo-chemically that when the ratio between the radius of the cation and the radius of the anion has a certain value, ions will arrange themselves in a certain

co-ordinating group. No condition was put in the definition of isotypy concerning the size of ionic radii which may vary within very wide limits. For this reason, the dimensions of the elementary polyhedron in isotypic compounds may vary widely.

Two isotypic compounds will therefore crystallize as separate individuals out of a solution or melt, and in such cases a substitution in the lattice leading to a mixed crystal is not possible. This fact determines also the different thermal behaviour specific to each separate individual both on heating and on cooling.

Isomorphous compounds. Isomorphism is taken to mean the property of some substances, different in nature but whose chemical formulas are similar, to crystallize in structural units of the same kind, giving crystal lattices of the same type. Hence, some crystalline species with a different chemical composition are so similar as to the crystallographic form that it is very hard to identify them.

Similar crystallographic forms are obtained when three conditions are met by isomorphous substances, namely: that the combination type should be identical (binary, ternary, etc.); that the relative size of the elements forming the combination should not differ too much; and that they should crystallize in the same lattice.

Unlike isotypic compounds, isomorphic compounds may crystallize together in the same structural edifice, a process which is called *syncrystallization*. Substances so crystallized are also called *solid solutions* because they correspond physically both to solutions (being ionic mixtures of several compounds), and to solids (because the ions of the compounds are arranged in lattices).

From the viewpoint of the way of formation of isomorphous-solid solutions several types are known, and these types are called *isomorphous series*. These series will be dealt with in detail when discussing chemical processes of solid solutions.

4.2 CHEMICAL PROCESSES DETECTABLE BY THERMAL ANALYSIS

In order to be able to discuss chemical processes which take place when a solid product is heated or cooled it is necessary to present briefly the chemical characteristics of natural products. As was shown, most minerals encountered in nature are represented by chemical compounds. From a mineralogical viewpoint these compound are classified into several groups presented in the following.

Definite simple compounds. These are simple chemical compounds which rigorously obey the law of conservation of matter, the law of multiple proportions, and the law of constant proportions. The group of definite compounds include oxides, various oxygenated salts, sulphides, halides, etc. A characteristic fact for these compounds is that they differ from one another by a series of special physical properties which in many cases appear on thermal curves as a result of chemical or physical processes.

Definite double compounds. These combinations represent definite compounds consisting of two simple compounds combined with each other in multiple proportion. In most cases these compounds are double through their cations, more rarely through their anions or simultaneously through cations and anions. Dolomite, glauberite, langbeinite are combinations which may be mentioned to illustrate this class.

From a comparison of the formulas of double compounds it follows that cations entering into their composition may not mutually be substituted isomorphously owing to the significant difference between their ionic radii. It follows from this that they differ from simple compounds by some peculiarities of the crystalline structure and frequently also by physical and chemical properties. For example, if from the viewpoint of their behaviour on heating the components which make up the definite double compound are taken separately, they have their own temperature ranges in which specific thermal processes take place. But when they are in the form of double compounds these temperature ranges are completely different. Figure 4.5 illustrates the thermal curves of an isomorphous association of magnesite-dolomite-calcite which are very telling from this point of view. Whilst magnesium carbonate, $MgCO_3$, crystallized as magnesite, decomposes under the action of thermal energy from 550 to 700 °C, magnesium carbonate from the dolomitic lattice decomposes at a temperature higher by 100 °C. In the case of calcium carbonate the situation is reversed: calcium carbonate crystallized as calcite decomposes at a temperature of 930 °C, whereas calcium carbonate from the dolomite lattice decomposes at a temperature by 50 to 100 °C lower. This behaviour on heating of double compounds against the constituent compounds taken separately is of real use in determining these minerals.

Compounds of variable composition. There are many native compounds whose composition varies within wider or narrower limits, while it is not possible to assign these variations of the composition to mechanical admixtures of foreign matter. From a crystallochemical viewpoint the variable composition of these compounds is explained by the low solubility of the components entering into their constitution.

Figure 4.5 Thermal curves of an association of magnesite-dolomite-calcite.

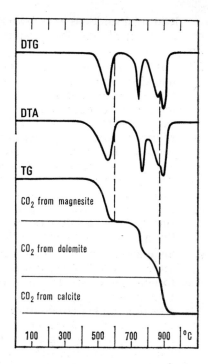

These chemical compounds of a mineral nature were termed *compounds with variable composition* (Betehtin, 1953). They do not differ in their properties from solid solutions, and therefore they must be considered as such, since the components of which they are formed have a limited miscibility.

Solid solutions. The capacity of crystalline substances to form mixtures of varying composition but with the same crystalline structure is largely based on isomorphism. From a genetic viewpoint, solid solutions are divided into two main groups: real solid solutions, and pseudosolid solutions. These in turn are subdivided into other groups.

Real solid solutions or *isomorphous associations* as they are called in mineralogy, represent perfectly homogeneous associations considered from the viewpoint of their crystalline structure. The definite chemical compounds from which they arise form associations in any proportions without entering into chemical combinations.
Physical and chemical properties of real solid solutions are additive, that is, they change gradually and regularly with increasing contents of the second component. Thus will change for instance, the melting point or the decomposition temperature, which is so specific for the isomorphous series. Hence, if all the properties of a mineral species are known, it is possible to determine its composition without having recourse to chemical analysis.

Real solid solutions are of two types: solid solutions *of substitution* or solutions of the first kind, and solid solutions *of impregnation* or solutions of the second kind:

(i)   Solid substitution solutions are particularly characteristic for metal minerals and ionic combinations. Essentially they consist of compounds with similar crystal lattices atoms or ions of one compound are substituted for atoms or ions from another compound. Thus, for example, are the isomorphous series $ZnCO_3 - FeCO_3$ and $MnWO_4 - FeWO_4$.

Mutually substituting elements have almost equal ionic radii (differences between radii should not exceed 15 per cent). In the periodic system of the elements, the values of ionic radii preserve a constant value on the diagonal, particularly in groups I to IV. It follows hence that isomorphous substitution is not connected with valency. But the substitution of ions with a different valency is possible only on condition that the sum of positive valencies be equal to the sum of negative valencies, in order that the valency balance in the structure should remain unchanged.

(ii)   Solid impregnation solutions are those solutions in which the second component settles only in the free spaces, that is, in the spaces between the atoms or ions forming the crystal lattice of the first compound. This impregnation is, therefore, possible only when there are failures in the periodic arrangement of the structure in the crystal lattice. Crystals arising in these cases may be of several kinds, namely: mixed crystals with an ordered distribution in the lattice; mixed crystals with gaps in the lattice; mixed crystals with supernumerary ions; mixed crystals with ions missing in the nodes but present in the voids of the lattice.

Failures of crystal lattices involving the formation of mixed crystals affect the equilibria of these crystal lattices. The excess, lack or disordered distribution of ions in a lattice affects the field of electrostatic forces of the lattice in the sense that the lattices become less stable.

Gradual substitution of some elements in a lattice leads, as was seen, to the formation of isomorphous series. Between the limit terms of these series there exists an infinity of mixed crystals. Graphical representations of these series on rectangular diagrams with the whole composition range of the mixed crystals of the series plotted as abscissas *vs.* the values of the respective properties related to the composition of the mixed crystals as ordinates have shown that four types of mixed crystals may be distinguished.

(1)   Some substances form mixed crystals in any proportion from zero to 100%, that is, the miscibility of the two components is unlimited. Such a series is called a *continuous isomorphous series*. Compounds belonging to a continuous isomorphous series behave homogeneously on heating; they give thermal effects as if these were generated by a simple compound. The only thing that varies is the peak temperature of the effect. For example, in the case of the native compound manganocalcite (Figure 5.62), at first sight one might be inclined to think that two thermal decomposition effects will be obtained, one for manganese carbonate and

the other for calcium carbonate. As a matter of fact, this compound gives only one thermal decomposition effect whose peak temperature varies linearly depending on the substitution ratio of one cation to the detriment of the other (Popa and Todor, 1971).

(2) Other substances form mixed crystals only in certain proportions, having a lacunar miscibility. These substances form *discontinuous isomorphous series*. Compounds from such a series behave differently on heating, giving thermal effects either specific to mixed crystals or specific to a mechanical mixture of two substances. For example, by crystallization out of a solution of the mixture of copper sulphate, $CuSO_4$, and ferrous sulphate, $FeSO_4$, (Figure 5.43) crystals are obtained which on being subjected to thermal analysis give three types of curves depending on the mixing ratio. When copper sulphate is predominant, thermal effects and the loss of mass recorded as a result of dehydration correspond to a compound crystallized with five molecules of water. When iron sulphate is predominant, thermal effects and the loss of mass recorded as a result of dehydration correspond to a compund crystallized with seven molecules of water. When the two sulphates are in an approximatelly equal ratio, thermal effects and the loss of mass indicate that crystallization no longer was unique: in this case copper sulphate has crystallized separately with five molecules of water, and ferrous sulphate has crystallized with seven molecules of water (Todor, 1971).

(3) Other substances form mixed crystals only at high temperatures, while separating into components at the ambient temperature. Since the mixed crystals which are formed under these conditions do not show any variation of mass, they can be studied only by the method of differential thermal analysis, recording the DTA curves both on heating and on cooling.

Some substances form crystals belonging to series called *isodimorphous* in which processes of polymorphism of the compound are involved besides the usually lacunar miscibility. As an example one cites the series $FeSO_4.7H_2O$ — $MgSO_4.7H_2O$. Pure ferrous sulphate crystallizes in the monoclinic system, while pure magnesium sulphate crystallizes in the rhombic system. The variation of physical properties including specific weight, refractive index, specific volume, etc., appear on a reticular diagram in the form of two parallel lines. It is possible to admit the existence of a monoclinic hypothetically polymorphous state of $MgSO_4.7H_2O$, which is inexistent with pure crystals, but which appears and is possible only with mixed crystals of ferrous sulphate and magnesium sulphate, as well an hypothetic rhombic polymorphous state for $FeSO_4.7H_2O$ which does not exist as pure crystals but exists only with mixed crystals (Solacolu, 1968). Compounds from this series behave on thermal analysis similarly to those from the continuous isomorphous series.

Solid pseudosolutions are distinguished from real ones by the fact that they contain mixtures of finely dispersed substances whose presence cannot be explained on the basis of crystallochemical laws. As examples of pseudosolutions one cites crystallosols and semitransparent minerals such as red quartz, red calcite, etc. Semitransparent minerals seem to be perfectly homogeneous, showing how finely the colouring pigment is dispersed in them.

The colour of many minerals originates in their composition itself, involving some chromofore, that is, a coloured chemical element. However, some minerals may be coloured in a certain shade although no chromophorous chemical element is involved in their chemical formula.

Methods of thermal analysis do not lend themselves to the study of chromophorous elements which bring about the colouring of minerals.

Hydrated compounds. It must be stated precisely from the outset that only such substances are considered to be hydrated compunds which hold in their composition electrically neutral water molecules. Hydrated compounds were earlier considered also to be those minerals which contained OH^- groups in their molecule. It is, however, obvious that there is an essential difference between H_2O molecules and the negatively charged OH^- ion which reflects notably on the physical and chemical properties of minerals. Ionic hydroxyl groups are capable of replacing in chemical compounds other negatively charged ions; hence, they are held very tightly bound in chemical lattices. Water molecules do not have this property; they are loosely bound in a compound, and participate only in the formation of the crystal lattice and are, therefore, quite readily removed on heating.

Removal of hydroxyl groups under the action of thermal energy leads to a breakdown of the molecule of the compound and in most cases precludes a renewed hydration of these molecules. Water molecules are much more readily removed under the action of thermal energy; their removal has no influence on the molecule of the compound, affecting only the crystal lattice, which is destroyed as a result. On renewed hydration the same crystal lattice may be formed again.

Water is retained in the structure of the compound in two ways:

(i)   As water of crystallization or of constitution entering into the crystal lattice of the mineral.

(ii)   As free water which does not participate in the formation of the crystal lattice.

The main aspects of the behaviour on dehydration of some hydrated compounds will be shown in the following, depending on the way in which water participates in the lattice of the respective compound.

Water of constitution or *water of crystallization* participates in the lattice in the form of water molecules, occupying strictly determined positions. The number of water molecules is found in a simple ratio to the other constituents of the compound. Let the following combinations be taken as examples: soda, $Na_2CO_3.10H_2O$; gypsum, $CaSO_4.2H_2O$; and melanterite, $FeSO_4.7H_2O$. These combinations are the so-called crystallohydrates which, according to Werner, must be considered complex compounds in which water molecules are constituent particles arranged in a certain order around certain ions.

Crystallohydrates are readily dehydrated on heating, and water is removed in steps, losing water molecules periodically. In this case, the lattice is reconstructed by preserving rational ratios between water molecules and the number of molecules of the base compound. For example, chalcanthite, $CuSO_4.5H_2O$, on heating loses at first two water molecules (from 90 to 130 °C), with formation of $CuSO_4 \cdot 3H_2O$, then two more water molecules (from 130 to 240 °C), with formation of $CuSO_4.H_2O$, and in the end the last water molecule is removed at higher temperatures (from 240 to 340 °C), resulting anhydrous copper sulphate (Figure 4.6).

Water of crystallization is removed from various chemical compounds at different temperatures; some of them lose this water at room temperature, others at higher temperatures, even of the order of hundreds of degrees.

Free (mineral) water fails to participate directly in the construction of the crystal lattice of minerals. On heating it is removed gradually and not by steps as the water of crystallization. From the way in which it is retained by minerals, one may distinguish three kinds of free mineral water, namely: zeolitic water, colloidal water, and hygroscopic water.

Zeolitic water was so termed after the group of minerals called zeolites in which the peculiarities of its presence most obviously manifest themselves. It was established that water molecules from this group of minerals do not take a well-defined position in the crystal lattice, settling only in free spaces. On heating, this water is removed from 80 to 400 °C continuously, giving a very wide thermal effect attended by a loss in weight, corresponding to the total water content of

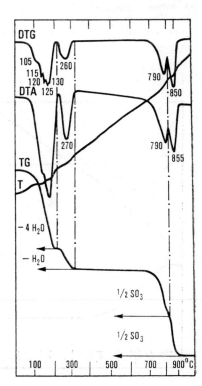

Figure 4.6 Thermal curves of copper sulphate synthetically crystallized with five molecules of water.

the compound. Thermal curves obtained are analogous to those illustrated in Figure 4.7.

Mineral substances containing zeolitic water, when they are carefully dehydrated, that is, when they are heated slowly without heating being continued over the dehydration temperature, may retrieve their physical properties, including their capacity to absorb water. If they are subjected to renewed analysis after being previously hydrated, thermal curves analogous to the preceding ones are obtained. This property is very useful in identifying compounds which generate such processes.

Colloidal water is the constitutional water of hydrogels in which it is held back at the surface of the dispersed phases by very feeble linking forces. In reality, this is a kind of water of absorption and can be removed comparatively readily under the action of thermal energy, like zeolitic water, but with the difference that the temperature range is much lower.

Hygroscopic water also called *capillary water* is held back by some substances in fine cracks, in pores or in powdery masses by the forces of surface tension. It is readily removed for the most part by heating up to a temperature of 110°C. It is not possible to make a demarcation on thermal curves between capillary and colloidal water, from a thermic point of view.

Basic compounds is the name given to those combinations which contain hydroxyl ions in their molecules. As a rule, these ions neutralize the supplementary charges of the cation.

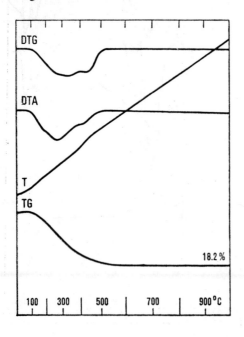

Figure 4.7 Thermal dehydration curves of a natural zeolite obtained at a heating rate of 10 °C min⁻¹

On heating, such hydroxyl groups containing compounds behave as follows: If the compounds are also hydrated, the water of crystallization is removed at first, followed by the removal of hydroxyl ions, and in the end the compound undergoes physical or chemical transformations. It often happens that the removal of hydroxyl groups takes place almost simultaneously with the other thermal transformations, in very close temperature ranges, yielding highly specific thermal curves.

Thermal processes of basic compounds are illustrated in Figure 4.8 very well by means of the thermal curves of a sample of hydromagnesite. One may notice on these curves that water of crystallization is removed at first, in two stages, followed by the removal of hydroxyl groups, and in the end by the decomposition of magnesium carbonate, also in two stages.

From what has been mentioned earlier it follows that on heating, basic compounds yield dehydration reactions, dehydroxylation reactions, and decomposition reactions, but in the case of native compounds another series of chemical reactions may also appear which will be described in Chapter 5.

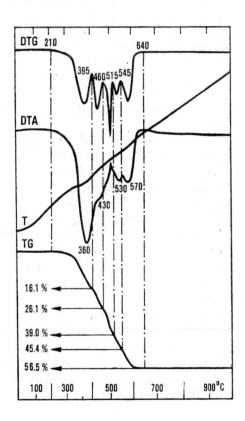

Figure 4.8 Thermal curves of a sample of hydromagnesite from Tişoviţa — Romania (Popa and Todor, 1971).

Dissociation reactions of solid solutions. These reactions are thermal dissociations by which complex molecules are resolved into simpler molecules. Two cases may be distinguished in the process of thermal dissociation:

(1) When the crystalline compound consists of an association of two or more well-defined molecules. This case is frequently encountered in double or triple sulphates from salt deposits. On heating, such combinations yield, before the thermal process caused by melting or decomposition, a small endothermal effect recorded on the DTA curve.

(2) When one or more molecules pass by dissociation into the gaseous state, being thus removed from the system. An example in this sense is the thermal dissociation of ammonium chloride. These dissociations are recorded on thermal curves by a marked endothermal effect and a loss in weight corresponding to the product evolved. Dissociations of this kind are encountered in a series of organic compounds which on heating liberate free radicals.

Combination and exchange reactions in solid state. Thermal analysis methods are suited to the study of combination and exchange reactions, but only of those which take place in the solid phase or when one or more components from the mixture pass into the liquid phase because of their melting. The presence of the molten liquid phase is particularly important in regard to the progress of reactions. Compounds which are formed as a result of these reactions are insoluble in the melt and crystallize from it. There are, however, reactions which start at much lower temperatures, before the liquid phase sets in; these are in fact solid state reactions.

It is known that there is a characteristic temperature for each compound, depending on the nature of the crystalline structure, at which temperature the atoms or groups of atoms obtain the necessary mobility for changing their position. At these temperatures, thermal agitation begins to manifest itself at first by a vibration of the atoms in the points which they occupy in the lattice. By further raising the temperature the vibrations of the atoms are amplified, and a change in their positions becomes thus possible. From a thermodynamic viewpoint the reaction between crystals develops in the sense in which heat is yielded, and the equilibrium of the reaction is established at a certain temperature. Solid state reactions are exothermic reactions and they are made obvious by differential thermal analysis methods. The curves obtained mark the temperature limits within which the reaction takes place; the surface of the thermal effect recorded on the DTA curve is proportional to the heat of reaction.

Silicates are less reactive in the solid state than other inorganic or metal compounds. This fact was also proved by crystallization processes in which metals and inorganic compounds are more liable to be arranged in crystal lattices than silicates.

Typical examples of this kind of reactions are those which take place in the formation of orthosilicates. Thus the formation of magnesium silicate takes place at a temperature of 1170 °C, according to the reaction:

$$2\,MgO + SiO_2 \longrightarrow Mg_2SiO_4$$

For this kind of reactions to take place, it is necessary that at least one of the reactants should diffuse through the solid state which separates the initial substances from each other.

These reactions are also known very well and used in the case when dry decomposition is carried out, for example: $MeSiO_4 + Na_2CO_3$. To illustrate such a reaction, Figure 4.9 shows the thermal curves of the disintegration of quartz with sodium carbonate.

Reduction reactions. Reactions taking place with an electron gain are called *reduction reactions.* Noting the metal ion which is reduced by Me^{2+} and the electron by e^-, the reaction may be expressed as $Me^{2+} + e^- \rightleftarrows Me^+$. Hydrogen is generally the donor of electrons.

The study of reduction processes by thermal methods is carried out in special equipment, in a controlled atmosphere. The thermal process of reduction generally appears on thermal curves as an endothermic effect attended by a loss in weight.

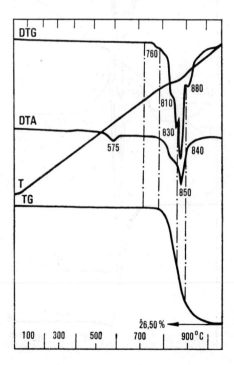

Figure 4.9 Thermal curves of an artificial mixture of quartz and sodium carbonate.

Oxidation reactions. Reactions taking place with a loss of electrons are called *oxidation reactions.* Also noting by Me^+ the metal ion which is oxidized, and by e^- an electron, the reaction may be represented as: $Me^+ - e^- \rightleftarrows Me^{2+}$. Generally, oxygen is the acceptor of electrons.

By oxidation of minerals one should understand the aggressive action of oxygen on a metal product. Oxidized products are covered with oxidizing layers at different rates and according to different laws, depending on the affinity of the metal for the surrounding atmosphere, and on the nature of the initiating layer which is formed, and which is determined by the crystalline structure.

The study of oxidation processes by thermal methods is carried out in an atmosphere of oxygen or air. The thermal process of oxidation appears on thermal curves as an exothermic process attended by an increase in weight. The most telling example is the oxidation of FeO or of MnO, resulted from the decomposition of siderite or rhodochrosite (Figure 4.10).

Naturally, sulphurations and chlorinations of some metals are also oxidation processes.

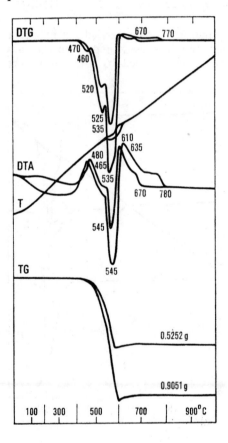

Figure 4.10 Thermal curves of a siderite sample taken in different amounts from which results an exothermic effect in the temperature range from 600 to 800 °C.

5

Thermal Behaviour of Minerals

As mentioned in previous chapters, the methods of thermal analysis applied either separately or combined, yield good results in the study of the physical and chemical processes, which take place as an effect of the action of heat on a solid product. A knowledge of these processes, whose intensity is closely connected with the compound which is analysed, implicitly leads to the determination of the compound.

Minerals are usually chemical compounds and rather seldom native elements. Therefore, only native chemical compounds which appear in the solid state at the temperature and pressure of the surroundings will be discussed in the following. Native elements are determined relatively easily by quite a number of other physical or chemical methods, which are much more adequate. For this reason, thermal methods have been applied rather sporadically to their analysis. However, in order to establish the temperature at which a change in their state of aggregation takes place, and particularly to determine the melting temperature, the method of differential thermal analysis is widely used. It is also used in the case of native elements.

For practical reasons, and to give a most conclusive picture of the behaviour of minerals on heating, it was necessary to depart from the general conventional classification of minerals, found in handbooks of mineralogy. Let us make it clear that this departure is not based on mineralogical or chemical considerations; the aim is only to help render the account more systematic.

Contradictory experimental data from the specialised literature were checked for some of the minerals, and the results are reported in the following.

5.1 OXIDES

Minerals belonging to this class for the most part behave similarly on heating. Thermal processes specific to this class of minerals are connected with the polymorphous transformations which minerals undergo on heating. These polymorphous transformations occur only at well defined temperatures and may be investigated exclusively by the method of differential thermal analysis.

Thermal processes connected with oxidation appear with some oxides also when the related cation changes to a higher valency state. Again, with other oxides thermal processes connected with reduction appear when the related oxide loses some of the oxygen, which sometimes results in a reduction of its positive charge. Since these transformations take place with variations of mass, they may also be investigated by gravimetric thermal methods. In the following, thermal processes taking place with the main native oxides on heating will be briefly presented.

5.1.1 Copper oxides

Both copper oxides — tenorite, CuO, and cuprite, Cu_2O — behave analogously on heating. At temperatures above 950 °C tenorite passes into cuprite, releasing oxygen. This process is recorded on the DTA and DTG curves as an endothermic process, and the TG curve shows a loss of mass.

With rising temperature, cuprite (either the native product or that resulting from thermal dissociation of tenorite) loses its oxygen and passes into metallic copper. The thermal effect is analogous to that of tenorite, the only difference being that it gives a much better defined endothermal process on the DTA curve in the temperature range from 1000 to 1050 °C. This fact is due to two thermal processes overlapping while they occur simultaneously the decomposition of cuprite, on the one hand, and the melting of the metallic copper which resulted from decomposition, on the other hand. Summing up, the transitions of these two compounds may be expressed by the following sequence of reactions:

$$2\,CuO \xrightarrow{\;950-1000\,°C\;} Cu_2O \xrightarrow{\;1000-1050\,°C\;} Cu \quad (metallic)$$

5.1.2 Aluminium oxide

Corindone, α-Al$_2$O$_3$. This is the only oxide and at the same time the purest form of native aluminium oxide. Artificially prepared aluminium oxide can exist in three polymorphous forms: γ, β, and α. On heating above 1000 °C, the γ and β forms pass into the α form. This transformation does not occur at a fixed temperature point, unlike polymorphous transformations. This fact has led a number of researchers to state that the γ and β forms are not, properly speaking, polymorphous states (Solacolu, 1968). In fact, when these artificial products are heated, no conclusive effect will apeear on thermal curves.

It is, nevertheless, well to recall to mind that artificial aluminium oxide, which is the thermally inert material most currently used in differential thermal analysis, must previously be subjected to calcination at 1400 °C for a few hours in order to ensure full thermal stability.

5.1.3 Iron oxides

Wüstite, FeO. This is the only oxide of bivalent iron, and it is rarely encountered in nature. On heating, wüstite is oxidized at comparatively low temperatures, passing into haematite, Fe_2O_3. On thermal curves, a marked endothermic effect shows wüstite oxidation around a temperature in the range 275—325°C. This effect is associated with an increase of mass, as a result of the absorption of oxygen. According to some authors, with rising temperatures, the resulting haematite fails to show any thermal effect; other authors, on the contrary, allege that a feeble polymorphous transformation effect shows at about 500 °C on the DTA curve.

Haematite, Fe$_2$O$_3$. This oxide of tervalent iron, which exists both in a γ and an α form, fails to show any thermal transformation up to 1000 °C. If any thermal effects should appear on thermal curves obtained when this product is heated, these are certainly due to one or more compounds associated with haematite.

Magnetite, Fe$_3$O$_4$. This compound consists of one bivalent and two tervalent iron ions. On heating, it undergoes a first thermal transformation due to the oxidation of the bivalent ion. This oxidation appears on thermal curves as an exothermic effect attended by a slight increase of mass in the temperature range 350—400°C. As a result of the thermal process, Fe_2O_3 is produced which, with rising temperature, will pass through a polymorphous transformation into the α form of haematite. This causes a slight endothermic effect to appear on the DTA curve between 650—800 °C.

Figure 5.1 illustrates the thermal curves of the three mineral iron oxides.

5.1.4 Manganese oxides

Manganosite, MnO. As a mineral, this oxide is extremely rare and for this reason investigations were carried out only with artificial samples. The thermal curves obtained show a first exothermic effect at a temperature of about 350 °C, as a result of the oxidation of Mn^{2+} to Mn^{4+}, when the oxide passes into pyrolusite. This thermal transformation is attended by an increase of mass. There is a marked thermal effect on all three thermal curves. With rising temperature, the oxide formed behaves similarly to pyrolusite.

Pyrolusite, MnO$_2$. The first thermal transformation which pyrolusite undergoes takes place at 650—700 °C, when it passes into braunite, β-Mn_2O_3. This transformation takes place with absorption of heat and hence, on the thermal curves, there is an endothermic effect attended by a negative mass variation.

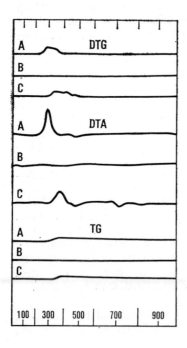

Figure 5.1   Thermal curves of iron oxides: *A*, wüstite; *B*, haematite; *C*, magnetite.

With raising temperatures, the β-Mn_2O_3 formed will pass into hausmannite, $Mn^{2+}2Mn^{3+}O_4$, betwwen 950 and 1050 °C. In this case too, the transformation is shown on the thermal curves by an endothermic effect attended by a negative mass variation. In the specialised literature, a rhombic modification of manganese dioxide called *ramseite* is described; on thermal curves, unlike pyrolusite, this shows only a slight exothermic effect at about 500 °C, recorded only on the DTA curve. This exothermic effect is caused by the transformation of ramseite into pyrolusite and is, in fact, an irreversible polymorphous transformation.

Braunite, Mn_2O_3. As is to be expected, the thermal curves of this mineral exhibit a first thermal effect caused by its transformation into hausmannite. The transformation takes place between 950 and 1050 °C, and appears on the thermal curves as an endothermic effect attended by a loss of mass. At higher temperatures, between 1150 and 1200 °C, the hausmannite formed will undergo a polymorphous transformation, passing from the β into the α form, a fact which causes a slight endothermic effect to appear on the DTA curve.

Data from the literature referring to the transformation of braunite into hausmannite is contradictory. According to Mackenzie (1962) the transformation of braunite into hausmannite takes place as described above, but Topor (1964) has shown that this transformation takes place simultaneously with a change in the polymorphous condition, in the temperature range from 1100 to 1200 °C. Treiber (1967) shows that braunite is, in fact, a compound oxide or rather an oxisilicate of the type $(MnSi)_2O_3$. According to Kulp and Perfetti (1950), this compound actually fails to show a thermal effect up to 1000 °C. I believe that the compound $(MnSi)_2O_3$ is a mechanical mixture of SiO_2 and Mn_2O_3, and that one should be able to obtain the transformation effect of quartz, either on heating or on cooling, by using a sensitive instrumental equipment.

Hausmannite, Mn_3O_4. Similarly to magnetite, this compound consists of one bivalent and two tervalent manganese ions. Nevertheless, according to data from the literature it does not show on thermal curves an effect specific to the bivalent ion, like magnetite, but an effect of polymorphous transformation only. This effect appears in the temperature range from 900 to 970 °C, when the γ form passes into the β form; further, between 1150 and 1200 °C, hausmannite undergoes a second polymorphous transformation, when the β form passes into the α form. These two transformations are marked on the DTA curve in the form of some small endothermic effects.

Figure 5.2. illustrates the thermal curves of the manganese oxides discussed.

5.1.5 Silicon Dioxide

While apparently simple, the composition of silicon dioxide, SiO_2, represents, in fact, a series of polymorphous modifications. Owing to its crystalline structure, this oxide takes a special position among native oxides. The crystalline structure of silicon dioxide is actually connected directly with that of silicates. This is the

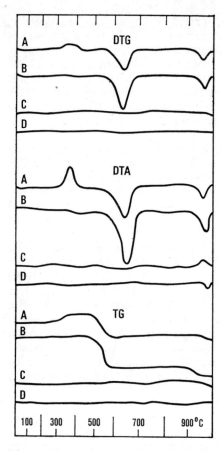

Figure 5.2 Thermal curves of manganese oxides: *A*, manganosite; *B*, pyrolusite; *C*, braunite; *D*, hausmannite.

reason for some authors considering this mineral to belong to the silicates group. However, considering that quartz is a typical oxide, both from the viewpoint of its chemical composition and of its thermal behaviour, it will be examined in this chapter.

From the eleven polymorphous states assigned to silicon dioxide, three have independent designations in mineralogy: quartz, tridymite, and cristobalite. These polymorphous modifications are denoted by the greek letters α and β depending on the temperature range in which they are stable. Some authors denote the low temperature modification by α and the high temperature one by β; others denote the low temperature modification by β and the high temperature one by α. However, the latter notation is by far the more common.

The general scheme of the polymorphous transformation of quartz at different temperatures may be represented as follows:

$$\beta\text{-quartz} \underset{}{\overset{573\,°C}{\rightleftharpoons}} \alpha\text{-quartz} \underset{}{\overset{870\,°C}{\rightleftharpoons}} \alpha\text{-tridymite} \underset{}{\overset{1470\,°C}{\rightleftharpoons}} \alpha\text{-cristobalite}.$$

In addition to these polymorphous transformations, two more enantiotropic transformations are known for tridymite and cristobalite. By sudden cooling of α-tridymite, this polymorphous form is preserved at temperatures below 870 °C, and at still lower temperatures it passes into the low temperature forms:

$$\alpha\text{-tridymite} \underset{}{\overset{163\,°C}{\rightleftharpoons}} \beta\text{-tridymite} \underset{}{\overset{117\,°C}{\rightleftharpoons}} \gamma\text{-tridymite}.$$

Likewise, by sudden cooling of α-cristobalite, this form is stabilized below 1470 °C and at low temperatures the following polymorphous transformation takes place:

$$\alpha\text{-cristobalite} \underset{}{\overset{180 - 270\,°C}{\rightleftharpoons}} \beta\text{-cristobalite}.$$

Amorphous silica occurs native associated with water, $SiO_2.nH_2O$, in the mineral opal. This mineral will be examined separately at the end of this chapter.

Quartz, SiO_2. The polymorphous transformation of β-quartz into α-quartz occurs readily at about 573 °C; this transformation was made obvious by the variation of different properties. Thus, at 573 °C ± 40 °C, a sharp endothermic effect appears on the DTA curve. Owing to the fact that this transformation takes place with a small heat absorption of about 3.1 calories per gramme, the area of the thermal effect is very small. The transformation process is reversible, and this allows the polymorphous transformation effect to be made obvious ever in the case of associations with other minerals. This is achieved either by cooling the sample, when a small exothermic effect appears on the DTA curve at 573 °C, or by reheating the sample after having previously cooled it below 500 °C, when only the polymorphous endothermic transformation effect of quartz appears on the DTA curve.

According to Faust (1948), this polymorphous transformation effect of quartz is independent of the process of its formation. Faust therefore suggests its use as a temperature standard for instrument calibration. More recent investigations, however, show that the polymorphous transformation temperature of quartz depends on its temperature of formation, and, for this reason, there may be up to 38 °C difference in transformation temperature.

Solacolu (1968) shows that the polymorphous transition point of quartz varies by a few degrees with certain crystals. For instance, very finely ground crystals and crystals repeatedly calcinated at high temperatures have different transition points. This is because the structural balance of the quartz lattice has been disturbed, giving rise to structural defects, and causing the transformation to proceed at a faster pace. Another cause of variation of the transition temperature is the isomorphous addition of alien elements to the quartz lattice. For example, B_2O_3, P_2O_3, etc. have an activation effect on the transformation, producing a drop in the transition temperature.

There are comparatively few data relating to the transformation of α-quartz into α-tridymite recorded on thermal curves. This transformation takes place, as was already shown, at 870 °C, but most authors assert that it cannot be made obvious by the methods of differential thermal analysis. Nevertheless, Földvári

(1958), by heating "Maramuresh Diamond", a very pure quartz, obtained a slight bend on the DTA curve around a temperature of 870 °C. This polymorphous transformation of quartz, because it is not complete even on overheating, is difficult to record, since most instruments are not sensitive enough to detect it.

The transformation of α-tridymite into α-cristobalite is also very difficult, to monitor as it requires a very long exposure to high temperatures, particularly in the case of pure crystals. On passing from tridymite into cristobalite, silicon tetrahedrons turn about the axis (111), and the reorganization of the tetrahedrons in the new position in the lattice is the real cause of the inertia of this transformation.

At temperatures above 1500 °C silicon dioxide melts. According to Solacolu (1968), the melting points of the various forms differ as follows: the melting point of α-cristobalite is 1713 °C $\pm$ 5 °C, that of α-tridymite is 1670 °C $\pm$ 10 °C, and that of α-quartz is 1580 °C.

Tridymite. Because both polymorphous transformations of tridymite develop readily and at a high rate, they can be recorded on the DTA curve only with very sensitive instruments. According to data from the literature, a small endothermic effect appears on the DTA curve in the range 75—125 °C with a thermal maximum at 117 °C. The second polymorphous transformation takes place similarly to the previous one but with an endothermic effect between 125 and 175 °C and with a thermal maximum at about 163 °C. Both thermal effects are reversible, and if the sample is cooled off at the same rate at which it was heated, two small endothermic effects then appear on the DTA curve.

Cristobalite. The polymorphous transformation of α-cristobalite into β-cristobalite does not take place at a fixed temperature. The maximum of the thermal effect varies between 180—270 °C. This variation is closely linked with the nature of the sample from which cristobalite was taken (namely whether it was formed from crystalline quartz or from amorphous silica), and with the cooling rate at which the cristobalite was obtained.

The transformation process of cristobalite as a function of the cooling rate differs according to the formation of its crystal lattice. If the cristobalite formed has an ordered lattice, then its polymorphous transformation process appears at temperatures towards 270 °C, but if the arising lattice is lacunary, that is, it has defects, the transition temperature drops below 200 °C.

Opal. This native product is a typical solid hydrogel, and therefore thermal processes arising when it is heated are closely connected with the removal of water. The water content varies from one sample to another, and is most frequently included between one and five per cent, but there are varieties with higher contents, reaching up to as much as 34 per cent. Opal varieties lose water at low temperatures, most of them between 100 and 150 °C; some may lose water even at 300 °C. Water removal under the action of thermal energy is a continuous process. Therefore, on thermal curves, in the temperature range shown, there will appear an extended endothermic effect, without a well-defined maximum.

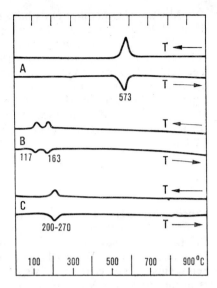

Figure 5.3 DTA curves of various forms of silicon dioxide: *A*, quartz; *B*, tridymite; *C*, cristobalite.

Opal occurs with various hues depending on the presence of impurities. At first sight one might think that these impurities could be detected by thermal methods. This is, however, very difficult, because the impurities are present in very small amounts, and their possible thermal effects cannot be detected by present-day instruments.

Amorphous silica. In nature, amorphous silica occurs mainly in quartzites and in volcanic ashes. Amorphous silica is stable up to 1000 °C, no transition occurring on thermal curves. Above this temperature it begins to crystallize into α-cristobalite, and this crystallization is more marked towards 1200 °C. When it is cooled, the cristobalite changes at 230 °C into β-cristobalite, a transformation which takes place with volume variation; as was already mentioned, this transformation is recorded on the DTA curve as a small exothermic effect.

Figure 5.3 illustrates the thermal curves of various forms of silicon dioxide.

5.2 HYDROXIDES

Native hydroxides, unlike artificial ones, are well-defined compounds which were formed by chemical precipitation in strongly alkaline conditions. Most of the native hydroxides have arisen in zones of marked oxidation of ore deposits. The fact that their solubility in water is for the most part very slight suggests that highly saturated solutions were formed in the process of oxidation, from which hydroxides were subsequently deposited in crypto-crystalline and colloidal masses.

Most of these compounds have stratified lattices characterized by an hexagonal or near hexagonal and very compact arrangement.

Thermal processes on which the identification and determination of hydroxides is based are processes connected with the removal of OH groups from their lattices. The removal of hydroxyls in the form of water molecules generally takes place at different temperatures specific to the respective compound. As a result of this expulsion, the lattice of the crystalline system is destroyed. With rising temperature after the thermal dehydroxylation process, some of these compounds, which have been turned into oxides, undergo new structural organizations similar to those of oxides.

5.2.1 Magnesium hydroxide

Brucite, $Mg(OH)_2$. On heating, this mineral expels a molecule of water as a result of its dehydroxylation. This causes a marked endothermic effect to appear on the thermal curves in the temperature range from 400 to 500 °C, corresponding to a loss of mass. When the compound is a simple mineral, the loss of mass represents 31 per cent of its weight. With rising temperatures, the residue, which is in fact periclase, MgO, undergoes no other thermal transformation (Figure 5.4).

Brucite sometimes contains iron and manganese in the form of isomorphous associations, called *ferrobrucite* and *manganobrucite*, respectively. In such cases the colour of the residue will be red or brown with a black hue, instead of white, depending on the amount of iron or manganese, and the colour of the residue is the only indication that the brucite is mixed with other oxides.

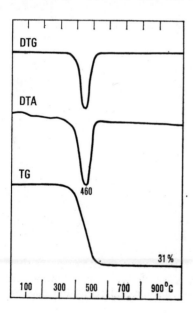

Figure 5.4   Thermal curves of brucite.

Brucite is similar in appearance to talc, $Mg_3[Si_4O_{10}]$ $[OH]_2$, to pyrophyllite, $Al_2[Si_4O_{10}]$ $[OH]_2$, and to hydrargillite, $Al(OH)_3$. It is clearly distinguished from these compounds on thermal curves by the temperature range in which thermal effects occur as a result of the expulsion of OH groups from their lattice.

5.2.2 Aluminium hydroxides

Gibbsite or **hydrargillite, $Al(OH)_3$.** The thermal curves of this mineral show a marked endothermic effect between 310 and 350 °C, attended by a loss of mass as a result of the total or partial removal of OH groups from its lattice. It is not clear what kind of a compound gibbsite is changed into after this hydroxyl expulsion. Some researchers assume that gibbsite first changes into boehmite, $AlO(OH)$, which at a higher temperature expels the hydroxyl and forms γ-alumina.

From data obtained by Paulik, Paulik and Erdey (1961), both with native and artificial compounds, it follows that gibbsite decomposes in three stages with a loss of mass corresponding to the loss of 0.5, 2.0, and 0.5 mols of water, respectively. The temperature ranges in which the three effects are situated are as follows: the first, from 240 to 290 °C, is a feeble endothermic effect; the second, from 300 to 350 °C, is more marked; the third, from 515 to 560 °C is also of lesser intensity.

With natural gibbsite, hydroxyls are usually expelled in a continuous process, preventing thermal effects from being clearly distinguished.

Many data from the literature show that only the endothermic effect in the temperature range from 310 to 350 °C appears conclusively on the DTA curve, whereas the thermal effect of the dehydroxylation of the boehmite formed is blurred and inconclusive. This fact led Sasvári and Hegedüs (1955) to conduct detailed investigations. They heated native gibbsite at a temperature of 300 °C for an interval of an hour, and then analysed the partly dehydroxylated product by means of X-ray diffraction. In this way they were able to prove that the product contained boehmite, but they did not find the specific lines for α-Al_2O_3. They concluded that on heating native gibbsite is changed into Al_2O_3, passing through boehmite. Boehmite, and possibly the amorphous aluminium oxyhydrate, $Al_2O_3.H_2O$, which is present, decompose slowly, even at a slight rise in temperature, without yielding the endothermic effect specific to boehmite.

Tivodor (1964), investigating bauxite samples from India, in which the prevalent mineral is hydrargillite, obtained on thermal curves (Figure 5.5) a second endothermic effect, which is, in fact, the so-called deficiency effect of boehmite. There fact is also a loss of mass shown on the DTG and TG curves in this temperature range confirming the existence of an endothermic effect.

Boehmite, γ-$AlO(OH)$. Another important component mineral in bauxite deposits, besides hydrargillite, is boehmite. On heating, this mineral decomposes in a single reaction into aluminium oxide and water in the temperature range from

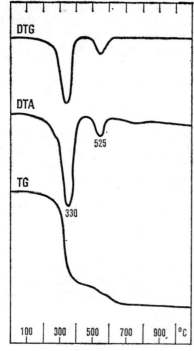

Figure 5.5　Thermal curves of hydrargillite *(after Tivodor, 1964).*

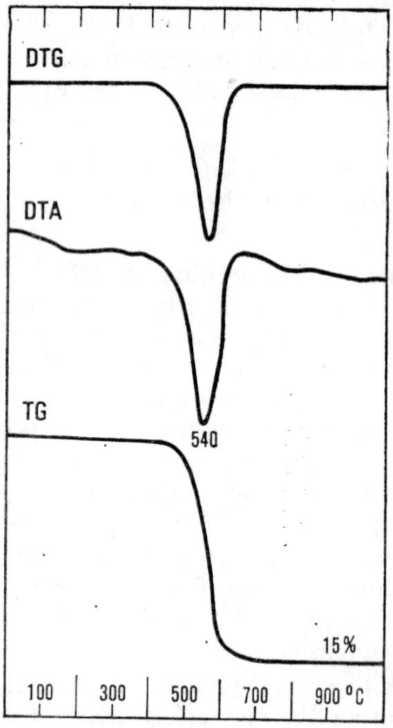

Figure 5.6　Thermal curves of boehmite *(after Tivodor, 1964).*

490 to 580°C. As a result of this thermic process, boehmite when it is a mono-mineral presents on thermal curves a loss of mass of 15.03 per cent (Figure 5.6).

Diaspore, α-A10(OH). Identification and determination of diaspore with thermal methods is difficult, because on heating it behaves similarly to boehmite.

5.2.3 Iron Hydroxides

Goethite, α-FeO(OH) and **Limonite, α-FeO(OH)$\cdot n$H$_2$O.** From a chemical viewpoint these minerals are represented by a single compound whose ratio of Fe$_2$O$_3$ to H$_2$O is 1 : 1 (water being considered as a constituent from OH groups). This was proved by means of X-ray diffraction, showing that both compounds have a well-defined lattice. All varieties of iron hydroxide that are richer in water are in fact hydrated gels, holding water adsorbed in various amounts.

Theoretically, the chemical composition of goethite is: 89.90 per cent Fe$_2$O$_3$ and 10.10 per cent H$_2$O. When the water content is higher than indicated by the formula, the mineral is called *limonite*.

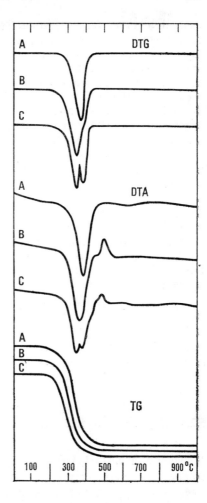

Figure 5.7 Thermal curves of iron hydroxides: A, goethite-limonite; B, lepidocrocite; C, limoni-te-lepidocrocite.

On thermal curves, minerals of the goethite-limonite type show a single endothermic effect, associated with a loss of mass, as a result of the removal of OH groups, and the remaining ferric oxide passes into haematite (Figure 5.7A).

According to Topor's (1964) data, the thermal dehydration effect of goethite is situated between 250 and 360 °C, and that of limonite between 350 and 400 °C. Nevertheless, with regard to the thermal curves of limonite, many contradictions appear in data from the literature since the presence of impurities causes a shift in the temperature of the thermal effect, and supplementary effects improperly ascribed to limonite may simultaneously appear on thermal curves.

Lepidocrocite, γ-FeO(OH). The chemical composition of this mineral is identical to that of goethite, but analytical determinations carried out by various methods and on different samples have shown that it contains much fewer impurities than goethite. On heating, lepidocrocite behaves similarly to goethite in regard to the elimination of OH groups. On the DTA curve, however, a visible distinction appears between the two minerals. In the case of goethite, after the endothermic effect caused by the removal of OH groups, thermal curves fail to indicate a change occurring in the mass of the residue. In the case of lepidocrocite, however, after the endothermic effect caused by the removal of OH groups, an exothermic effect appears on the DTA curve between 400 and 500 °C as a result of a polymorphous transformation of γ-Fe_2O_3 into α-Fe_2O_3.

This difference in thermal behaviour of the two minerals results from the fact that α-haematite is formed directly by decomposition of goethite, whereas γ-haematite is formed at first by decomposition of lepidocrocite, and this is then changed by an exothermic process into an α-type modification. According to Treiber (1967), the difference in the behaviour on heating is due to the difference existing in the crystal structure of these two minerals. In goethite, hydrogen plays the part of the cation, whereas in lepidocrocite hydrogen occurs in independent OH groups. In addition, the structure of lepidocrocite is a less compact one, and this accounts for the fact that lepidocrocite decomposes at a temperature 30 to 50 degrees centigrade lower than that of goethite (Figure 3.7 *B*) (Kulp and Trites, 1951).

In nature, these two minerals are usually found associated in highly variable proportions, and for this reason on thermal analysis they yield curves indicating a double endothermic dehydroxylation effect in the form of two clearly separate peaks; in these cases, however, the exothermic polymorphous transformation effect is much less pronounced (Figure 3.7 *B*).

5.2.4 Manganese Hydroxides

Manganite, Mn.MnO$_2$(OH)$_2$. Theoretically, the native compound has the following composition: 40.4 per cent MnO; 49.4 per cent MnO_2; and 10.2 per cent H_2O. Thermal curves obtained when this mineral is analysed show a succession of endothermic effects, leading us to consider that its chemical formula could be more correctly written as MnO_2.$Mn(OH)_2$. Such a formula shows that of the two manganese ions entering into the composition of this mineral, one is tervalent and the other tetravalent.

The first effect which appears on heating is an endothermic effect situated between 350 and 400 °C, associated with a loss of mass as a result of the elimination of hydroxyl ions. The residue remaining after this thermal process is MnO . MnO_2, and with rising temperature this undergoes a series of transformations. Data from the literature in connection with these transformations is contradictory. Thus, according to Kulp and Perfetti (1950) this residue is changed between 950 and 980 °C (with heat absorption) into hausmannite (Mn_3O_4), thus producing a second

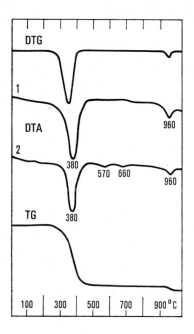

Figure 5.8 Thermal curves of manganite
(after Kulp and Perfetti. 1950).

endothermic effect (see DTA curve *1* in Figure 5.8). But the authors mentioned above, while conducting investigations only by differential thermal analysis, fail to mention that by this transition the compound suffers a loss of mass as a result of the elimination of an oxygen atom. If the assumptions of Topor (1964) are agreed, namely that the residue remaining after the decomposition of manganite undergoes several transformations, then indeed the effect in the temperature range from 950 to 980 °C is associated with a negative mass variation. According to Topor, the residue remaining after the decomposition of manganite undergoes a first thermal transformation between 500 and 570 °C, when the residue in an amorphous state will pass into α-Mn_2O_3 by an absorption of heat, which appears on the DTA curve as a slight endothermic effect. Further, between 640 and 700 °C the α form of Mn_2O_3 will pass into β-Mn_2O_3, and this transition also appears on the DTA curve as a slight endothermic effect. Passage of the β form of Mn_2O_3 into hausmannite (Mn_3O_4) takes place, according to Kulp and Perfetti, and to Topor, in the same temperature range. With rising temperature, the hausmannite formed would undergo a new polymorphous transformation, which takes place in the temperature range from 1180 to 1250 °C, which is also marked on the DTA curve by a slight endothermic effect.

To enable a comparison of the mentioned effects, Figure 5.8 shows the thermal curves of this mineral.

5.3 SULPHIDES

Except for hydrogen sulphide, all native combinations between the anion S^{2-} and metallic cations are solid crystalline substances. These combinations must be considered as ionic compounds, although some properties invalidate this fact. The intense affinity of sulphur for heavy metals is demonstrated by the fact that it forms compounds that are almost water insoluble. Native sulphides can be simple or double, depending on the nature of the metals which participate in their formation. They frequently form solid solutions between themselves in the form of continuous series or with limited miscibility in the solid state. In nature, these minerals are also distributed in various polymorphous series. This fact, together with other shortcomings of an experimental nature, adversely affect thermo-analytical determinations; hence, thermal methods of investigation of sulphides are rarely used.

All sulphides for which thermal curves are to be found in the literature indicate exothermic effects corresponding to oxidation reactions in various temperature ranges.

In determining sulphides, volatile products may arise during the thermal process, which will attack the equipment and other products may also be formed as a result of melting which will completely or partly destroy the reaction crucible or the thermocouple. In such cases, it is advisable to use grooves made of non-porous ceramics, and to insulate the thermocouple from the sulphides either by the grooves themselves or by a separate quartz screening. When sulphides occur in an association with other minerals, and especially when these minerals have ions of heavy metals in their structure, thermal curves will record a series of sham effects. These sham effects are due, in the first place, to the oxidation of sulphur into sulphur oxides which are highly reactive in the nascent state and attack the lattice of the mineral present in the association, partly or totally destroying it. To avoid this drawback, the thermal analysis should be carried out in an oxygen-free atmosphere, for instance, in nitrogen, but for this special equipment with a number of devices permitting the access and removal of the gas is needed. The thermal behaviour of the main natural sulphides will be described below.

Chalcocite, Cu_2S. On DTA curves this mineral show a slight endothermic effect between 90 and 95 °C. This effect emerges as a result of a polymorphous modification of the type $\alpha \rightleftharpoons \beta$. Immediately after this effect some samples analysed have shown another effect, which was also endothermic, in the temperature range from 100 to 106 °C. The cause of this effect is not known, but it is believed to arise because of the presence of some inclusions of other elements in the chalcocite lattice.

With rising temperature, chalcocite remains stable up to about 300 °C, when a new endothermic effect, also of slight intensity, appears. This too is caused by a reversible polymorphous transformation. Immediately after this effect begins a marked exothermic effect, whose maximum is situated between 475 and 525 °C, caused by the oxidation of chalcocite. Upwards of about 600 °C thermal curves indicate an extended endothermic effect with a sharp maximum at about 820 °C. The cause of this extended endothermic effect is not well understood, but the final product remaining after this reaction is thought to be tenorite, CuO, since the behaviour of the product on further heating, is analogous to that of tenorite, showing a slight endothermic effect associated with a loss of mass between 950 and 1000 °C, when CuO passes into Cu_2O. Simultaneously with this transformation, an incipient melting sets in, which is proved by the appearance of the residue, presenting in the end the characteristics of a melt.

Covellite, CuS. The structure of covellite, which is formed of two kinds of sulphur ions (single S^{2-} ions and double S_2^{2-} ions) and from mono and bivalent copper ions (Cu^+ and Cu^{2+}), causes it to have a different thermal behaviour than that of chalcocite.

On heating, covellite shows stability on thermal curves up to 350 °C. It undergoes a first transformation between 375 and 425 °C, recorded on the curves as a moderately marked exothermic effect, which commonly shows two thermal maxima. The ca u se of this effect is not very clear. It is ascribed either to a polymorphous transformation or to inclusions present in its mass, for example, iron sulphide.

The thermal effect specific to this mineral starts at about 450 °C, when a marked endothermic effect appears, caused by thermal dissociation of covellite, according to the reaction $2(Cu_2S.CuS_2) \rightarrow 3Cu_2S + 3S$. With rising temperatures, when determinations are conducted in the air or in an oxygen enriched atmosphere, a new endothermic effect appears, caused by a new oxidation of sulphur, resuting in a final product of the chalcocite type, but possibly also a final product according to the reaction described by Treiber (1967): $Cu_2S + 2Cu_2O \rightleftarrows 6Cu + SO_4^{2-}$.

If the reaction were to proceed as described by Treiber, then further thermal effects must necessarily appear on thermal curves caused by the reactivity of the resultant SO_4^{2-} anion on metallic copper. Thus copper sulphate would be formed, which at higher temperatures would decompose, as shown in the case of chalcantite.

Figure 5.9 illustrates the thermal curves of the two sulphides of copper.

Galena, PbS. Thermal curves obtained on this mineral are complicated, because oxidation processes are not completed in the same temperature range, but take place by stages. This is due to the preferential oxidation of the material which comes in direct contact with oxygen, for instance of the material at the surface of the reaction groove. DTA curves indicated in the literature fail to show a thermal transformation up to 300—350 °C, which is the beginning of the first exothermic effect, with a maximum at about 375 °C and a slight break at 410 °C. This effect is followed by another exothermic effect, more marked, with a sharp maximum at about 520 °C,

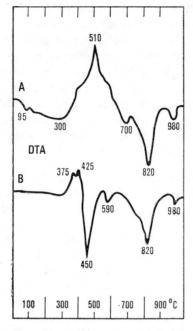 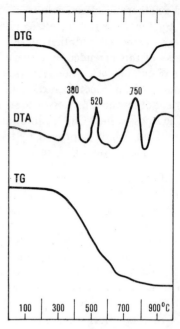

Figure 5.9 DTA curves of copper   Figure 5.10   Thermal curves of
sulphides: *A,* chalcocite; *B,* covellite.   galena.

and then by another, also exothermic effect, with a maximum at 750 °C (Figure 5.10).

The reversion of the DTA curve to the base line in the temperature range upwards of 800 °C is caused by the fact that the residue melts. Galena gives a multitude of maximum exothermic effects and the temperatures of these maxima depend primarily on the characteristics of the instrument, on the amount of sample worked, and on the amount of oxygen present in the oven atmosphere.

It is highly important to remember that no metal crucibles, (including platinum crucibles), should be used when analysing this sulphide, because they would be destroyed. Likewise, the wires of thermocouples must be completely insulated from the sulphide, possibly with a protecting quartz layer.

Zincblende, ZnS. On the DTA curve, the pure mineral shows a thermal stability up to 500 °C. Above this temperature a slight exothermic effect appears, situated in some cases at about 500 °C, and in others at about 700 °C. This temperature fluctuation of the thermal effect is caused, some believe, by the grinding degree of the sample in the mortar as well as by oxygen access to the sample, and the effect is thus due to a superficial oxidation of the particles. This superficial oxidation will further protect the particles, causing the thermal effect proper of the oxidation of

Figure 5.11   Thermal curves of zincblende.

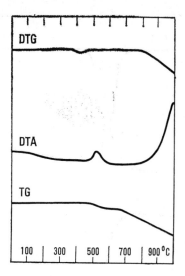

zincblende to appear at a higher temperature, upwards of 850 °C (Figure 5.11). After the oxidation reaction, no thermal maximum appears on the DTA curve up to 950 °C, when the mineral begins to volatilize.

Cinnabar, HgS. Although cinnabar can readily be detected by its red colour, it lends itself well to thermal determinations both qualitative and quantitative, owing to its sublimation in a very narrow temperature range. Sublimation takes place at about 400 °C and an endothermic effect appears on thermal curves, attended by a loss of mass corresponding to the total amount of cinnabar present in the sample.

When determinations are conducted in an inert atmosphere, the sublimate is black and will be deposited on the cooler parts of the instrumental installation, whereas when determinations are conducted in the presence of oxygen, sublimation takes place simultaneously with oxidation, according to the reaction: $HgS + O_2 \rightarrow Hg + SO_2$. On the DTA curve, sublimation appears as an exothermic effect, and on the DTG curve as an endothermic effect.

Cinnabar is known to occur native as a raw mineral, representing, in fact, a cryptocrystalline mass consisting of cinnabar and siliceous minerals, and in some cases also of organic compounds. In this case, cinnabar can readily be detected by an endothermic effect appearing on the DTG curve at about 400 °C. Figure 5.12 shows the thermal curves of a cinnabar sample from Sîntimbru, Romania.

Pyrite, FeS₂. Pyrite being one of the most frequently ecountered native sulphides, curves obtained by thermal analysis have been studied more intensely than for other sulphides. Characteristic of pyrite is a marked exothermic effect which begins at about 350 °C and has a maximum included between 400 and 450 °C. The configuration of thermal curves, and particularly of the DTA curve, is highly varied.

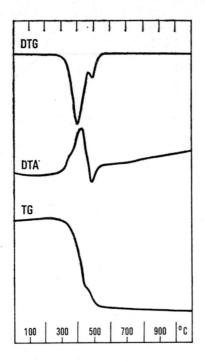

Figure 5.12 Thermal curves of a sample of cinnabar from Sîntimbru, Romania.

On thermal curves, the exothermic effect frequently appears with two and even three maxima. This shows that the oxidation of pyrite depends on its amount in a sample and on the grinding degree, hence implicitly on the amount of oxygen which brings about the oxidation. It has been postulated that these double or treble maxima of the exothermic oxidation effect of pyrite might be closely connected with the way in which this mineral appears native, but there is not enough evidence to substantiate this theory.

I consider more plausible Mackenzie's (1957) assumption which, in fact, is valid for the whole range of sulphides giving exothermic effects with several maxima. This assumption is based on the fact that the oxidation of sulphides takes place successively but nevertheless by leaps, because when oxygen penetrates into the sample it causes a first oxidation at the surface of the particles as a result of which sulphur oxides low in oxygen are evolved abundantly, and these come in contact with new layers of oxygen immediately around the crucible, combining with it. This, for a time, prevents oxygen from penetrating the sample, and the mineral is practically in an inert atmosphere for this interval of time. The temperature will consequently drop in the sample and exothermic maxima will hence appear. In a completely inert atmosphere, pyrite gives one single marked endothermic effect situated between 600 and 800 °C.

For comparison, Figure 5.13 shows the DTA curves of pyrite both as a simple mineral and in association with other minerals.

Marcasite, FeS$_2$. This mineral, which is the low temperature form of iron sulphide, yields thermal curves that are simpler than those of pyrite because the exothermic reaction is less complicated. Oxidation begins from about 370 °C, and its thermal maximum is at 430—440 °C. Several thermal maxima can appear but fewer than with pyrite.

Some authors, such as Kracek (1942) and Topor (1964), assert that there might be a marcasite-pyrite transformation at about 410 °C, but this is not recorded on thermal curves. Moreover, investigations carried out with marcasite in an inert atmosphere fail to show this transformation which, if it had existed, should have appeared.

A comparison between the thermal behaviour of the two sulphides of iron shows that the oxidation of marcasite occurs much more readily than that of pyrite. When the amount of sample subjected to the analysis is the same, marcasite presents the thermal maximum at a temperature somewhat lower than that of pyrite.

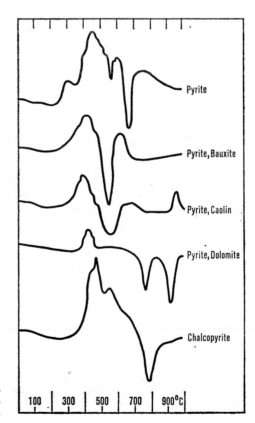

Figure 5.13 DTA curves of pyrite as a simple mineral, of pyrite in association with other minerals, and of chalcopyrite.

Pyrotine, $Fe_{(1-x)}$ S. Values for x generally vary from 0.1 to 0.2, and for this reason the formula of pyrotine is written as FeS.

Specific to the thermal curves of this mineral, unlike the other sulphides of iron, is the slight endothermic effect from 130—140 °C, caused by a reversible polymorphous transformation. Further, with increasing temperatures pyrotine shows an exothermic oxidation effect specific to iron sulphides, except that the beginning of the range of this effect as well as the maximum of the effect are situated at a somewhat lower temperature.

Chalcopyrite, $CuFeS_2$. On thermal analysis, chalcopyrite shows a single oxidation reaction marked on thermal curves by a sharp exothermic effect. On the DTA curve the beginning of the reaction is recorded at about 300 °C. The curve becomes abrupt at about 340 °C, having the maximum of the exothermic effect at about 450 °C, the end of the reaction reaching temperatures of 600—650 °C.

Data from the literature indicate that with rising temperatures an endothermic effect appears at about 770 °C, but the nature of this effect is not clear. It is believed to arise because the product remaining after oxidation attacks the crucible, when this is made of metal, or the thermocouple, when this is in direct contact with the sample. As a matter of fact, the same thing happens also with the other sulphides. It was found that the crucible shows substantial loss of mass after a sulphide analysis when it has been cleaned in an acid medium.

5.4 CHLORIDES

The thermal behaviour of these minerals has not been studied in depth and only the method of differential thermal analysis has been used. I shall not discuss the thermal behaviour of halite, NaCl, and of sylvite, KCl, because in pure conditions these minerals give very simple thermal curves. The only thermal process of physical nature is that of melting, and this is recorded only on the DTA curve. The thermal process caused by melting was described in some detail in Chapter 4. The melting point of sodium chloride, when in the state of a simple compund, is at 801 °C and that of potassium chloride at 770 °C. Figure 2.7 illustrates the way in which the melting point is affected when the two minerals are mixed in different proportions.

Bischofite, $MgCl_2 \cdot 6H_2O$. Bischofite is a simple mineral with very restricted distribution. It was found in the upper levels of salt deposits, above the carnalite bed, as well as in the crystallized salts from some lakes rich in magnesium. This mineral was studied by the method of differential thermal analysis by Ivanova (1961) who, however, has not made any statement as to the nature of the thermal effects.

From the thermal curves that I have obtained, it can be concluded that simultaneously with the removal of the water of crystallization of this mineral there occurs a partial hydrolysis of the type: $MgCl_2 + H_2O \rightarrow MgO + 2HCl$. But, also experimentally, it was found that at the same rate of heating the thermal process of dehydration-hydrolysis is constant in respect to the loss of mass. From the thermal curves hydrolysis is shown to begin after about three molecules of water of crystallization have been removed, that is, above 240 °C, and that hydrolysis is more intense between 400 and 700 °C (Figure 5.14). Owing to the process of hydrolysis, on the one hand, and to the fact that magnesium chloride is highly hygroscopic, forming a series of hydrates with 2, 4, 8 and 12 molecules of water, on the other hand, the quantitative determination of bischofite is difficult. When bischofite is subjected to thermal analysis one must also keep in mind that, owing to hydrolysis, part of the substance migrates out of the sample groove, and the instruments become contaminated. Because of this, it was not possible to calculate precisely the loss of mass in any of the samples that I have analysed.

Carnalite, MgKCl$_3$. 6H$_2$O. This mineral is one of the last to be formed as a result of the evaporation process of the water from salt lakes rich in Mg^{2+} and K$^+$ ions. Hence it is encountered native always in the upper horizons of salt deposits. Br$^-$, Rb$^+$ and Cs$^+$ ions are known to be present in carnalite in an isomorphic association, but these elementatts are found in very small amounts and are not perceptible by thermal analyses; they could at most modify the melting point of carnalite.

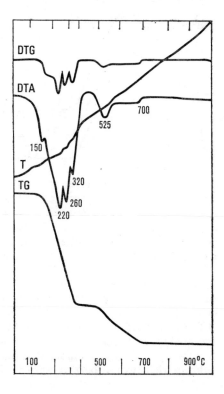

Figure 5.14   Thermal   curves   of   bischofite.

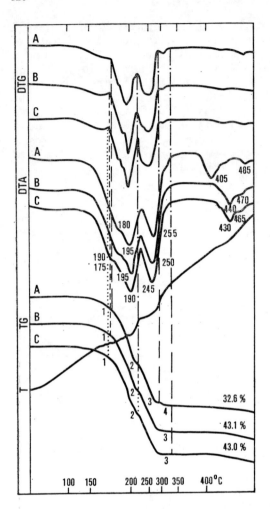

Figure 5.15 Thermal curves obtained on samples of carnalite of various origin: *A*, Stemnik (U.S.S.R.); *B*, Stassfurt (Germany); *C*, Tazlău (Romania).

From the thermal curves I have obtained at a heating rate of 5 °C per minute (Figure 5.15) it follows that the dehydration of carnalite begins at about 130 °C and ends at about 350 °C. At this rate, dehydration proceeds in several stages. Above the temperature of 350 °C two endothermic effects appear on the DTA curve assumed to be caused by melting of the anhydrous association. With some samples, only the peak temperature of the effect varies and the variation is closely connected with the purity degree of the sample. It is found that in the case of curve *A* from Figure 5.15 the first effect occurs at a temperature about 40 °C lower than the analogous effect in *B* and *C*. From chemical analyses I have carried out on these samples, it was concluded that the sample for curve *A* contained more potassium chloride than would be necessary in the carnalite lattice. This was also confirmed by the losses of mass, which are smaller than in samples *B* and *C*. Simultaneously with this effect, it was found that TG and DTG curves show an incipient loss of mass due to a volatility from the mass of the sample. These effects could also be observed when the samples were heated at a rate of 10 °C per minute. After removal of the water of crystallization in the two well-defined stages, the mass of the sample continuously decreases up to 1000 °C. At this heating rate no level portion is found on the TG and DTG curves up to a temperature of 1000 °C to enable quantitative determinations to be made. As in the case of bischofite, on heating the sample above 400—450 °C the instruments are contaminated by products volatilized from the sample.

To conclude, it may be stated that methods of thermal analysis are adequate for the determination of carnalite only in the range of temperatures in which water of crystallization is removed, and that the results are not very conclusive from a quantitative viewpoint, because the mineral is hygroscopic and absorbs water from the atmosphere.

Tachihydrite, $2MgCl_2.CaCl_2.12H_2O$. This mineral is the last to be deposited in the process of water evaporation from salt lakes and it has not been widely discussed in mineralogy since it is of comparatively minor importance and it is not frequently encountered, as it is highly unstable. No studies have been made on the mineral in the native state, but only on artificial samples obtained by crystallization of the compound from solutions. Thermal curves (Figure 5.16) show that this compound undergoes two kinds of transformations, the first as a result of dehydration and the second due to partial hydrolysis. The latter reaction takes place vigorously, and as a result, a large part of the sample is thrown out of the reaction groove.

Kainite, $MgSO_4KCl.3H_2O$. In spite of the fact that, from the viewpoint of its components, kainite takes an intermediate place between the chloride group and the sulphate group, it is treated with the former because of its similar thermal behaviour.

It frequently occurs native in the form of granular masses, which is of particular practical importance in its use as raw material for the production of fertilizers, and for production of potassium and magnesium salts. Kainite was studied as a mineral by thermal methods of analysis by Cocco (1952) and Kassner (1958) but they have recorded only the DTA curves.

According to my data, kainite presents highly characteristic thermal curves (Figure 5.17). Water of crystallization is removed in two stages: at first two molecules are expelled together in the temperature range from 160—300 °C; in the second stage, the third water molecule is removed between the temperatures of 300 and 420 °C. From the shape of the thermal curves and from the temperature range in which the last water molecule is removed, it may be assumed that this last molecule of water of crystallization is bound only to magnesium sulphate, and that after the removal of the first two water molecules, the mineral separates into sylvite, KCl, and kieserite, $MgSO_4.H_2O$.

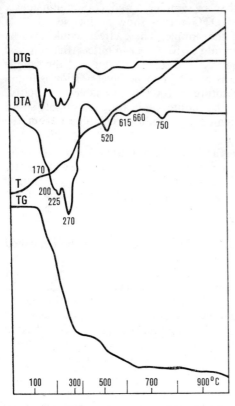

Figure 5.16 Thermal curves of artificial tachihydrite.

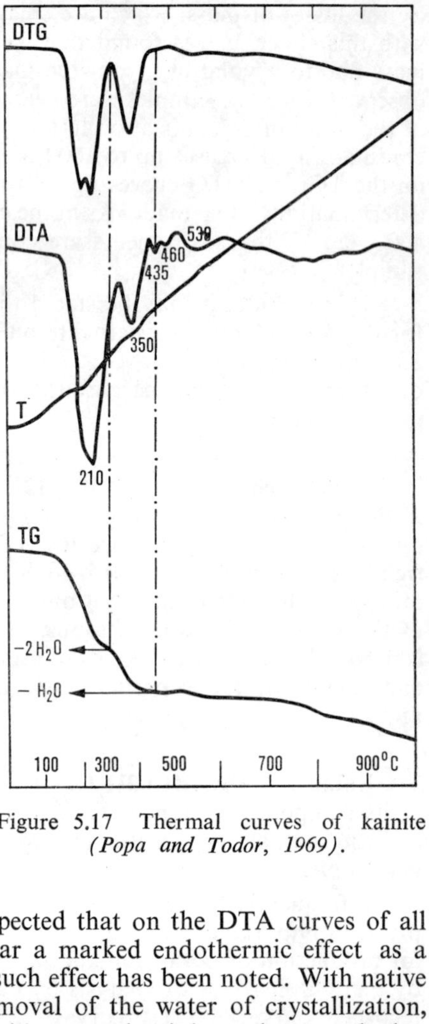

Figure 5.17 Thermal curves of kainite *(Popa and Todor, 1969).*

With rising temperature, it would be expected that on the DTA curves of all minerals from this group there should appear a marked endothermic effect as a result of the melting of the material, but no such effect has been noted. With native samples, however, immediately after the removal of the water of crystallization, one or two endothermic effects of small area will appear, but it is not known whether they are due to the impurities or to kainite. With artificial associations obtained by crystallization, which cannot be stated with certainty to represent kainite (because it contains more water of crystallization than indicated by the theoretical compound), these thermal effects failed to appear. An endothermic effect appears, however, around a temperature of 500 °C both with native and with artificial products. This effect could be ascribed to incipient melting, but only of potassium chloride, because after that TG and DTG curves indicate a continuous loss of mass. In this case also, if experiments are conducted at temperatures higher than 500 °C the instruments become contaminated.

5.5 SULPHATES

Native sulphates include minerals of a sedimentary chemical nature representing combinations of the SO_4^{2-} anion with metallic cations. Most frequently bound with the SO_4^{2-} anion are the cations of alkaline and alkaline-earth metals, but sulphates of the other metal cations and especially of heavy metals are also encountered.

Native sulphates may be simple, double, or treble, and have arisen as a result of well defined chemical processes, either by precipitation or by crystallization from solutions. Generally, almost all native sulphates crystallize with a fixed number of water molecules which, under the action of thermal energy, are removed in well-defined temperature ranges and always in constant proportions.

With regard to their behaviour on heating for the purpose of thermal analysis, sulphates are divided into two completely different classes. The first class includes sulphates that melt on heating at certain temperatures, that is, they give melting points, and after that, on cooling they crystallize again. The second class includes sulphates that decompose on heating, releasing SO_3 and giving a residue in the form oxides; these oxides may exhibit thermal stability or may undergo a number of transformations with increasing temperatures.

5.5.1 Natural Sulphates of Alkaline and Alkaline-Earth Metals

5.5.1.1. Alkaline sulphates group

Unlike the wide range of synthetic sulphates, only four alkaline sulphates occur native, namely thenardite, Na_2SO_4, mirabilite, $Na_2SO_4 . 10H_2O$, arkanite, K_2SO_4, and gloserite, $K_3Na(SO_4)_2$.

From a thermal viewpoint, the four minerals generally behave in an analogous way, except mirabilite which readily loses its water of crystallization. All four minerals yield specific melting points if they are not contaminated with other salts; as a rule, however, they are contaminated with halite which is almost always present in the company of these sulphates.

Thenardite, Na_2SO_4. In thermal analyses, thenardite shows two endothermic effects, recorded only on the DTA curve (Figure 5.18). The first effect, which takes place as result of a polymorphous transformation, occurs in the temperature range from 200—300 °C, and the second, which is due to the melting point, occurs at 885 °C. No weight variation is indicated by the TG and DTG curves if the product analysed is a simple mineral. With some samples in which sodium chloride was found present, the melting point is somewhat lower, and after this thermal effect there also occurs a loss of mass as a result of the volatilization of a part of the sodium chloride present.

If the sample subjected to analysis is cooled at the same rate as that at which it was heated, the two thermal effects are again recorded on the DTA curve, but this time the process takes place with evolution of heat.

Mirabilite, $Na_2SO_4.10H_2O$. At a heating rate of 10 °C per minute, mirabilite loses the water of crystallization completely between 40 and 180 °C. The DTA curve records a marked endothermic effect caused by the removal of the water of crystallization. This effect has two maxima: the first, situated below a temperature of 60 °C, is due to a sham melting effect, or to a dissolution of sodium sulphate in its own water of crystallization; the second, situated at about 120 °C, is the maximum proper of the removal process of the water of crystallization.

Duval (1948) has shown that at a temperature of 72 °C there would arise an intermediate product of the type $Na_2SO_4. 4.75H_2O$, but subsequent investigations have not confirmed this fact.

Further, the anhydrous product behaves analogously to thenardite. TG and DTG curves show that the loss of the water of crystallization takes place continuously, in a straight line, and not by jumps, the removal of water beginning from the temperature at which the effect of dissolution in its own water of crystallization takes place, and continuing up to about 160 °C (Figure 5.19).

Arkanite, K_2SO_4. Thermal effects produced on heating both native and artificial arkanite can be studied only by the method of differential analysis. An endothermic effect appears in the temperature range from 520—600 °C caused by a polymorphous

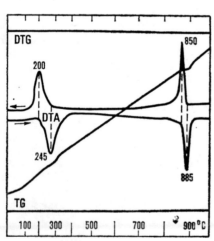

Figure 5.18 Thermal curves obtained on heating and cooling thenardite.

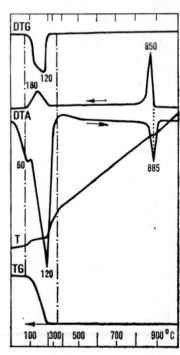

Figure 5.19 Thermal curves obtained on heating and cooling mirabilite.

Figure 5.20 Thermal curves obtained on heating and cooling arkanite.

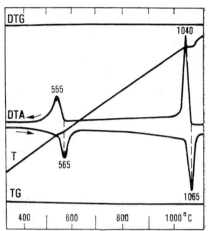

transformation, and at 1060 °C a second effect appears, which is also endothermic, due to melting of the compound (Figure 5.20). Also, with arkanite, if the sample in cooled after the melting point has been passed, both effects will again be recorded on the DTA curve.

Gloserite, $K_3Na(SO_4)_2$. Thermal effects of gloserite are analogous to those of thenardite and arkanite, the only difference being that the temperatures at which these effects occur with gloserite are situated between the temperatures of the other two compounds. Thus, the temperature of the polymorphous transformation effect lies at about 400 °C, and that of the melting effect at about 970 °C. Like thenardite and arkanite, the thermal curves gloserite recording weight variations fail to show any modification.

Figure 5.21 illustrates DTA curves obtained on heating and cooling both a mechanical mixture of potassium and sodium sulphates and of the product obtained by evaporation of the solution in which both sulphates were dissolved, which is in fact gloserite. The series of curves (a) show that in the case of a mechanical mixture of Na_2SO_4 and K_2SO_4 the DTA curve will indicate very clearly the thermal effects of polymorphous transformation both for Na_2SO_4 and for K_2SO_4, the melting point of this mixture lying at about 960 °C, as in the case of gloserite. The area of the thermal effect is, however, larger. On cooling, the thermal effect caused by the polymorphous process is recorded as a single effect. When the association was obtained from a solution, whereby both sulphates were crystallized together, the DTA curves (b) record the polymorphous process both on heating and on cooling as a single efect. The comparison between the two curves aims to prove that the method of differential thermal analysis can accurately show if the product is a mechanical mixture or if the compounds were crystallized together.

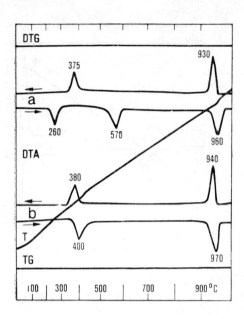

Figure 5.21 Thermal curves obtained on heating and cooling gloserite: a, mechanical mixture of K_2SO_4 and Na_2SO_4 not crystallized; b, mechanical mixture of K_2SO_4 and Na_2SO_4 crystallized.

In summing up, it may be concluded that methods of thermal analysis and, more precisely, differential thermal analysis, enable an identification of alkaline sulphates, but no quantitative determinations. Nevertheless, in the case of mirabilite it is possible to evaluate its amount in an association from the amount of water of crystallization removed, but errors are large.

5.5.1.2 Gypsum group

The natural compounds from this group are gypsum and anhydrite. Plaster, which is a synthetic transition product between gypsum and anhydrite is known to occur native, but it is not sufficiently important to be taken into consideration here.

These minerals are products of chemical sedimentation arising as a result of the reaction between SO_4^{2-} and Ca^{2+} ions. Between gypsum and anhydrite there exists a continuity of exchange, depending on moisture and pressure, as a result of the absorption or expulsion of water. Hence, in most cases gypsum and anhydrite are found together.

Gypsum, $CaSO_4.2H_2O$. Native gypsum was studied by Mitsuki (1952), Yamanchi and Togai (1953), West and Sutton (1954) and Sudhir (1958), using the methods of differential thermal analysis; Duval (1963) made a comparative study by thermal gravimetry between data obtained on artificial and native samples.

At a heating rate of 5 °C per minute, gypsum expels the water of crystallization in three clearly distinct stages, which may be seen particularly well on the DTG curve. At first one water molecule is removed, followed immediately by the removal of half a water molecule. As a result of these expulsions, gypsum passes into a stable form called *plaster*, $2\,CaSO_4 . H_2O$. After this stage follows the removal of the last half of the water molecule, when gypsum passes into anhydrite. On further heating, in the temperature range from 380—450 °C a new thermal transformation will occur which is recorded only on the DTA curve by an exothermic effect, as a result of the polymorphous transformation of gypsum.

At a heating rate of 10 °C per minute, thermal curves show only two effects determined by the removal of the water of crystallization (Figure 5.22). In this case, one and a half molecules of water are removed at first, as a result of which gypsum passes into plaster; then, with rising temperatures, the other half of a water molecule is removed too. After this the processes are the same as in the case of heating at a rate of 5 °C per minute. After the transitions shown above, gypsum fails to suffer any thermal transformation up to temperatures above 1200 °C.

Many gypsum samples yield thermal effects at temperatures above 450 °C; these effects are caused by the presence in the sample of other minerals, such as clays and carbonates.

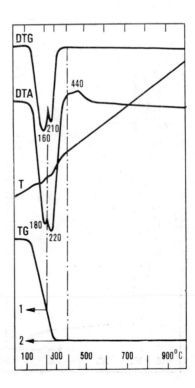

Figure 5.22   Thermal curves of gypsum at a heating
              rate of 10 °C per minute.

Plaster, CaSO$_4 \cdot \frac{1}{2}$H$_2$O. Plaster is, as already mentioned, an intermediate product between gypsum and anhydrite, obtained artificially, and thermal determinations have been carried out only on artificial products. After the thermal effect caused by the removal of half a molecule of water of crystallization, a sample of pure gypsum undergoes the same transformations as gypsum. But most samples from various industrial sources also contain impurities, particularly carbonates and argillaceous minerals. Figure 5.23 illustrates the thermal curves of such a sample. It may be noticed that in the temperature range in which water of crystallization is, as a rule, removed, three clearly distinct effects appear on the DTG curve. The first effect is due to the removal of the water absorbed as moisture; the second is caused by the removal of the water of crystallization from gypsum, which goes to prove that during the industrial process not all gypsum was converted into plaster; the third effect, which is much more intense, is due to the removal of the water of crystallization of gypsum. At about 420 °C the exothermic effect of the polymorphous transformation, shown also in the case of gypsum, appears on the DTA curves Around a temperature of 850 °C, thermal curves indicate an endothermic effect due to a loss of mass as a result of the decomposition of calcite present in the sample.

Anhydrite, CaSO$_4$. In the pure state, anhydrite undergoes no thermal transformation up to a temperature of 1200 °C, hence it cannot be determined by thermal

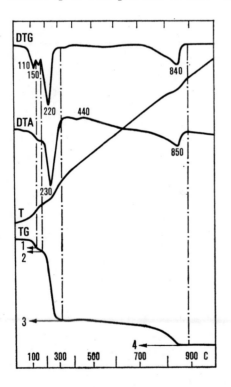

Figure 5.23   Thermal curves of a sample of industrial gypsum.

methods. Some determinations are made, however, for the identification of the impurities present in anhydrite samples.

Gypsum and plaster were seen to lend themselves well to quantitative determinations by thermal methods. These determinations are based on the loss of mass as a result of the removal of the water of crystallization, which is bound strongly in the lattice of minerals. Satisfactory results were obtained also in the investigation of the nature of the minerals present as impurities in the gypsum mass (Todor, 1971).

5.5.1.3 Baryte and Celestite Group

Sulphates from this group arise by evaporation of the native solutions from sulphurous salt lakes rich in magnesium ions. Epsomite is deposited at first. As the solutions evaporate, magnesium sulphate with seven molecules of water of crystallization becomes increasingly unstable, yielding its place to the hexahydrate. Kieserite is formed by direct crystallization from salt solutions rich in SO_4^{2-} and Mg^{2+} ions.

Epsomite, $MgSO_4 . 7H_2O$. Both the native and the artificial products have been studied by differential thermal analysis on the one hand, and by thermal gravimetry, on the other hand. A complex thermal analysis was performed by Lóránt (1966) on an artificial product, showing the way in which water of crystallization is removed at two heating rates, namely at 5 °C per minute and at 10 °C per minute. In both cases, epsomite expels water of crystallization in two clearly distinct stages. In the first stage six water molecules are expelled up to a temperature of 290 °C when the heating rate was of 5 °C per minute, and up to a temperature of 305 °C when the heating rate was 10 °C per minute. The removal of the last molecule of water of crystallization requires higher temperatures, namely 400 °C. When the heating rate was 5 °C per minute, an endothermic effect was recorded on the DTA curve around 80 °C, due to the sham melting effect in its own water of crystallization.

At both heating rates, it was found that the seven water molecules are removed in several stages, but it was not possible to calculate exactly how much was expelled at every stage. Above the temperature of 400 °C, at which the removal of the water of crystallization is complete, the anhydrous salt remains constant in weight up to a temperature of about 900 °C. Thermal curves (Figure 5.24) show that around a temperature of 910 °C a slight endothermic effect will appear, possibly indicating an incipient melting of magnesium sulphate, but on thermal curves a loss of mass is simultaneously recorded as a result of the desulphuration of magnesium sulphate according to the reaction $MgSO_4 \rightarrow MgO + SO_3$.

In samples which are contaminated with sodium chloride, the mixture melts at a much lower temperature, and after that the loss of mass begins.

Hexahydrite, $MgSO_4.6H_2O$. At both heating rates, the hexahydrite behaves analogously to epsomite, the only difference being that five molecules of water of crystallization are removed in several stages. The last molecule is removed at a higher temperature.

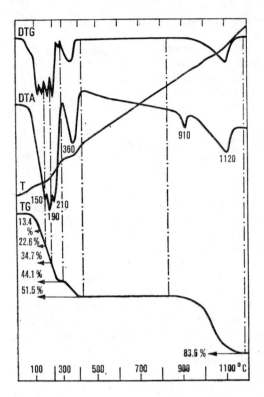

Figure 5.24   Thermal curves of epsomite at a heating rate of 10 °C per minute.

Kieserite, MgSO₄.H₂O. This mineral, frequently encountered in potassium salt deposits, was studied by Cocco (1952), employing the methods of differential thermal analysis. Popa and Todor (1969) show that kieserite expels its molecule of water of crystallization in the temperature range 300—400 °C. The loss of mass of simple mineral samples as a result of this thermal process is in the order of 13 per cent. With rising temperatures, the thermal curves (Figure 5.25) of kieserite are analogous to those of epsomite. In very many samples, kieserite is associated with other minerals, especially with halite. In such cases, the loss of mass due to the removal of the water of crystallization is the only possible method for determining kieserite.

The three minerals making up the epsomite group lend themselves particularly well to quantitative analytical determinations by thermal methods. If their determination is less exact or even inconclusive after the first thermal effect caused by the loss of the water of crystallization, things are different with the second thermal effect caused by the removal of the last molecule of water of crystallization. As it was seen, in the end all three minerals lose the last molecule of water of crystallization in a well-defined range of temperatures, and on account of this removal they lend themselves to the determination of the magnesium sulphate present in the sample.

5.5.1.4 Double and Treble Sulphates Group in Salt Deposits

These native sulphates are formed from salt solutions rich in Mg^{2+}, Ca^{2+}, Na^+, and K^+ cations by their combination with the SO_4^{2-} anion. This combination takes place in the temperature range from 0 to 80 °C. These minerals are extensively distributed in nature, forming the potassium salt deposits which occur both as clearly distinct and fully stable simple mineral beds in deposits, and as associations among themselves or among themselves and other salts, and particularly sodium and potassium chlorides.

The great difficulty in their determination is due to the fact that they undergo a series of transformations from the moment when they are collected, until they are analysed. Thus, in moist surroundings some of them are hydrated, passing into other forms. For instance, langbeinite is converted with time, in the presence of atmospheric humidity, into leonite or schönite and magnesium sulphate of the kieserite or epsomite type, according to the reaction:

$$2K_2Mg_2(SO_4)_3 \xrightarrow{nH_2O} \begin{cases} K_2Mg(SO_4)_2 \cdot 4H_2O \\ K_2Mg(SO_4)_2 \cdot 6H_2O \end{cases} + 3MgSO_4 \cdot nH_2O$$

Sulphates crystallized with water molecules, particularly leonite and schönite, if kept in dry surroundings will dehydrate with time, being resolved into potassium and magnesium sulphates. This fact led a number of investigators to assume the existence of potassium sulphate as a mineral on its own.

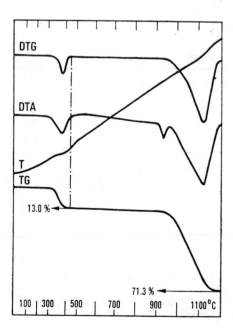

Figure 5.25 Thermal curves of a kieserite sample from Tazlău, Romania.

As a result of the instability mentioned overleaf, the same samples by whichever method they are analysed generally lead to different results. To avoid such an occurrence, all samples collected should be kept in hermetically closed plastic bags in which they will remain unchanged for a longer time.

Since data related to the thermal behaviour of minerals from this group is scant and refers only to differential thermal analysis, I shall discuss my own investigations. The investigations were conducted with an extended range of simple mineral samples from the deposits at Tazlău-Cucuieti in Romania, as well as with a number of samples originating from Stassfurt (Federal Republic of Germany) and Stemnik (the Ukraine).

Langbeinite, $K_2Mg_2(SO_4)_3$. Since this mineral crystallizes without water and fails to decompose on heating, it can be determined as a simple mineral only by differential thermal analysis. Thermal curves obtained at a heating rate of 10 °C per minute present two endothermic effects (Figure 5.26). The first effect, of small area, is situated at a temperature of about 640 °C and is due to a polymorphous transformation. The second endothermic effect is highly intensive; it is recorded at the temperature of 950 °C and is due to the melting point. Both effects are reversible, that is, if the sample analyzed is cooled at a rate approximately equal to that of heating, it will be of equal intensity but exothermic.

In most cases, langbeinite is contaminated with a number of other minerals, particularly with halite, kieserite, sylvite, kainite, and insoluble minerals of an argillaceous nature. As a result, other thermal effects will appear on the thermal curves of langbeinite, either only on the DTA curve or on all curves, when the accessory minerals also show mass variations.

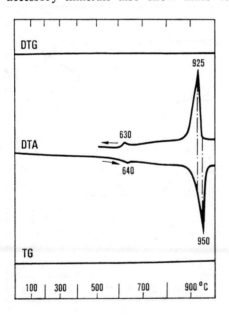

Figure 5.26 Thermal curves obtained on heating and cooling a sample of langbeinite from Tazlău, Romania *(Popa and Todor. 1969).*

One of the main indications as to the purity of langbeinite is its melting point. If the sample contains an alien mineral with a lower melting point than the melting point of langbeinite, then the latter will also be lowered. If the Cl^- ion is contained in the molecule of the alien mineral, a loss of mass will be found on TG and DTG curves after the melting point of the mixture, due to the volatility of the respective chloride. These considerations are valid for the whole range of minerals included in the sulphate group.

To sum up, langbeinite may be identified very well by means of thermal methods of analysis, but no quantitative determinations can be made.

Schönite, $K_2Mg(SO_4)_2.6H_2O$. The mineral is a double sulphate crystallized with six water molecules. The water of crystallization is expelled under the action of thermal energy in a way typical of this mineral. Thermal curves obtained both with samples of the native and of the artificial mineral produced by crystallization of the mineral from solution show three endothermic effects of like intensity in the temperature range 25—350 °C (Figure 5.27). By measuring the height of the TG curve it was established that in all cases schönite gives off water molecules in pairs. This fact allows quantitative determinations to be performed.

With rising temperatures, schönite fails to show any mass variation, hence the TG and DTG curves further remain constant. The DTA curve, however, will present two more endothermic effects. The first effect, of small intensity, recorded around a temperature of 575 °C, is due to a polymorphous transformation, and the second, of much greater intensity, recorded around a temperature of 750 °C, is due to melting of the potassium and magnesium sulphate mixture. These two thermal effects are reversible on cooling.

If it is intended to perform quantitative determinations based on the loss of mass, and when the samples are contaminated with halite, experiments should be conducted only until the melting point is reached.

Leonite, $K_2Mg(SO_4)_2.4H_2O$. This mineral is similar to schönite, the only difference being that it crystallizes with four water molecules only. As a rule it occurs in salt deposits much more frequently than schönite, sometimes forming well-defined simple mineral beds. Figure 5.28 illustrates the thermal curves of a simple mineral sample. It can be seen on these curves that with this mineral, as with schönite, the water of crystallization is expelled in series of two molecules each. This process is shown on DTA and DTG curves by the two endothermic effects. After these effects, the DTA curve shows the polymorphous transformation effect at about 570 °C as well as the endothermic effect due to melting at about 570 °C. The thermal effects are reversible on cooling.

Polyhalite, $K_2MgCa_2(SO_4)_4.2H_2O$. Polyhalite almost always occurs as a simple mineral, forming thick beds in deposits and being thereby particularly interesting. Thermal methods have not been used much to investigate the mineral polyhalite and other minerals from this group. Cocco (1952) and Ivanova (1961) show it on DTA curves in samples originating from potassium salt deposits. Popa and Todor have examined in detail the behaviour of polyhalite on heating, and have shown

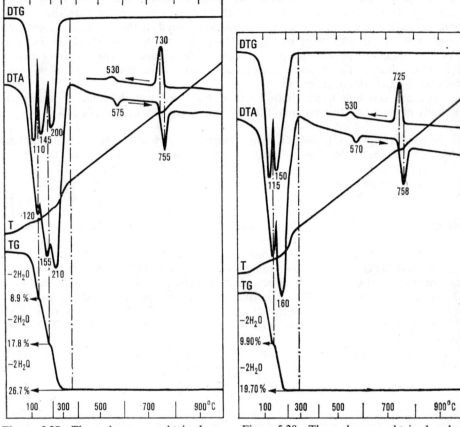

Figure 5.27 Thermal curves obtained on heating and cooling a sample of schönite.

Figure 5.28 Thermal curves obtained on heating and cooling a sample of leonite from Tazlău, Romania *(Popa and Todor, 1969).*

how it can be identified in native mixtures and how it can be quantitatively determined (Popa and Todor, 1969).

Thermal curves of polyhalite (Figure 5.29) show that the water of crystallization is expelled at a high temperature, between 300 and 450 °C, a fact which clearly separates it from the other representatives of the group. Further, as the temperature rises, at about 640 °C on the DTA curve a slight endothermic effect appears, caused by a polymorphous transformation, and at 880 °C there is a marked endothermic effect due to melting. On cooling, both thermal effects are reversible.

In order to establish the influence of some salts on polyhalite when heated, various artificial mixtures were prepared from a simple mineral sample of polyhalite with different salts added. Thermal curves were recorded both on heating and on cooling. It was found that the added salts did not affect the removal of the water

Figure 5.29 Thermal curves obtained on heating and cooling a sample of polyhalite from Tazlău, Romania *(Popa and Todor, 1969)*.

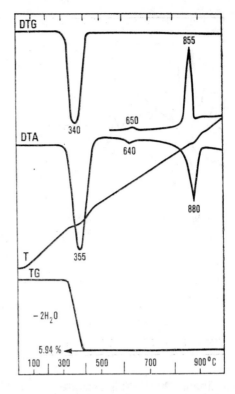

of crystallization, but they did alter the melting point. However, it is not advisable to conduct experiments beyond the melting point when it is intended to carry out quantitative determinations.

Astrakanite, $Na_2Mg(SO_4)_2.4H_2O$. Thermal curves (Figure 5.30) obtained both with native and artificial samples show that in the temperature range $100-350\,°C$ the water of crystallization is expelled. This expulsion takes place in two stages, two molecules being given off at each stage. As a result of this, two endothermic effects appear on the thermal curves; the first, having a maximum between 140 and $200\,°C$, depending on the degree of purity of the sample, corresponds to the removal of the first two water molecules; the second, whose maximum is between 260 and $300\,°C$, is similar in form and intensity with the first, and corresponds to the removal of the remaining two water molecules.

With rising temperatures, at $620\,°C$ another endothermic effect is recorded only on the DTA curve. This effect is of low intensity and is due to a polymorphous transformation or more correctly to a resolution of astrakanite into its constituents, that is, Na_2SO_4 and $MgSO_4$. When heating is continued, an endothermic effect appears, having two maxima, one around $670\,°C$ and another

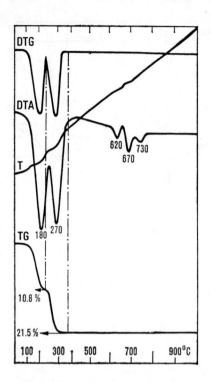

Figure 5.30 Thermal curves of a sample
fo astrakanite from Tazlău (Romania).

at about 720 °C; this extended thermal effect with double peaks is due to melting of the mixture.

Unlike the other representatives of the group, in the case of astrakanite the thermal effects recorded at the melting point are more extended, and the conversions take place in a wider temperature range.

Glauberite, $Na_2Ca(SO_4)_2$. On heating, glauberite suffers no change of mass up to a temperature of 1200 °C; therefore, it can be studied by the method of differential thermal analysis. According to Mackenzie (1962), glauberite shows two endothermic effects on the DTA curve, the first from 450 to 527 °C, and the second from 875 to 925 °C. The thermal curves I have obtained at a heating rate of 10 °C per minute (Figure 5.31) show that the first endothermic effect is situated at a lower temperature, namely, around 270 °C and is due to a polymorphous transformation. It may be assumed that the real temperature of this effect is at about 270 °C, because the polymorphous transformation is caused by the presence of Na_2SO_4, and as can be seen from the discussion on thenardite, this transformation takes place in the temperature range 200—300 °C.

Other compounds mentioned in handbooks of mineralogy also belong to this sulphate group of salt deposits, but it was not possible to separate these compounds

Figure 5.31 Thermal curves obtained on heating and cooling of glauberite.

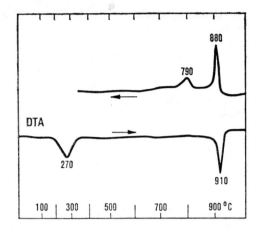

as simple mineral individuals, to enable the investigation of their behaviour on heating.

As we have seen, a native sample may contain either a single mineral or an association of minerals. Therefore, one should not lose sight of the fact that in a native sample of potassium salts, containing various minerals, each mineral represents a complex function in relation to analytical results, either chemical or thermal, and it is at the same time affected by the way in which various ions may combine with each other and by the errors involved in the analysis. Hence, it is always better when the components in a sample are established quantitatively to compare and correlate the results obtained by several methods.

5.5.2 Native Sulphates of Heavy Metals

Unlike native sulphates of alkaline and alkaline earth metals, compounds resulted from a combination of the SO_4^{2-} ion with heavy metals are comparatively few in number. They are not very often found as simple minerals (except chalcantite and melantherite), but they are frequently encountered in associations when they are isomorphously crystallized, with ratios between anions and cations varying within very wide limits. All native sulphates of heavy metals are crystallized with water molecules which are readily given off to the surroundings; hence they must be kept in tight containers such as plastic bags or jars with paraffined stoppers.

Thermal processes specific to these minerals are dehydration and decomposition or rather desulphuration, where the oxide passes into the oxide of the cation and sulphur oxides are released from the system. Although these sulphates rarely occur as simple minerals, the thermal curves of similar artificial compounds will be discussed, because these artificial compounds behave analogously to the native minerals.

Chalcantite, CuSO₄.5H₂O. The artificially prepared product was investigated by Berg, Nikolaiev, and Rode (1944) and Cocco (1952), using differential thermal analysis, and by a number of researchers employing thermogravimetry whose papers are published in Duval's *Thermal Gravimetry* (1963). Lóránt (1966) also describes the thermal behaviour of the artificial product, when studied by the method of the derivative thermogravimetry. I investigated both artificial and native samples to find the degree of purity of the native product. My data are generally similar to those given in the literature. However, there was a difference between the native and artificial samples in that the three stages of dehydration (Figure 5.32) were much more clearly defined on the DTG curve in the case of the native samples.

I shall now examine the behaviour on heating of crystallized copper sulphate. The first four water molecules are removed quite readily in two clearly distinct stages, two molecules at a time. The last molecule is expelled with greater difficulty, at a higher temperature. This fits in well with the known facts that in the crystal structure of CuSO₄.5H₂O only four molecules are coordinatively bound to the copper ion, whereas the fifth is retained by hydrogen bonds. As a matter of fact, the monohydrate does not contain any water as such, but only OH groups bound as CuSO₅H₂. After the last molecule of wtaer is expelled, the anhydrous sulphate

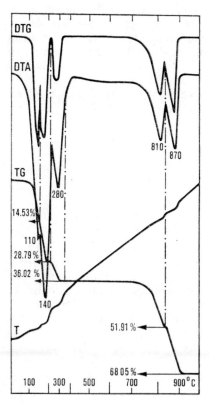

Figure 5.32 Thermal curve of a chalcantite sample.

remains stable up to 700 °C, when desulphuration begins. This desulphuration takes place in two stages. At first, half a molecule of SO_3 is expelled, and the compound passes into a basic salt of the form $Cu_2O.SO_4$ which is then further desulphurized, giving rise to the second thermal effect. If the temperature rises above 1000 °C the cupric oxide formed begins to expel oxygen, passing into cuprous oxide which, in turn, with rising temperatures may pass by melting into metallic copper.

Melantherite, $FeSO_4.7H_2O$. Ferrous sulphate crystallized with seven molecules of water was analysed by Tvetkov and Voliashikina (1953) and Ivanova (1961), using differential thermal analysis, and by Duval (1959), Ostrov and Sanderson (1959), employing thermogravimetry. These authors showed how the artificial product behaved on heating, but since they used only one of the thermal methods, the results were not conclusive. Lóránt (1966) investigated the synthetic product by the methods of derivative thermogravimetry, obtaining a clear picture of the thermal processes of this compound.

On heating, melantherite expels the seven molecules of water of crystallization at well-defined temperature intervals. Oxidation of Fe^{2+} to Fe^{3+} also takes place simultaneously with the expulsion of water, but this process is disputed in the specialized literature, some asserting that oxidation takes place at the same time as dehydration, others maintaining that oxidation occurs much later. In order to clear up this question, I have carried out determinations at low heating rates, below 5 °C per minute, in the temperature range at which dehydration takes place (Todor, 1971). After analytical interpretation of the thermal curves obtained, I have found that oxidation begins only when the first six molecules of water have been removed. In this determination, the sample must necessarily be covered, because otherwise it would be thrown out of the crucible as a result of the vigorous dehydration process. Oxidation begins after the first six molecules of water have been removed since the vapours abundantly given off during the expulsion of the first six molecules of water prevent the oxygen from penetrating into the sample. As soon as this heavy release of water vapours has ceased, oxygen penetrates into the sample and the oxidation process begins. As a rule, however, in the temperature range in which the last water molecule is removed there is only partial oxidation. This fact can be seen very well on the TG and DTG curves (Figure 5.33) which indicate an increase of mass after the dehydration process, while the DTA curve shows two endothermic effects due to overlapping processes (dehydration and oxidation). The thermal effect caused by oxidation comes to an end at about 500 °C. As a result of this all the ferrous sulphate passes into basic sulphate of the form $Fe_2O(SO_4)_2$.

With rising temperatures begins the desulphuration of the basic sulphate formed. Unlike other workers, I have found that this desulphuration takes place in two forms, namely with some samples desulphuration comes off in a single stage, while with others in two stages, according to the following scheme:

$$\text{Case I: } Fe_2O(SO_4)_2 \xrightarrow{500-800\,°C} Fe_2O_3 + 2SO_3$$

$$\text{Case II: } 2Fe_2O(SO_4)_2 \xrightarrow{500-670\,°C} Fe_2(SO_4)_3 + Fe_2O_3 + SO_3$$

$$Fe_2(SO_4)_3 \xrightarrow{670-800\,°C} Fe_2O_3 + 3SO_3$$

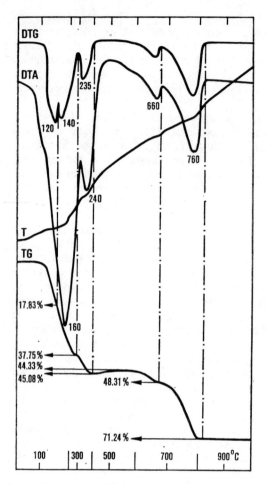

Figure 5.33 Thermal curves of melantherite at a heating rate of 10 °C per
minute.

To sum up, it may be stated that dehydration, and particularly desulphuration, may adequately represent points of the quantitative analytical determination, but it must first be established if the desulphuration of the basic sulphate formed takes place directly or through the agency of ferric sulphate.

More conclusive analytical results are obtained when the analysis of this compound is performed at a heating rate of 5 °C per minute. In this case, oxidation is completed in the temperature range at which dehydration occurs, a fact which is shown very well on the DTA curve in Figure 5.34 in which the endothermic effect caused by the expulsion of the last molecule of water is completely missing, its place being taken by the exothermic effect due to oxidation. From Figure 5.34 it follows that oxidation was completely finished when dehydration came to an end, and the basic sulphate formed remains constant in weight up to 500 °C, when the first desulphuration takes place and the compound passes into ferric sulphate,

Figure 5.34 Thermal curves of melantherite at a heating rate of 5° C per minute.

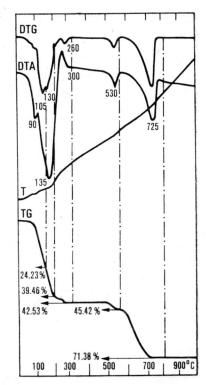

which is then further desulphurized. When oxidation takes place simultaneously with dehydration, it is found that desulphuration occurs at a much lower temperature than in the case of a high heating rate. On this evidence we may assume that the two kinds of desulphuration encountered in the case of melantherite are connected with the way in which oxidation was brought about.

Mallardite, MnSO$_4$.nH$_2$O ($n = 7$, 5 and 4). Manganese sulphate crystals with seven molecules of water of crystallization are also known, but they are stable only at temperatures below 10 °C. At the temperature of the surroundings it crystallizes as pentahydrate, and at temperatures above 26 °C a tetrahydrate is formed, which is the ordinary commercial form. Thermal investigations of this compound have been carried out only with the pentahydrate.

Thermal curves obtained (Figure 5.35) show that the water of crystallization is removed in two stages: in the first stage four water molecules are expelled, and in the second stage the last molecule.

From Figure 5.35 it may be seen that the DTA curve records two feeble endothermic effects at about 45 and 80 °C, caused by the dissolution of the product in its own water of crystallization. At temperatures higher than 300 °C the anhydrous product is stable up to about 800 °C, when the desulphuration

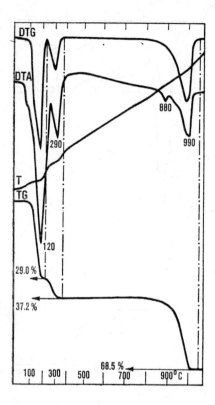

Figure 5.35 Thermal curves of synthetic mallardite.

process sets in. Desulphuration is complete at about 1000 °C. Simultaneously with the beginning of desulphuration, the DTA curve shows an endothermic effect at 880 °C, which is due to incipient melting of the anhydrous manganese sulphate. The final product obtained as a residue is a manganese oxide of the form Mn_2O_3 and not an association of MnO and Mn_2O_3, as is stated in some handbooks of inorganic chemistry,

As regards the oxidation of manganese, data from the literature is contradictory. Lóránt (1966) maintains that oxidation takes place simultaneously with dehydration, a basic manganese sulphate of the form $Mn_2O(SO_4)_2$ being formed first. My analyses run counter to this opinion. I have found in all cases that the value of the mass variation caused by dehydration is within the limits of experimental errors and is close to the theoretically calculated one, while the values of the mass variations as a result of desulphuration are by about 3.3 per cent lower than the theoretically calculated ones. In fact, the mass variation corresponds to oxidation. I consider that the oxidation of manganese takes place through the agency of the basic manganese sulphate, but this oxidation occurs in the desulphuration process. Moreover, the product obtained after dehydration is not dark-coloured specific to oxidized manganese, and by simple dissolution of this product in water and recrystallization it gives thermal curves analogous to those described overleaf.

Morenosite, $NiSO_4.7H_2O$. Anhydrous nickel sulphate was studied under this name by Ostrov and Sanderson (1958) using the methods of thermogravimetry, and the heptahydrate was analysed using the same methods by Fruchart and Michel (1958). A study employing differential thermal analysis is mentioned in a paper signed by Berg and co-workers (1944), and another, using derivative thermogravimetry in Lóránt's (1966) paper.

When heating is performed at a rate of 5 °C per minute, the water of crystallization is removed in five stages. The first six water molecules are expelled in a narrow temperature range, and the last molecule is driven off at a much higher temperature. When the heating rate is 10 °C per minute, dehydration occurs in only three steps. After the dehydration process is terminated, that is, in the temperature range from 450 to 750 °C, anhydrous nickel sulphate remains constant in weight (Figure 5.36). Desulphuration begins around this temperature, develops in a single stage, and is completed at about 950 °C, a residue of nickel oxide being obtained.

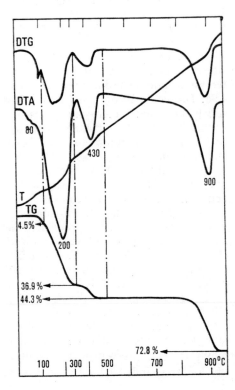

Figure 5.36 Thermal curves of morenosite.

Goslarite, $ZnSO_4.7H_2O$. This zinc sulphate crystallized with sev enmolecules of water of crystallization behaves similarly to epsomite when heated, and it is, in fact, isomorphous with this sulphate. According to some authors, goslarite should be the name given to a simple mineral zinc sulphate product, whilst others maintain that goslarite is an association of several sulphates of Zn, Mg, Mn, and Cd.

At a heating rate of 5 °C per minute, goslarite is completely dehydrated at a temperature of 400 °C. This finding contradicts Lóránt (1966) who claimed that until the desulphuration temperature is reached, that is, above 750 °C, the product still retains half a molecule of water of crystallization. According to Lóránt, six water molecules are removed in the first stage; there then follow two more stages in which the last molecule of water of crystallization is expelled.

With rising temperatures, a feeble endothermic effect is recorded on the DTA curve at a temperature of about 730 °C. This effect is of a physical nature, and indicates an incipient melting of the anhydrous zinc sulphate. Desulphuration begins immediately after this physical process, and it is recorded on all three thermal curves (Figure 5.37). Desulphuration takes place in two stages, according to some authors by passing through the sulphite form, whilst others maintain that one third of the SO_3 is removed at first, and the remaining two thirds of the SO_3 are expelled in the second stage.

Ferrous sulphate, $Fe_2(SO_4)_3.nH_2O$. Since in nature it is very unlikely that one would find ferrous sulphate as a simple mineral, and since both the data from the literature and those we have obtained with different artificial products differ widely, I have tried to prepare this product in the laboratory. To do this I started from Fe_2O_3 which I dissolved in sulphuric acid by applying heat. Although Fe_2O_3 was added until an amount of unsolved oxide remained in the solution, on recrystallization I found that the crystals contained a certain amount of sulphuric acid. This could be observed very well on the thermal curves obtained (Figure 5.38) which show that the crystals formed are an association of water of crystallization, sulphuric acid, and ferric sulphate. The boiling point of sulphuric acid is known to lie at a temperature of 338 °C. Its dissociation begins at this temperature and is completed at 450 °C. These changes are recorded on the thermal curves by an endothermic effect which occurs between 300 and 450 °C. By the loss of mass due to this effect, it is possible to determine accurately the amount of sulphuric acid included in such mixtures.

In order to obtain ferric sulphate free of sulphuric acid, but crystallized with n molecules of water, the product obtained was heated at a temperature of 500 °C, and then dissolved and recrystallized from water. Conventional handbooks of chemistry, show that ferric sulphate crystallizes with six or nine molecules of water, but the sulphate obtained by the method above was crystallized with only seven molecules of water. This water of crystallization is removed in two stages: five molecules are expelled in the first stage, and the remaining two molecules are driven off in the second stage. Nevertheless, from the thermal curves illustrated in Figure 5.39, and more exactly from the DTG curve, it follows that the last two molecules of water are removed one by one. In associations crystallized together with sulphuric acid, the water of crystallization is removed between 100 and 210 °C, which corresponds well with there being nine molecules of water for one molecule

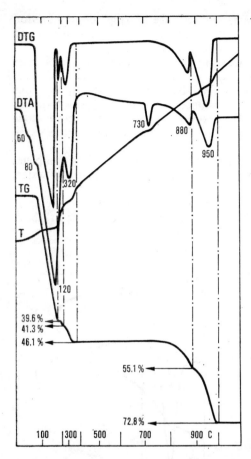

← Figure 5.37   Thermal curves of goslarite.

Figure 5.38   Thermal curves of a mixture of $H_2SO_4 + Fe_2(SO_4)_3 + nH_2O$, obtained at a heating rate of 5 °C per minute in the dehydration range, and of 10 °C per minute in the desulphurizing range.

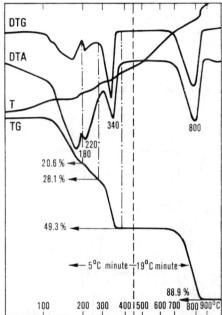

of ferric sulphate. The water removed in this case between 210 and 300 °C is retained in the compound owing to the presence of sulphuric acid.

In both cases, the product remaining after dehydration, that is, anhydrous ferric sulphate, is stable from 450—600 °C and this range can be used for quantitative determinations.

With regard to desulphuration, the only data that have been found complete in the literature are those of Lórant (1966), who maintains that ferric sulphate is desulphurized in two steps, according to the following scheme:

$$Fe_2(SO_4)_3 \longrightarrow Fe_2O_2(SO_4) + 2SO_3$$

$$Fe_2O_2(SO_4) \longrightarrow Fe_2O_3 + SO_3.$$

All the analyses I have carried out have shown, however, that desulphuration takes place in a single step. This can be accounted for if one follows up the way in which ferrous sulphate is desulphurized (Figure 5.33), since in the last step this passes also through ferric sulphate. The temperature range in which desulphuration takes place in the case of a heating rate of 10 °C per minute lies between 650 and 850 °C.

Aluminium sulphate, $Al_2(SO_4)_3.18H_2O$. Owing to the large number of molecules of water of crystallization, the dehydration of aluminium sulphate involves melting of the substance in its own water of crystallization, followed by vigorous boiling. While this boiling takes place, the substance tends to be thrown out of the reaction groove, and when the sample is covered there will be a continuous oscillation of the balance as a result of which the DTG curves take on the shape of saw teeth (Figure 5.40).

At a temperature of about 400 °C dehydration is complete or almost complete, because in many cases aluminium sulphate expels only 17.5 molecules of water, and the loss of mass on desulphuration is somewhat larger than the theoretically calculated one. From 400 to 650 °C the weight of aluminium sulphate remains constant. Above this temperature desulphuration begins, being complete at about 900 °C.

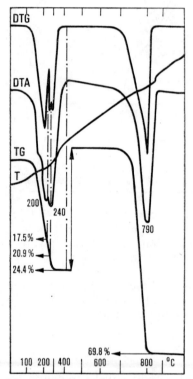

Figure 5.39 Thermal curves of $Fe_2(SO_4)_3.7H_2O$, obtained at a heating rate of 10 °C per minute.

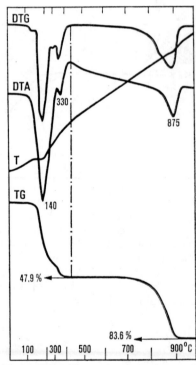

Figure 5.40 Thermal curves of crystallized aluminium sulphate.

5.5.3 Native and Artificial Associations of Heavy Metal Sulphates

The associations I have obtained artificially by crystallization from solutions at the temperature of the surroundings are widely represented in nature. Analytical observations that can be made by studying the thermal curves can be of two kinds. In the first place, one can establish the kind of isomorphism into which these mixtures are classified, knowing that the isomorphous series are three in number, namely, continuous isomorphous series, discontinuous isomorphous series, and isodimorphous series.

The kind of the isomorphism can be determined on the thermal curves by studying the way in which the water of crystallization is removed at a low heating rate. This is particularly characteristic in the case of the last molecule of water which, as could be seen in the case of simple sulphates, is always removed separately from the other molecules. The process of isomorphism is discussed in Chapter 4. Figure 5.41 illustrates the thermal curves of a continuous isomorphous series, and Figure 5.42 the thermal curves of a discontinuous isomorphous series.

Figure 5.42   Thermal curves of a discontinuous series of $(Zn, Mn)SO_4.nH_2O$.

Figure 5.41   Thermal curves of a continuous series of $(Cu, Mn)SO_4.nH_2O$.

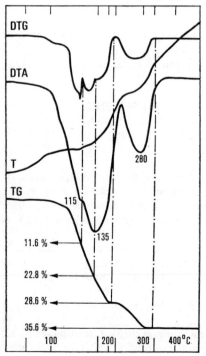

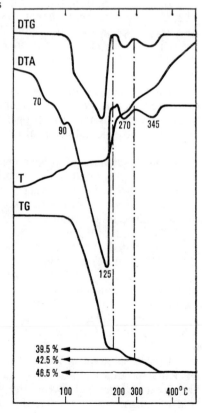

In the second place, on thermal curves it is possible to make observations finally leading to quantitative determinations based on the fact that, on heating, sulphates from this class undergo desulphuration with a loss of mass in proportion to the amount of the sulphates present in the mixture. As a rule, this desulphuration takes place in a different temperature range for each separate sulphate.

Double sulphate of iron and copper, $(Cu, Fe)\underline{So}_4.nH_2O$ ($n = 5$ or 7). This association of copper and iron sulphates, frequently encountered in nature, is named according to the number of molecules of water of crystallization. The compound crystallized with five molecules of water is called *ferrochalcantite*, and that crystallized with seven molecules of water is called *pisomite*.

I have analysed both forms and have reached the conclusion that where the copper sulphate content of the mixture is higher than $10-15$ per cent, the product is ferrochalcantite and below that amount the crystals are of the pisomite type. This contention results from the way in which the water of crystallization is removed as well as from the percentile content of water of crystallization which is greater for ferrochalcantite than for pisomite.

In this association, the desulphuration process begins at a temperature of about $650\,^{\circ}C$, ferrous sulphate being desulphurized at first, after it has been oxidized, and then copper sulphate is desulphurized. Desulphuration of the mixture takes place in four stages as shown in Figure 5.43: the first two thermal effects are due to ferrous sulphate, and the last two to copper sulphate (Figure 5.43).

Double sulphate of copper and zinc, $(Cu, Zn) SO_4.5H_2O$. The native product is called *zinchalcantite* and on heating behaves similarly to ferrochalcantite. The only difference is that the copper sulphate is desulphurized at first in two stages, and then the zinc sulphate, also in two stages.

Double sulphate of copper and manganese, $(Cu, Mn) SO_4.5H_2O$. In spite of the fact that this mixture has been found in nature, it bears no name as a mineral. By analogy with the other double sulphates of copper, let it be called *manganochalcantite*. But unlike the previous ones, this association shows isomorphism of continuous series.

With regard to desulphuration it behaves as follows: at first, copper sulphate is decomposed in two stages, and then manganese sulphate. Unlike the desulphuration of manganese sulphate as a simple compound, which takes place in one stage only, in this association the thermal curves (Figure 5.44) show several stages of desulphuration. The process is ascribed to an overlapping of the desulphuration process of manganese sulphate with the reduction of copper oxide into cuprous oxide, and further perhaps into metallic copper. Large errors occur when the thermal curves of such a mixture are interpreted quantitatively.

Double sulphate of iron and magnesium, $(Fe, Mg)SO_4.7H_2O$. In the terminology of Russian mineralogists this native compound is named *kurovite*. Because of the great difference between the desulphuration temperature of ferrous sulphate and of magnesium sulphate, this association lends itself very well to quantitative

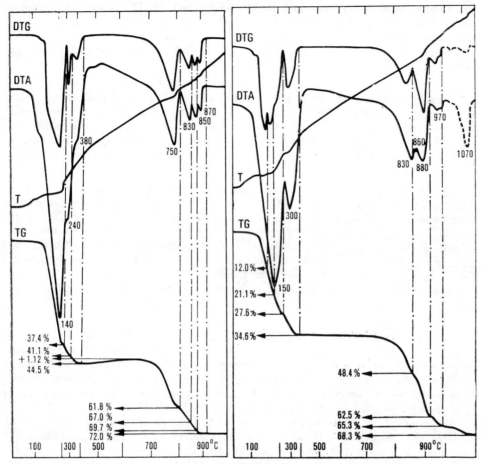

Figure 5.43 Thermal curves of pisomite.   Figure 5.44 Thermal curves of manganochalcantite.

analytical determinations. This association is the most representative case of isodimorphism. Desulphuration of this double sulphate takes place in two stages: in the first stage ferrous sulphate is desulphurized through the agency of the basic sulphate, and in the second magnesium sulphate is desulphurized.

Double sulphate of iron and zinc, (Fe, Zn) SO$_4$. 7H$_2$O. The isomorphous crystalline association of these two sulphates behaves similarly to kurovite, with naturally different temperature ranges. At first the native ferrous sulphate is desulphurized through the agency of the basic sulphate, then the zinc sulphate is desulphurized.

Double sulphate of iron and nickel, $(Fe,Ni)SO_4.7H_2O$. This isomorphous association of the discontinuous series type behaves analogously to the last two associations mentioned, but the temperature range in which ferrous sulphate is desulphurized first, and that in which nickel sulphate is desulphurized next, are very close.

Double sulphate of iron and manganese, $(Fe,Mn)SO_4.7H_2O$. This iso- morphously crystallized association is of the discontinuous series type and presents thermal curves similar to those of kurovite. Removal of the water of crystallization is complete up to 400 °C, after which oxidation begins, and this is followed by the desulphuration of ferrous sulphate, and then of manganese sulphate.

Double sulphate of manganese and magnesium, $(Mn,Mg)SO_4.7H_2O$. The native product is named *fauserite*, and belongs to the discontinuous isomorphous series. With regard to dehydration, this association behaves analogously to the other associations. Its desulphuration takes place at a high enough temperature upwards of 800 °C, and is complete at about 1200 °C. On this account it is difficult to make a sharp distinction between the desulphurations of these two sulphates. Therefore, for a quantitative calculation the loss of mass caused by desulphuration is taken together for both sulphates, so that the total content of sulphate present is determined, and not that of each sulphate separately.

Double sulphate of zinc and manganese, $(Zn, Mn) SO_4 \cdot nH_2O$. Thermal analysis of this isomorphous association has brought to light a peculiarity of its structure compared to the other representatives of the group. It was found that in some cases the association crystallizes with seven molecules of water, and in other cases seven molecules of water are alloted to zinc sulphate and only five molecules of water of crystallization to manganese sulphate.

From analytical data it has been shown that if the manganese sulphate content is higher than 40 per cent, the association crystallizes with only five molecules of water instead of seven and compounds containing less than 40 per cent manganese sulphate crystallize with seven molecules of water.

Although the temperature ranges in which both sulphates are desulphurized are high, the loss of mass corresponding to zinc sulphate (the first to be desulphurized) and that corresponding to manganese sulphate can be determined with sufficient accuracy.

Double sulphate of zinc and magnesium, $(Zn,Mg)SO_4.7H_2O$. This iso- morphous association from the isodimorphous series expels the last molecule of water of crystallization in two stages specific for each sulphate from the association. The thermal process of desulphuration takes place at high temperatures, beginning at 800 °C and being complete above 1150 °C. The way in which desulphuration develops is also specific to each sulphate separately, zinc sulphate being desulphurized first, and then manganese sulphate.

Double sulphate of aluminium and potassium (potash alum, kalinite), KAl (SO$_4$)$_2$·12H$_2$O. Potash alum occurs native as the result of the weathering of iron pyrites and alkali rocks, forming earthy masses, efflorescences, crusts, and even compact granular masses, as a rule in the oxidation zones of pyrite deposits, most frequently in admixture with other sulphates. It is even possible to prepare it on a commercial scale from alum-earth by calcination and digestion of the mass with water, and subsequent recrystallization of the alum from solution.

Dehydration of alum develops analogously with that of aluminium sulphate; eight molecules of water of crystallization come off first and the last two molecules come off later. Between dehydration and desulphuration, the DTA curve records a feeble endothermic effect at about 650 °C, which is due to a polymorphous transformation. Desulphuration begins at over 700 °C, basic aluminium sulphate being formed first. The final product of desulphuration is a mixture of aluminium oxide and potassium sulphate which, by raising the temperature, show on the DTA curve an effect specific to melting.

Ternary and quaternary mixtures. I have prepared a wide range of crystallized, ternary and quaternary mixtures formed from heavy metal cations and the SO$_4^{2-}$ anion for the purpose of studying their behaviour on heating.

Although many samples, especially of ternary mixtures, are found native, thermal methods can provide quantitative data giving only the total content of water of crystallization and the total content of SO$_4^{2-}$ as a result of mass variations produced by the dehydration and desulfuration of the associations. This shortcoming is due to the overlap of the thermal effects so that there are no clearly defined peaks on the graphs.

For quantitative interpretations, errors of analysis would be extremely high, and some compounds would even be lost. However, these curves give sufficient qualitative information concerning the number of sulphates present in the association. Naturally, these qualitative data can be obtained only by comparing the curves of the unknown sample with the curves obtained from known samples.

5.5.4 Alunite and Jarosite Group

Alunite, KAl$_3$ (OH)$_6$ (SO$_4$)$_2$. Alunite is a native basic sulphate whose chemical formula must be taken as double, because analysis always reveals six molecules of water. Potassium may partly be replaced with sodium, and the mineral is then called *sodium-alunite*, but no distinction can be made from the macro- and microcrystalline appearance. Alunite may readily be mistaken for other minerals, especially with clays and its identification and determination from the data of chemical analysis is quite difficult.

The method of differential thermal analysis was successfully applied by Asada (1940) and Gad (1950) in studying the decomposition of alunites, and the DTA curves obtained gave qualitative information as to the presence of this compound in a number of argillaceous minerals. These studies were subsequently resumed by Popa and Todor (1971) by thermal derivatography, establishing in this way the intermediate stages of decomposition, as well as the way in which thermal curves are to be interpreted for quantitative purposes.

Thermal curves obtained show that in the temperature range 500—640 °C alunite undergoes a first thermal modification associated with a loss of mass. This loss of mass corresponds to the removal of six molecules of water as a result of which the compound passes into a dehydroxylated basic sulphate, according to the reaction:

$$2[KAl_3(OH)_6(SO_4)_2] \longrightarrow 2[KAl_3O_3(SO_4)_2] + 6H_2O.$$

It was noticed that with somes samples the removal of water takes place in two stages as a result of a modification in the crystal lattice of alunite. Indeed, at a heating rate of 5 °C per minute, all samples analysed have shown that the removal of water takes place in two stages, a fact which can be seen especially on the DTG curve (Figure 5.45), which shows much more conclusively than the DTA curve this stage of dehydroxylation. The removal of water in two stages may be accounted for if we admit that the formula of alunite is $2[KAl(OH)_2SO_4.Al_2(OH)_4.SO_4]$. In this case, in the first stage the four molecules of water will be removed, giving basic aluminium sulphate, and in the second stage, which follows immediately,

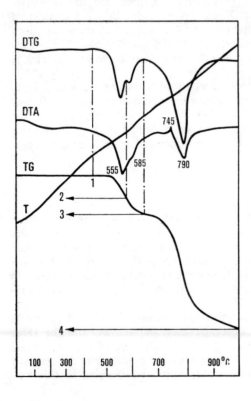

Figure 5.45 Thermal curves of an alunite sample from the Zlatna basin (Romania).

the remaining two molecules are removed from aluminium and potassium sulphate, according to the reactions:

$$2[KAl_3(SO_4)_2(OH)_6] \xrightarrow{500-565\ °C} 2[KAlSO_4(OH)_2(Al_2O_2SO_4)] + 4H_2O$$

$$2[KAlSO_4(OH)_2(Al_2O_2SO_4)] \xrightarrow{565-640\ °C} 2[KAl_3O_3(SO_4)_2] + 2H_2O$$

After the endothermic effect due to dehydration, there follows an exothermic effect recorded only on the DTA curve in the temperature range 720—750 °C. This exothermic effect is mentioned in the literature without any precise statement as to its nature. I believe that the energy set free is due to the broken bonds in the basic sulphate, which leads to the creation of a new crystalline form, releasing aluminium oxide according to the reaction:

$$2[KAl_3O_3(SO_4)_2] \xrightarrow{640-750\ °C} 2[KAl(SO_4)_2] + 2Al_2O_3.$$

Simultaneously with this new structural arrangement the desulphuration of the double sulphate of aluminium and potassium also begins.

Comparing the desulphuration of alunite with that of potash alum, one finds that the mechanism of desulphuration is different. In the case of potash alum, the desulphuration of aluminium sulphate is retarded by the presence of potassium sulphate as compared to pure aluminium sulphate (Figure 5.46), but desulphuration

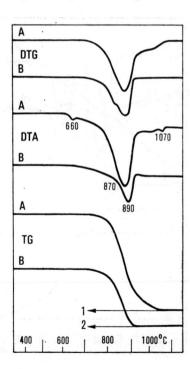

Figure 5.46 Comparative thermal curves of desulphuration: *A*, double sulphate of aluminium and potassium; *B*, aluminium sulphate.

is total in both cases below a temperature of 1070 °C. In alunite, total desulphuration will not take place before reaching 1200 °C, which shows that the structure of alunite is different from that of potash alum. In potash alum, as it might be recollected, the two sulphates do not form a chemical combination, unlike alunite in which one of the valencies of the SO_4^{2-} anion is bound to potassium and the other to aluminium.

As it was shown, simultaneously with the new structural organization of the anhydrous double sulphate begins the desulphuration, by which according to Gad (1950), Kulp and Adler (1950), three molecules of water would be expelled up to 1000 °C, whereas according to Kashkai and Babaev (1959) almost three would be expelled. Desulphuration, however, continues beyond this temperature, and it is not complete even at 1200 °C. It is, therefore, difficult to state precisely from the thermal curves which are the intermediate stages of the desulphuration of alunite. In the first part, when a massive desulphuration takes place in a closer range of temperatures, recorded on the thermal curves by a marked endothermic effect, about two molecules of SO_3 are removed, followed by a slow desulphuration. I find that this intermediate stage can be explained by the formation of a basic aluminium and potassium sulphate, according to the reaction:

$$2[KAl(SO_4)_2] \xrightarrow{640-800\,°C} 2(KAlO.SO_4) + 2SO_3.$$

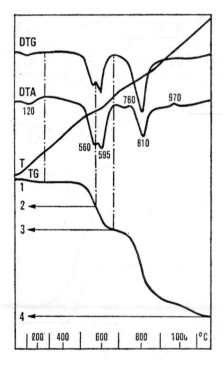

Figure 5.47 Thermal curves of an association of alunite and kaolinite.

After this bulky desulphuration no further intermediate stage may be pointed out up to the final product which should theoretically be an association of Al_2O_3 and K_2O, according to the reaction:

$$2(KAlO.SO_4) \xrightarrow{\text{above } 800 \text{ °C}} 2SO_3 + (Al_2O_3.K_2O).$$

But in the residue after decomposition, there is practically no free K_2O, because (in the case of an alunite free from contamination) this combines with Al_2O_3 giving an aluminate similar to high temperature artificial aluminates. In most cases, however, alunite is contaminated with quartz, with argillaceous minerals or other minerals, and then the K_2O resulted combines with SiO_2 and with Al_2O_3, yielding aluminosilicates of the type $K_2O\text{-}Al_2O_3\text{-}SiO_2$.

In conclusion, it may be stated that thermal methods lend themselves well for the identification and determination of alunites. In case it is intended to make quantitative determinations based on thermal curves, the only temperature range in which these determinations can be made is from 500 to 640 °C corresponding to the expulsion of OH groups. A quantitative interpretation of the alunite content can be made also in the case when argillaceous minerals or quartz are present besides alunite. This rests on the fact that quartz does not show any loss of mass on the curves, and the temperature ranges in which OH groups are expelled from alunite and from argillaceous minerals, though close, are not the same. By dropping perpendiculars from the cusps of the DTG curve on the TG curve, the TG curve is divided into various segments, corresp nding to the loss of mass of each separate reaction. These segments related to the total loss of mass of the sample, yield the loss corresponding to each separate reaction. By interpreting the DTA, TG, and DTG curves from Figure 5.47, which were obtained on an artificial association of alunite with kaolinite, it follows that water adsorbed by kaolinite is given off in the range from 0—1, the OH groups from alunite are removed in the range from 1—2, the OH groups from the kaolinite lattice are expelled from 2—3, and partial desulphuration of the alunite present in the mixture takes place from 3—4.

Jarosite, $KFe_3(OH)_6(SO_4)_2$. Thermal curves obtained on this mineral are similar to those of alunite, the only difference being that the thermal effects take place at a temperature about 100 °C lower than in the case of alunite.

5.6 PHOSPHATES

This class includes a large number of minerals having a chemical structure analogous to that of the arsenates and vanadates, together with which they frequently cccur associated in isomorphous series.

The PO_4^{3-} anion, whose dimensions are large, forms anhydrous and very stable combinations of the type $MePO_4$ with tervalent cations (also of very large dimensions).

When the phosphoric anion combines with cations of small dimensions, then the resulting compounds will for the most part be hydrated, and when the cations are bivalent the compounds will include other anions such as OH⁻, F⁻, O²⁻, and even Cl⁻. All these considerations are also valid in respect of the behaviour of phosphates on heating, producing thermal processes due to dehydration, dissociation in the solid state, and structural reorganizations.

Thermal analyses of these compounds are difficult, owing, on the one hand, to the fact that they occur associated with other minerals from which they are very difficult to separate as simple compounds, and on the other hand to the fact that they can show considerable variations in composition, whilst the thermal curves of one and the same mineral may frequently be different.

Mauly (1950) recorded the thermal curves for a large number of phosphates, but only the minerals which were studied in detail will be described in the following.

Wavellite or Kingite, $Al_6(PO_4)_4(OH)_6.9H_2O$. In thermal analyses this mineral undergoes a specific dehydration which is shown on thermal curves by a marked endothermic effect whose maximum lies at 275 °C, followed by second endothermic effect whose maximum lies at 315 °C (Figure 5.48). With rising temperatures, the dehydrated compound will suffer a structural reorganization marked on the DTA curve by an exothermic effect situated around a temperature of 700 °C. The temperature at which the effect is produced and the intensity of the effect may vary with the nature of the sample and the degree of grinding of the sample. It is believed that the new structural organization is due to the formation of phosphotridymite.

Vivianite, $Fe_3(PO_4)_2 \cdot 8H_2O$. The thermal curves of this mineral (Figure 5.49) show that the removal of water takes place in three distinct stages. The first stage, corresponding to the removal of five molecules of water, is recorded on the curve by the thermal effect whose maximum is at about 260 °C. The second stage,

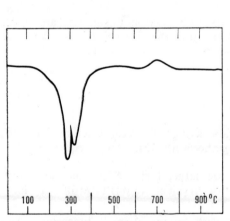

Figure 5.48 DTA curve of wavallite (according to Mauly, 1950).

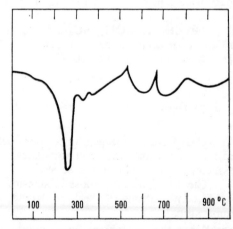

Figure 5.49 DTA crrve of vivianite (after Mauly, 1950).

corresponding to the removal of two more molecules of water shows a thermal maximum at about 330 °C. The third stage, corresponding to the expulsion of the last molecule of water, has a thermal maximum at 380 °C.

The exothermic effect, or rather the exothermic effects (because with some samples several maxima appear) are situated between 500 and 700 °C. This is caused in the first place by the oxidation of iron from the bivalent form to the tervalent form; this fact can readily be observed on the DTG and TG curves, which indicate an increase of mass, as well as a new structural organization.

Ambligonite, (Li, Na)AlPO$_4$(F,OH). Since no molecules of water are found in this very stable compound, it does not show any thermal transformations at low temperatures. On the thermal curves a segment of endo-exothermic effects appear in the temperature range 700—800 °C. According to some researchers, the endothermic effect is situated between 725 and 775 °C. In this range also there is an exothermic effect having its maximum at 760 °C. According to other researchers, the temperature range in which these endo-exothermic effects appear is higher by about 50 °C (Mackenzie, 1962).

Apatite, Ca$_5$(PO$_4$)$_3$(F,Cl). In the structure of apatite, OH groups are frequently present, replacing the F$^-$ or Cl$^-$ ion, and for this reason the mineral fails to yield very characteristic thermal curves. With many samples, a series of feeble endothermic effects appeared on the thermal curves. These were situated below 500 °C, and it is believed that they were due to the presence of alien elements in the samples of apatite. Transformations specific to this mineral occur in the temperature range 825—875 °C, and they are shown on the DTA curve by an extended effect, which is believed to indicate partial melting of apatite.

Augellite, Al$_2$PO$_4$(OH)$_3$. On thermal curves this mineral presents an endothermic effect in the temperature range 675—725 °C as a result of the expulsion of OH groups. On further heating, an exothermic effect appears on the DTA curve between 925 and 1000 °C, corresponding to renewed structural reorganization.

Autunite, Ca(UO$_2$)$_2$(PO$_4$)$_2$.12H$_2$O. The water of crystallization of this compound begins to be expelled below 100 °C, and at 225 °C it is completely removed. This causes a marked endothermic effect on thermal curves. On further heating, new structural organization of the dehydrated product take place, marked on the DTA curve by a feeble exothermic effect between 275 and 325 °C. With rising temperatures up to 1000 °C, the compound fails to show any further thermal effect on thermal curves.

Berlinite, AlPO$_4$. In thermal analyses, berlinite manifests only an effect of polymorphous transformation recorded on the DTA curve in the temperature range 575—625 °C .

Bosphorite, Fe$_3$(PO$_4$)$_2$(OH)$_3$.7H$_2$O. The water of crystallization of this compound is removed analogously to that of the sulphates, giving a marked endothermic effect on the thermal curves up to 225 °C, immediately followed by another more feeble one. The thermal effect caused by the expulsion of OH groups fails to appear very conclusively according to data from the literature. It is believed that these groups are removed in an extended range of temperatures from 300 °C (the final temperature of dehydration) to 625 °C (when the new structural reorganization begins). Structural reorganization takes place between 625 and 675 °C and is marked on the DTA curve as a feeble exothermic effect.

Bobierrite, $Mg_3(PO_4)_2.8H_2O$. The thermal curves of this compound show that the water of crystallization is removed beginning at about 100 °C and is fully expelled at 325 °C. With rising temperatures, a feeble endothermic effect appears between 425 and 275 °C.

Structural reorganization takes place from 675 to 710 °C and is marked on the DTA curve by an exothermic effect which, as a rule, has two maxima.

Evansite, $Al_3PO_4(OH)_6.6H_2O$. This mineral has not been well investigated. Accorrding to data given by Mackenzie (1962), it behaves on heating as follows. The water of crystallization is removed in an extended range of temperatures with a maximum at 260 °C, immediately followed by a more feeble effect whose thermal maximum is at 350 °C. With further heating, at about 515 °C a sharp endothermic effect marking the expulsion of OH groups appears. Structural reorganization takes place between 725 and 775 °C and is marked on the DTA curve by a feeble exothermic effect.

As it was stated in the introductory part of this chapter, phosphate minerals occurring native are much more numerous than those presented here. Thermal curves obtained on these minerals are not in the least conclusive, since they were obtained on different samples in which the phosphate minerals were associated with other minerals which in their turn yield thermal effects overlapping with those of the phosphates. For this reason, their description was not considered necessary.

5.7 CARBONATES

A large number of mineral species belong to the class of carbonate rocks. Some of these are widely scattered in nature either as simple minerals or associated with other minerals in the deposit. They are of particular economic value as such or in associations.

Compounds of the CO_3^{2-} anion with divalent metallic cations having medium and large ionic radii can be very stable. The number of these metallic cations is comparatively small. Chief among those forming anhydrous compounds are Mg^{2+}, Ca^{2+}, Sr^{2+}, Ba^{2+}, Zn^{2+}, Fe^{2+}, and Mn^{2+}; those forming compounds which include OH groups in their structure are Cu^{2+}, Mg^{2+}, Zn^{2+}, and Pb^{2+}. Compounds of the CO_3^{2-} anion with monovalent alkali ions are also encountered, but if anhydrous they must contain the H^+ cation in their structure, i.e. they must form acid salts.

It has already been shown that the natural compounds belonging to this class can be more or less stable, but they will generally decompose under the action of thermal energy. This decomposition takes place at a well defined temperature, carbon dioxide being evolved, and the metallic cation is left in the form of an oxide. This property of carbonates makes it possible accurately to determine the mineralogical composition of carbonate minerals by means of the methods of thermal analysis. Such determinations would be difficult if not impossible to achieve by other methods. Let us assume, for instance, that data yielded by the chemical analysis indicate only the anion CO_3^{2-}, and the cations Mg^{2+} and Ca^{2+} as constitutents of the compound. From these data it would not be possible to acquire certainty that the compound having yielded them is a dolomitic mineral or an association of two different minerals, i.e. a magnesite and a calcite. From a genetic point of view, however, and from that of the commercial uses, it is highly important to have an accurate knowledge of the nature of the mineral.

The specialized literature includes many data concerning the behaviour of such natural compounds on heating. To a certain extent these data are variable owing to differences between the analysed samples and to the various analysis techniques. Nevertheless thermal comparisons of minerals appear to be conclusive, in spite of the fact that these shortcomings complicate the comparison of thermal curves, provided we assume that only the temperatures of thermal effects are varying.

Some practical observations are necessary in order to achieve a good reproducibility of the thermal curves and a sensible interpretation of them. The most adequate heating rate for the investigation of carbonates is 10 °C per minute, and the largest amount of sample required is 0.5 g.

It is also necessary to take into account some visual observations concerning the colour of the sample to be analysed and of its residue, particularly when calcium and magnesium carbonates are concerned. These carbonates are generally white, but we shall show that they can assume various colours, depending on the impurities contained in the samples. Such observations concerning the colour of the samples and of the residue lead to more conclusive interpretations of the results even if these are only of a qualitative nature. It is also by these colour variations that conclusions are drawn concerning minor elements that might possibly be determined by other methods.

5.7.1 Simple Anhydrous Carbonates Group

Aragonite and calcite, CaCO₃. Calcium carbonate is the most widespread native carbonate. It appears in two crystalline forms, as *aragonite*, crystallized in the rhombic system, and as *calcite*, crystallized in the trigonal (rhombohedral) system. Under certain conditions, these forms can pass into each other at ordinary temperatures and at the prevailing atmospheric pressure. Aragonite, which is unstable with time, will change its form and pass into calcite; this transformation takes place at ordinary temperatures over very long periods of time. The precise temperature at which aragonite changes into calcite is not certain, but the rate of change is known to increase with rising temperatures.

According to data from the literature (Badalov, 1949; Faust, 1949 and Tzvetkov *et al.*, 1964), the transformation of aragonite into calcite is completed over a few minutes at temperatures ranging from 400 to 500 °C. The above-mentioned authors have recorded this polymorphic transformation by means of the method of differential thermal analysis, DTA, as a small endothermic effect; hence, the transformation takes place with an absorption of heat.

I made investigations in 1971 using combined thermal methods, proving that the cited experimental observations are erroneous. A large number of samples, optically assumed to have the structure of aragonite, were analysed. On the thermal curves, only a part of these have given the endothermal effect supposed to be due to the polymorphic transformation. It is a very interesting fact, that with all the samples which have produced this supposedly polymorphic transformation effect recorded by the thermal curves, it was actually a transformation associated with a loss of mass that was conclusively recorded on the TG and DTG curves (Figure 5.50). It is well known, however, that since a polymorphic transformation is only structural, it comes off without mass variation.

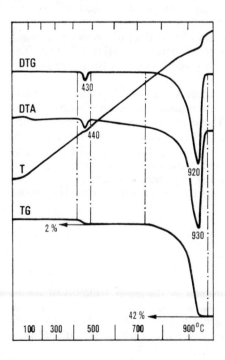

Figure 5.50 Thermal curves of aragonite.

The transformation of aragonite into calcite occurs indisputably, and it is speeded up with rising temperatures. However, it does not occur at a range of temperatures precise enough to enable its recording as a thermal effect with an endothermal maximum well outlined on the DTA curve. The endothermal effect recorded on the DTA curve at temperatures ranging from 400 to 500 °C, considered to be an effect caused by the polymorphic transformation of aragonite into calcite, is actually a thermal effect due to a removal of OH groups bonded to Ca^{2+} in the mass of aragonite. In all instances, the removal of OH groups corresponded to a loss of mass from 1.0 to 2.5 per cent; as to the temperature range, the process actually took place at about 450 °C (the same as that given by the authors mentioned overleaf) varying within narrow limits.

In connection with the presence of hydroxyl groups in the mass of aragonite, it can be assumed that, since aragonite is, generally, a first crystallization stage of calcium carbonate, it will also include molecules having OH groups in their structure. This statement is also borne out by the principle underlying the method of qualitative analysis of minerals called the "Meige reaction". In this reaction, which consists of boiling the fine aragonite powder in a dilute cobalt nitrate solution, if the powder takes on a bluish violet hue then we can infer that aragonite is contained in the sample. From a chemical point of view this means that, owing to the presence of OH groups, the added Co^{2+} cation forms cobalt hydroxide, which is in fact a fine precipitate coloured in a bluish violet hue, and which adheres on the fine particle of the aragonite. A number of research workers, including Cuthbert and Rowland (1947), Beck (1950), Kauffman and Dilling (1950), Heystek and Schmidt (1953), have shown that some of the samples analysed have not produced any thermal transformation on the DTA curve, in spite of the fact that they have presented the macro- and microcrystalline features of the aragonitic lattice. This proves that the OH groups are actually included in some aragonites, and these are the only aragonites presenting the thermal effect at a range of temperatures between 400 and 500 °C.

From a genetic point of view it can be explained that the aragonites which have OH groups included in the mass of their crystals have arisen in surroundings low in CO_2, while the solutions in which they have been precipitated had a pH-value on the alkaline side, unlike the aragonites which do not include OH groups in their mass, and which have arisen in surroundings high in CO_2, having therefore, an acid pH-value.

At temperatures above 500 °C, when the aragonite has already passed into calcite its behaviour will be similar to that of the latter. Thus, with rising temperatures, calcite will begin to decompose at about 675 °C, and at 950 °C its decomposition will be complete. These values of the decomposition temperature hold good only when the tests are carried out with mineral species or simple minerals. If calcite is associated with other minerals, its decomposition temperature will be appreciably lowered, depending on the percentage of it in the mixture.

In the case of a simple mineral calcite, the maximum of the thermal effect is at 930 to 940 °C, but when it is present in a mixture in proportions of only 10 to 15 per cent, the maximum of the thermal effect will then be depressed at about 800 °C. By measuring the loss of mass due to decomposition and evolution of the resulting CO_2 on the TG and DTG curves, it is possible to make quantitative determinations with about the same error as in the case of chemical determinations.

In what follows, we shall point out some analytical observations of a practical nature concerning the specification of the other minerals contained as impurities in the mass of calcite.

In the large majority of cases, limestones are white-coloured, but there are, nevertheless, many limestones with various colour shades, which may deepen, change, or even disappear on heating. If the raw sample has a pale grey hue, and the residue on heating is white-coloured, this means that the sample contains organic matter as finely dispersed inclusions in its mass. In this case, the resulting thermal curves must be considered with particular care at temperatures ranging from 200 to 500 °C, when the DTA curve shows an exothermal overstepping of the base-line, and the DTG curve a slight loss of mass resulting upon the combustion of the organic matter. When the limestone has the same pale grey hue, but will give a dark coloured residue on heating, which turns almost black, then the investigated sample contains sulphides finely dispersed in its mass. Their presence becomes manifest by the appearance of a well outlined exothermal effect on the DTA curve at a temperature of about 460 °C; this effect is sometimes associated with a small loss or even with an increase of mass. When the sample has a slightly reddish hue, and the colour of the residue on heating is a deeper shade of red, it then contains iron oxides as impurities, which in some cases give an exothermal effect similar to, but less intense than that of the sulphides. If the colour of the sample is white, and the residue is also white, while a slight endothermal effect appears on the DTA curve at 573 °C, then the sample contains quartz. In the case where both the sample and the residue are white, but the recorded thermal curves show effects associated with a loss of mass between 150 and 250 °C, then the investigated sample contains gypsum as an impurity. Finally, if the sample is white, but the residue takes on a brownish colour which turns almost black, then the sample contains manganese impurities in the form of manganese and calcium carbonates.

What has been said concerning the behaviour of calcite is of great significance for industrial uses, and from an analytical point of view it shows what analyses have to be carried out in each separate case. These observations hold good for the whole range of carbonates whose colour is different from that of the mineral when it occurs as a mineral species.

Magnesite, $MgCO_3$. Anhydrous magnesium carbonate occurs only native; the synthetically prepared product is a basic carbonate having roughly the composition $3MgCO_3.Mg(OH)_2.9H_2O$.

Native magnesite has been studied by Stone (1954), Kissinger (1957), Barchards (1960), Schramli and Becker (1961) *et al.*, using the method of differential thermal analysis and by Caillère and Pobéguie (1960) employing the method of thermal gravimetry.

Magnesite decomposes under the action of thermal energy at a comparatively low temperature: a slight decomposition begins at 450 °C, whilst at 640 °C decomposition reaches a maximum (Figure 5.51). After decomposition, the residue, which is MgO, will not undergo any further thermal transformations up to very high temperatures.

Witherite, BaCO₃. During heating up to 1100 °C, witherite does not show any loss of mass, hence the endothermal effect specific to the decomposition of carbonates takes place at a much higher temperature. Unlike the other carbonates, witherite undergoes two polymorphic transformations which take place below its decomposition temperature, and are recorded on the DTA curve as two reversible endothermal effects (Figure 5.52).

These transformations, recorded on the curve in the form of sudden effects, always have a specific and constant temperature; therefore, in addition to the fact that they afford a clue for the identification of witherite, they can also serve as standard temperature points for the purpose of thermocouple calibration. Thus, the first polymorphic transformation occurs at 810 °C and takes place with an appreciable heat consumption. The second transformation occurs at 970 to 980 °C and is also featured by a high heat consumption, which is, however, smaller than the preceding one. The latter transformation is recorded only by instruments with a high enough sensitivity to show the temperature difference, ΔT, between the sample and the thermally inert substance; in the opposite case this effect may be missing, as for instance in the studies of van der Marel (1956).

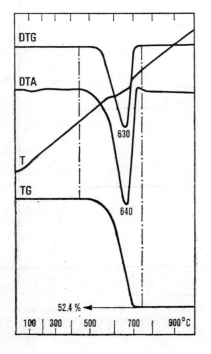

← Figure 5.51 Thermal curves of magnesite.

↓ Figure 5.52 Thermal curves of witherite.

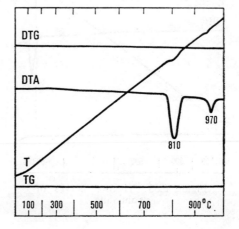

Strontianite, SrCO₃. According to data from the literature processed by Tzvetkov *et al.* (1964) relating to the investigation of strontium carbonate by the method of differential thermal analysis, it appears that at a temperature of 930 °C this will give an endothermal effect as a result of polymorphic transformation, similar to the first effect of witherite. From thermal investigations by means of combined methods performed on this mineral it has become known that a slight decomposition simultaneously begins with this polymorphic transformation, and that this decomposition is complete at a temperature of about 1200 °C (Figure 5.53).

As a rule, strontium, and barium carbonates are found together with calcium carbonate which, as has already been pointed out, decomposes at a lower temperature than that of the decomposition of these two minerals. In these cases, the endothermal effects caused by the polymorphic transformations of strontium and of witherite overlap the decomposition effects of calcite. These effects are recorded on the DTA curve in the form of thermal maxima which are located at temperatures specific to each carbonate separately and the TG and DTG curves show with sufficient accuracy the loss of mass caused by the decomposition of calcite (Figure 5.54).

Siderite, FeCO₃. For the determination of the percentage of siderite, a carbonate mineral frequently encountered in iron deposits, thermal methods have been used for a very long time. Thus, the thermal behaviour of siderite on differential thermal

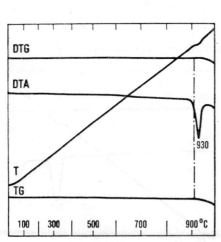

Figure 5.53 Thermal curves of strontianite.

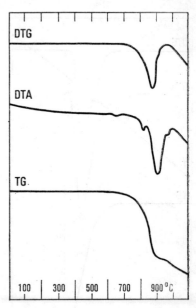

Figure 5.54 Thermal curves of a natural mixture of $CaCO_3 + SrCO_3 + BaCO_3$.

analysis has been described by Cuthbert and Rowland (1947), Kerr and Kulp (1947), Frederickson (1948), Rowland and Jonas (1949), Kaurkskii (1954), Kaurkskii and Polikin (1958), Schwab (1950) *et al.* The afore-mentioned authors have failed to make quantitative interpretations of the effects recorded on the DTA curve.

A quantitative study of siderite has been carried out by Popa and myself (1968 and 1970). We have established that siderite, as a monomineral, undergoes two transformations. The first transformation consists of the decomposition of iron carbonate. This decomposition takes place with an absorption of heat and is recorded on the thermal curves by an endothermal effect attended by a loss of mass corresponding to the amount of CO_2 evolved. The range of temperatures at which decomposition takes place is from 450 to 600 °C, having a thermal maximum of the effect at about 580 °C. It is only natural that this interval should vary, as has already been shown, depending on a number of experimental conditions. On a further rise of temperature, oxidation of the ferrous oxide resulted from the decomposition of the carbonate occurs immediately after the decomposition of the carbonate has been completed. This oxidation is marked on the thermal curves by an extended exothermal effect and by an increase of mass (Figure 5.55).

The temperature at which oxidation takes place is variable. Data from the literature in connexion with oxidation is very contradictory, because as a process it is closely linked with the admission of oxygen into the pores of the sample.

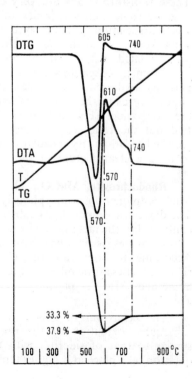

Figure 5.55 Thermal curves of a sample of siderite from Teliuc, Romania.

Another matter in dispute in the literature refers to the beginning of oxidation and its extent. Some authors, such as Schwab (1950), consider that the only possible oxidation reaction is $3Fe + CO_2 \rightarrow Fe_3O_4 + CO$. On the other hand, Rowland and Jonas (1949) have proved that oxidation takes place owing to the presence of oxygen in the atmosphere of the furnace and not on account of the carbon dioxide. To prove this, they have run the experiments in an atmosphere of carbon dioxide and have found that no oxidation takes place under such circumstances.

Kerr and Kulp (1947) have questioned the possibility of an immediate oxidation of the ferrous oxide, which after decomposition of the carbonate is in a very fine powder condition, and is covered by a protective layer of carbon dioxide. Rowland and Jonas (1949) have shown that the final product of oxidation at temperatures above 700 °C is Fe_2O_3.

Unlike the afore-mentioned authors, who have taken into account only the thermal effects on the DTA curve by also considering the thermal phenomena recorded on the TG and DTG curves, in our opinion the oxidation process occurs immediately after decomposition of the carbonate, and oxidation of FeO proceeds as far as Fe_3O_4 in case the tests are run in the surrounding atmosphere. The very marked exothermal effect on the DTA curve is due to a summing-up of two transformations, namely, the oxidation and the structural alteration of the resulting oxide, which passes from the trigonal form into the cubic form of magnetite. These transformations are very conclusively shown by the thermal curves in the case of some mineral-species of siderite. Things, however, become complicated when associations are involved as in the most commonly occurring samples. In what follows we shall refer to the most frequently encountered case, when siderite is associated with iron oxides.

From investigations carried out with samples of siderite which also contain partially hydrated iron oxides, it was shown that thermal methods give good indications as to the iron carbonate percentage and the OH groups removed from the iron oxides (Figure 5.56). It is not possible, however, by these methods to find out the total iron content present, and a chemical percentage analysis is required to do so. By means of the data obtained with both methods it is possible to have a clear picture of the compounds which make up the sample.

Rhodochrosite, $MnCO_3$. This carbonate is rare as a mineral species because Mn^{2+} is frequently isomorphously replaced in its structure with Fe^{2+}, Ca^{2+}, or Mg^{2+}. The degree of isomorphous substitution can be determined only by means of other analyses, but the fact that an isomorphous substitution and not a mechanical mixture of carbonates is involved can be proved only by thermal analysis methods. According to some authors (Logvinenko, Karpova, and Kosmatchev, 1961), rhodochrosites are members of the isomorphous series $MnCO_3$-$FeCO_3$-$CaCO_3$-$MgCO_3$. Sometimes Mn^{2+} is partially replaced in the composition of rhodochrosite with Zn^{2+}.

The behaviour of rhodochrosite on heating, i.e. its decomposition and the subsequent oxidation of the product remaining after decomposition, is wholly similar to that of siderite, with the sole difference that the transformations in question take place at a higher temperature. Two effects are typical of rhodochrosite

Figure 5.56 Thermal curves of a sample
of siderite with partly hydrated iron oxides.

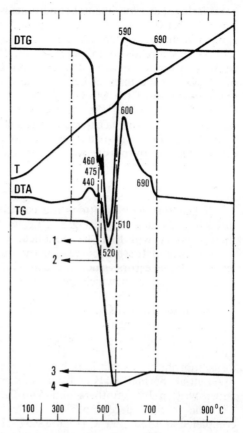

Figure 5.56 Thermal curves of a sample of siderite with partly hydrated iron oxides.

as they are also of siderite: an endothermal effect caused by the decomposition of the carbonate from 450 to 600 °C, and an exothermal effect caused by oxidation, which occurs shortly after the first. The thermal effect produced by oxidation may vary within fairly wide temperature limits, as we have shown in the case of siderite. The temperature of the thermal maximum in the decomposition of rhodochrosite is slightly higher than in that of siderite, and varies from one sample to another. This variation of the thermal maximum is due to the number of Ca^{2+}, Mg^{2+} and Fe^{2+} ions which are substituted for the Mn^{2+} ion in the rhodochrosite lattice. More often than not, Ca^{2+} and Mg^{2+} ions make for an increase in the temperature of thermal effects, whereas the Fe^{2+} ion leads to a decrease of these temperatures.

As in the case of siderite, the form in which the final residue appears after the decomposition and oxidation of rhodochrosite is still at issue in the literature. Since four manganese oxides are known, the question is which one of them will be obtained among the decomposition products of the manganese carbonate, considering that experimental conditions will affect the result. Indeed, the exchange intensity between the CO_2 evolved and the oxygen that has penetrated into the sample is different, depending most of all on these experimental conditions.

As has already been pointed out, the structure of $MnCO_3$ is destroyed on heating in air at between 450 and 500 °C, while at 650 °C appears the structure of Mn_2O_3. In the interval between the disappearance of the $MnCO_3$ structure and the appearance of the Mn_2O_3 structure, the sample is in an amorphous condition. On further increasing the temperature to 1000 °C the Mn_3O_4 structure will be formed. If heating is carried out at a slower rate, of about 3 to 4 °C per minute, then partial or total oxidation will take place during the decomposition of the carbonate, and pyrolusite will be formed according to the reaction:

$$MnCO_3 + \frac{1}{2} O_2 \rightarrow MnO_2 + CO_2.$$

When the determinations are carried out in other atmospheres, for instance in carbon dioxide or inert gases, i.e. in the absence of oxygen, a quite different final product will then be obtained.

The use of thermal curves for the quantitative determination of rhodochrosite leads to large errors, since the computation of mass variation is erroneous just because the form in which the final product appears is uncertain.

Smithsonite, $ZnCO_3$. When it appears as cryptocrystalline masses, smithsonite is difficult to distinguish from the minerals with which it occurs in paragenesis (opal, zinc, silicates, etc.). Thermal methods based on the decomposition of the carbonate are particularly useful for its determination. The simple mineral or its isomorphous associations have been investigated by means of the method of differential thermal analysis by a number of authors, as it appears from a review paper written by Smothers and Yao-Chiana (1966).

The thermal decomposition of this mineral begins at about 350 °C, and is completed at about 550 °C (Figure 5.57). The thermal curves obtained are analogous to those resulting from the decomposition of siderite, with the difference that the thermal phenomenon recorded as a result of the decomposition are located at lower temperatures than that of siderite, and that the oxidation effect specific to siderite fails to exist altogether. The appearance of a slight mass increase after decomposition, caused by the occurrence of oxidation, indicates that the investigated sample also contains siderite or rhodochrosite in addition to smithsonite.

The colour of smithsonite is white, with a slightly greenish hue, but there are also brown varieties which contain a certain amount of iron oxides. Samples of smithsonite associated with iron oxides are clearly distinguished on the thermal curves from the samples of smithsonite associated with siderite, just because the oxidation effect fails to exist. The thermal curves stand out distinctly also when the mineral is found in limestones, because the limestones are stable at the range of temperature at which smithsonite is resolved, so that calcite and dolomite decompose only at a much higher temperature. This fact makes quantitative determinations based on the loss of mass accurate enough for establishing the ratio $ZnCO_3 : CaCO_3$ or $ZnCO_3 : (MgCa)CO_3$.

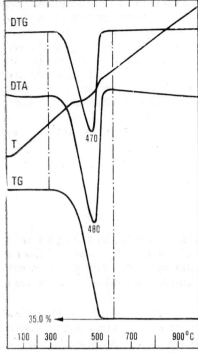

Figure 5.57 Thermal curves of a
specimen of smithsonite.

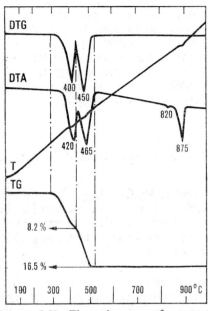

Figure 5.58 Thermal curves of a sample
of cerussite.

Cerussite, PbCO₃. Unlike the other carbonates from this group, on heating cerussite decomposes in two stages. Studies using the method of differential thermal analysis were carried out by Cuthbert and Rowland (1947), Beck (1950), Gruver (1950), Ivanova (1961), Warne and Bayliss (1962), and others, while Caillere and Pobeguin (1960) made use of the thermogravimetric method.

The first stage of the decomposition of cerussite takes place at temperatures ranging from 300 to 440 °C; it is of the form $2PbCO_3 \rightarrow PbO.PbCO_3 + CO_2$. In the second stage, which follows immediately, decomposition is of the form: $PbO.PbCO_3 \rightarrow 2Pb + CO_2$. The removal of carbon dioxide in two stages is a good starting point for the quantitative determination of cerussite (Figure 5.58).

With rising temperatures, the residue left after decomposition of the carbonate, i.e. lead oxide, undergoes two thermal transformations which are recorded only on the DTA curve. Thus, a slight thermal effect will appear on this curve at about 820 °C, which is caused by a polymorphic transformation of lead oxide. At a temperature of 870 °C the curve indicates another effect, which is also endothermal, caused by melting of the oxide.

When cerussite is investigated analytically by means of thermal methods, if the determinations are carried out in metal crucibles, particularly in platinum ones, care must be taken that the samples to be analysed should be free of sulphides. It is comparatively easy to ascertain that the samples contain perceptible amounts of sulphides, because their presence can be observed either with the naked eye or through a microscope or, better still, by treatment with HCl, when H_2S is evolved; in this case the samples are analysed in ceramic crucibles. Such precautions are necessary, as has already been shown in the case of galena, to avoid the destruction of metallic crucibles. For lack of ceramic crucibles, cerussite samples in admixture with sulphides can also be determined in metallic crucibles, in which case, however, the test must be run at temperatures not higher than 500 to 550 °C, at which lead sulphide does not yet react with the metal of the crucible, while the cerussite has already been decomposed.

5.7.2 Anhydrous Double Carbonates Group

Dolomite, Mg.Ca(CO₃)₂. This double carbonate of calcium and magnesium is widely scattered in nature and has been very much studied by means of thermal analysis methods. Data concerning the thermal behaviour of dolomite was systematized by Smothers and Yao-Chiang (1966) in a work entitled "Handbook of Differential Thermal Analysis".

Under the action of thermal energy, dolomite undergoes two characteristic transformations as it decomposes. The first transformation consists in a resolution of magnesium carbonate, which begins at about 600 °C and ends at 800 °C. The second transformation consists of the decomposition of calcium carbonate, and begins immediately after the decomposition of magnesium carbonate has been completed and holds on up to a temperature of 850 °C. A derivatogram typical for the thermal behaviour of dolomite is illustrated in Figure 5.59.

As in the case of calcite, it is possible to draw a number of conclusions concerning the impurities contained in the dolomite under investigation by considering the colour of the sample and of the residue.

The loss of mass corresponding to the decomposition of each carbonate separately is determined at first. Then follows a determination of the percentage of magnesium and calcium carbonates. According to these data, the dolomites are classified in several groups. Thus we can consider compounds whose ratios are

$$\frac{CO_2 \text{ in } MgCO_3}{CO_2 \text{ in } CaCO_3} \approx 1$$

to be dolomites proper.

If this ratio is higher than 1.0, the dolomites contain magnesium carbonate in excess and are designated *magnesian dolomites*. In such a case, i.e. when the ratio is higher than 1.0, the thermal curves must carefully be examined, since it possible that the sample should also contain magnesium carbonate, which is not bonded into the dolomitic lattice, and then, at about 600 °C there will appear a thermal

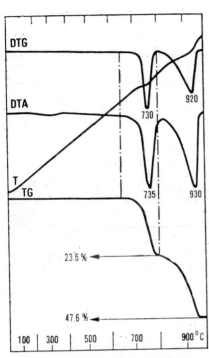

Figure 5.59 Thermal curves of
dolomite.

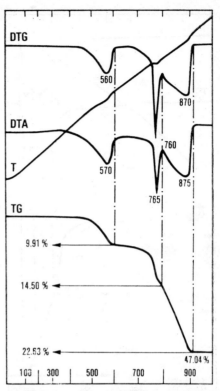

Figure 5.60 Thermal curves of a native
association of magnesite with dolomite.

effect with a loss of mass (Figure 5.60) corresponding to the percentage of magnesite contained in the dolomite. When the ratio is smaller than 1.0, the dolomites contain calcium carbonate in excess, and are called *calcitic dolomites*. If the content of unbonded calcite in the dolomitic lattice is larger than 10 per cent, two thermal effects will then appear, particularly on DTG curves (Figure 5.61), at a range of temperatures specific to the decomposition of calcium carbonate. As a matter of fact this is an endothermal effect with a double peak: the first effect corresponds to the calcium carbonate bonded in the dolomitic lattice, and the second, to calcium carbonate of the calcitic type. The presence of $MgCO_3$ or $CaCO_3$ outside the lattice of dolomite fails to be established from the percentage of the chemical analyses; this is possible only from the thermal curves.

Manganocalcite, (Mn, Ca)CO_3. In mineralogy, under this designation we commonly understand the mineral species from the uninterrupted isomorphous series rhodochrosite-calcite. This name is given to carbonated rocks which, according to the data of chemical analyses, also include Mn^{2+} ions in their structure. Data

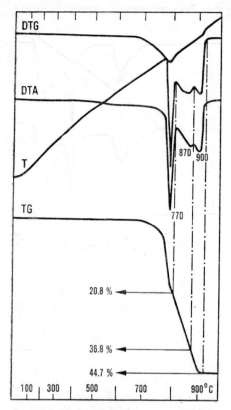

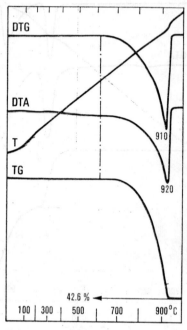

Figure 5.61 Thermal curves of a native sample of dolomite in which the calcium carbonate percentage is higher than for the lattice of dolomite.

Figure 5.62 Thermal curves of manganocalcite with a typical calcite lattice.

concerning the mineralogical percentage of these isomorphous compounds is scanty and incomplete.

Recent investigations (Popa and Todor, 1971) have proved that three types of manganocalcites can be identified by means of the combined thermal methods. These types, which represent either mechanical associations of calcium and magnesium carbonates or isomorphous substitutions from the same mineral group, behave differently on heating, and give thermal curves specific to each separate case. The large number of data existing in the literature, discussed by Tzvetkov et al. (1964), in the light of the differential thermal analysis, do not specify these differentiations. We will consider three types.

The first type consists of nicely crystallized manganocalcites with a transparent hue, and which on thermal analyses yield the curves characteristic of calcite (Figure 5.62). The essential difference in the behaviour on heating of the manganocalcites against calcite consists in the beginning of decomposition, which starts at temperatures about 50 °C lower than with calcite.

This depression of the decomposition temperature against that of calcite is valid, and depends on the degree of substitution of calcium by manganese, which takes place in the elementary crystallization cell of calcite. The larger the amount of Mn^{2+} which has been substituted for Ca^{2+}, the lower will be the decomposition temperature.

Characteristic of the exact determination of these types of manganocalcites is the black colour of the residue remaining after decomposition of the carbonates. With these types of manganocalcites iti s not possible quantitatively to determine both cations by means of thermal methods. At the most it is possible to determine the total CO_2 percentage evolved on thermal decomposition of the carbonates. However, these determinations based on mass variations are also to a certain extent erroneous, because an oxidation of MnO will take place simultaneously with the decomposition, higher forms of manganese oxides finally resulting as in the case of rhodochrosite. The fact that oxidation occurs simultaneously with decomposition is shown by the exothermal effect specific to oxidation failing to appear on the thermal curves.

For quantitative determinations, one should take as a starting base the amount of CO_2 obtained by thermal methods, and this will be correlated with the chemically determined percentages of Mn^{2+} and Ca^{2+}.

From a mineralogical point of view, this type of mineral is a manganocalcite in the true sense of the word, because manganese has partially been substituted for calcium in the elementary crystallization cell of calcite.

The second type of the manganocalcites consists of isomorphously crystallized mixtures of calcite and rhodochrosite, in which the two carbonates are crystallized in independent elementary cells. The crystals are extremely small and they are difficult to observe through the microscope.

On heating, these manganocalcites give thermal curves that are completely different from the previous ones. Thus, manganese carbonate decomposes at first, at temperatures ranging from 450 to 600 °C (Figure 5.63). The decomposition is recorded on the thermal curves by an endothermal effect attended by a loss in mass corresponding to the amount of CO_2 evolved on decomposition of the manganese carbonate. This endothermal effect is immediately followed by an exothermal effect, attended by an increase in mass, due to the oxidation of the MnO resulted from decomposition. The temperature at with this effect appears can vary within wide limits, and in addition to what has been shown in the case of rhodochrosite, the variation also depends on the ratio of $MnCO_3$ to $CaCO_3$; the larger the amount of manganese carbonate, the wider will be the temperature range in which oxidation takes place, and vice versa.

At temperatures higher than 700 °C the decomposition of calcium carbonate begins, recorded on the thermal curves by an endothermal effect attended by a loss in mass due to the CO_2 evolved. Above 940°C, the residue fails to undergoe any visible transformation. On the basis of the variations of mass recorded on the thermal curves, it is possible to make satisfactory quantitative interpretations of the

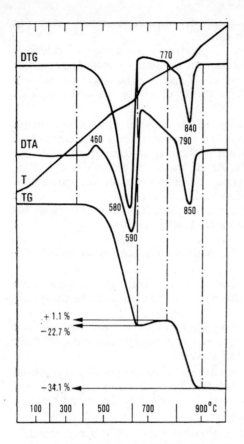

Figure 5.63 Thermal curves of a rhodo-chrosite-calcite type of manganocalcite.

percentages of rhodochrosite and calcite present in the isomorphously crystallized association.

The third type of manganocalcite consists of an association of calcite with manganese oxides included as impurities in its mass during the process or precipitation and crystallization. I believe that the designation of these minerals as mangano-calcites is a misnomer, since such a name can be given only to the carbonates; moreover, in most cases the manganese oxides are present associated with iron oxides. On heating, these minerals yield a thermal curve specific to calcite, with the sole difference that in many cases the DTA curve exhibits an exothermal effect of comparatively small extension, which is specific to the oxides (Figure 5.64), and is located at temperatures ranging from 400 to 500 °C.

Barytocalcite, (Ba,Ca)CO₃. This native association of the isomorphously crystallized calcium and barium carbonates preserves the thermal properties of the minerals as separate individuals, from the point of view of their behaviour on heating. Nevertheless, a very slight thermal effect appears on the DTA curve at temperatures.

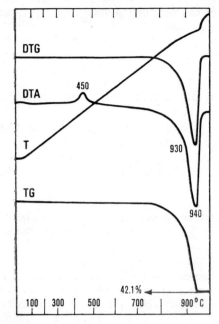

Figure 5.64 Thermal curves of a calcite containing finely dispersed sulphides.

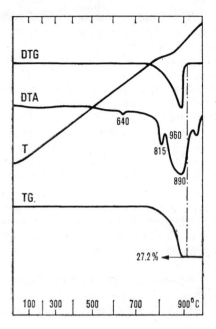

Figure 5.65 Thermal curves of a sample of barytocalcite.

ranging from 600 to 650 °C. This effect is properly assigned to a polymorphic transformation, because it is in fact a separation of the two carbonates. With rising temperatures the decomposition of calcium carbonate begins, and this is completed at a temperature of 950 °C. The DTA curve shows a much larger endothermal effect than the TG and DTG curves. This effect is due to overlapping of the thermal effects, i.e. on one hand to the decomposition of calcium carbonate, and on the other hand to the first effect of the polymorphic transformation of the barium carbonate, which takes place over the same range of temperatures as the decomposition of calcite. As has already been pointed out, witherite shows two endothermal effects caused by the polymorphic transformation, but the barytocalcite (which is the barium carbonate remaining after the decomposition of calcium carbonate) fails to present the second effect or, if this appears on the DTA curve, it is strongly diminished in intensity (Figure 5.65).

Manganosiderite, (Mn,Fe)CO$_3$. Manganosiderite or oligonite represents isomorphous associations of manganese and iron carbonates. It seems that the two designations used in mineralogy depend on the ratio of the percentages of iron to manganese. When siderite predominates, the mineral is called *manganosiderite*, and when rhodochrosite predominates, the mineral is styled *oligonite*, but this matter is not fully made clear in the literature.

This isomorphous mixture of carbonates has not been studied to a very great extent by thermal analysis. Tzvetkov, Valscihina, and Piloian (1964) have published some data concerning the differential thermal analysis of manganosiderite. My investigations have indicated that this isomorphous association is a purely mechanical one, and that the crystallization of the two carbonates takes place in separate elementary cells. The thermal curves (Figure 5.66) show that siderite decomposes at first, and then the rhodochrosite decomposes. On the DTG curve, these decompositions are clearly shown by two thermal maxima.

It is very difficult to determine the percentage of $FeCO_3$ and $MnCO_3$, respectively, on the basis of the losses of mass. However, this determination can be made but it will be inaccurate. Other methods of chemical analysis are also difficult, because these mixtures always contain free iron and manganese oxides.

If the process of thermal decomposition takes place in two stages, as has been shown (see discussion on siderite and rhodochrosite), the thermal process caused by oxidation of the two oxides produced from the decomposition occurs only in a single stage, which is visible on the thermal curves as an exothermal effect attended by an increase of mass.

Monheimite, $(Zn,Fe)CO_3$. This isomorphous association of zinc and iron carbonates is, like manganosiderite, a mechanical mixture in which the crystallization of the two carbonates occurs in separate elementary cells. The thermal curves obtained on these minerals are similar to those of the manganosiderites, the sole difference being that the decomposition of the carbonates takes place in a more restricted range of temperatures. Monheimite samples generally contain iron oxides. If the

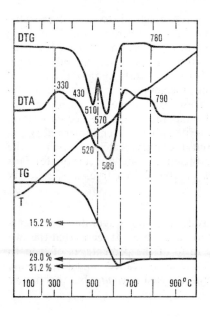

Figure 5.66   Thermal curves of a sample of manganosiderite.

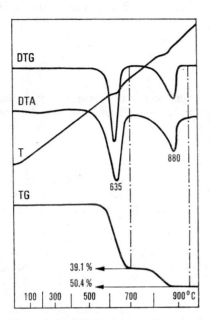

Figure 5.67   Thermal curves of a sample of huntite.

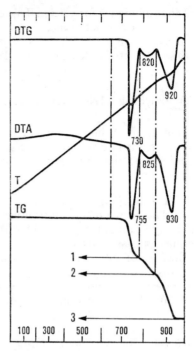

Figure 5.68   Thermal curves of a sample of ankerite.

thermal results are used in conjunction with the data from chemical analyses, it is possible to make precise quantitative interpretations based on the loss of mass, which indicates the total amount of CO_2 produced by the decomposition of the carbonates. In these mixtures, if the sample is free of sulphides, the Zn^{2+} cation is bound exclusively in the carbonate lattice, whereas iron may partially occur also as oxides. Hence, by calculating the amount of CO_2 corresponding to the amount of Zn^{2+} found, we get by difference the amount of CO_2 corresponding to $FeCO_3$.

Huntite, $Mg_3Ca(CO_3)_4$. This mineral is rarely encountered native, but has been discovered by Faust (1953) in the Current-Creek deposits from Nevada, where it occurs as cryptocrystalline masses similar to chalk. In the beginning it was considered to be a mechanical mixture of magnesite and calcite. The DTA curves obtained by Faust, also indicated that huntite was a mechanical mixture, but later X-ray diffraction studies revealed that another crystallization was involved, and for this reason it was suggested that it should be classified as an independent mineral.

The curves obtained by differential thermal analysis (Figure 5.67) have confirmed the presence of magnesite and calcite as the chief components, in a ratio of 3: 1. Moreover, with artificial mixtures of magnesite and calcite in the same ratio, the thermal effects obtained were identical except that the peak temperature of the effect was slightly higher for calcite. This can be accounted for by the fact that in huntite, the calcium carbonate remaining after decomposition of the magnesium carbonate is present as very fine particles, whereas with artificial mixtures the particle size is in the order of the degree of grinding.

5.7.3 Anhydrous Triple Carbonates Group

A number of carbonate minerals representing associations of three or even more carbonates also occur native. We shall discuss only ankerite and manganodolomite, because on heating the other associations behave similarly to the artificial association of the simple minerals, i.e, the thermal curves are identical.

Ankerite, (Mg, Fe)Ca(CO$_3$)$_2$. In the lattice of ankerite Fe^{2+} is substituted for Mg^{2+}. The degree of substitution varies widely. According to Kulp, Kent, and Kerr (1951), the amount of iron which replaces magnesite is from 5 to 70 per cent. In thermal analysis, this variation of the ratio between Mg^{2+} and Fe^{2+} leads to the production of different thermal curves.

Ankerite has characteristic thermal curves, which reflect the transformations that take place with increasing temperature. The variation of the ratio between Mg^{2+} and Fe^{2+} affects only the peak-temperatures of the thermal effects and their amplitude, but not the shape of the curves. The thermal effects specific to ankerite are shown as three endothermal effects (Figure 5.68), falling within the temperature range 700—900 °C. The decomposition temperatures of ankerite are higher than the decomposition and oxidation temperatures of siderite, which permits the determination of ankerite when it occurs together with siderite. The three thermal reactions which cause the three endothermal effects can be represented as follows:

$$(Mg, Fe)Ca(CO_3)_2 \longrightarrow MgO + CO_2 + (Fe)Ca(CO_3)_2$$
$$(Fe)Ca(CO_3)_2 \longrightarrow FeO + CO_2 + CaCO_3$$
$$CaCO_3 \longrightarrow CaO + CO_2$$

From a qualitative point of view, the decomposition of ankerite has been investigated on the DTA curve by Beck (1950), Guigue (1955), Koblenz and Tolnay (1961) and others. All these researchers have found that the larger the amount of iron in the lattice of ankerite, the lower will be the temperatures at which the thermal effects appear.

At first sight, it would seem that after the second endothermal effect there should also appear on the curves an exothermal effect, caused by the oxidation of the ferrous oxide which has arisen as a result of the decomposition of the carbonate. This effect, however, fails to occur, because in agreement with what has been shown in the case of siderite, oxidation does not take place in a CO$_2$ atmosphere. Moreover, the colour of the residue from the decomposition of the carbonates is neither red nor black, but after a time, as the residue is exposed to the air, it begins to develop colour due to oxidation.

From the macrocrystalline and microcrystalline aspect, we are very often tempted to attribute the designation of ankerite also to mixtures of dolomite with small amounts of free iron oxides and particularly of sulphides. However, not even the data of chemical analyses can make it clear whether an ankerite is involved or whether the mineral in question is a dolomite containing iron oxides, because, as we have seen, the Fe^{2+} percentage replaced for Mg^{2+} is apt to vary greatly. When the analytically determined percentage of iron is small, the iron can be assigned both to the lattice of ankerite and to the free oxides. Thermal methods show very well what kind of mixture is involved. Thus, for instance, where only 2 per cent of the mixture consists of sulphides, then an exothermal effect will appear on the DTA curve at about 460 °C (Figure 5.69).

Manganodolomite, (Mn,Mg,Ca)(CO₃)₂. As in the case of manganocalcites, the designation on manganodolomite is assigned to the mineral species belonging to the isomorphous dolomite-rhodochrosite series. In this case, the mineral in question is an isomorphously crystallized mechanical association of dolomite with rhodochrosite, which on the thermal curves shows one endothermal and three decomposition effects (Figure 5.70). Thus, an endothermal effect appears in the temperature range 550—600 °C, which is due to the decomposition of the manganese carbonate in the rhodochrosite lattice. This is immediately followed by an exothermal effect caused by the oxidation of the MnO produced by the decomposition. The two endothermal effects specific to the decomposition of dolomite appear subsequently.

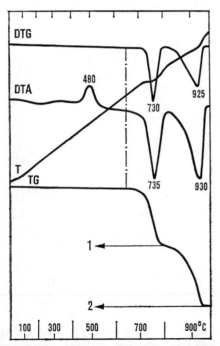

Figure 5.69 Thermal curves of a sample of dolomite with sulphides and iron oxides.

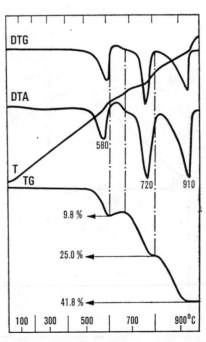

Figure 5.70 Thermal curves of a sample of rhodochrosite with dolomite.

By interpretation of the TG and DTG curves showing the variations of mass which are associated with these effects, it is possible to determine the amount of $MnCO_3$ present in this compound. In almost all cases, the manganodolomites also show a thermal effect specific to free manganese oxides on the DTA curves. The presence of these oxides in the samples can be attributed to the fact that the manganese carbonate contained in the mixture has been partially decomposed with time, but this, of course, occurs only in the zones where the sample came into direct contact with oxygen.

Data from the literature in connection with the thermal investigations of manganodolomites is very scanty. In what follows, I shall present some observations resulting from my researches concerning the behaviour of the minerals from this isomorphous series.

Besides the isomorphously crystallized mechanical associations of dolomite-rhodochrosite previously referred to, I have found that many samples subjected to thermal analyses show a lattice which is typical of ankerite, but in which manganese, instead of iron, has been substituted for magnesium. Since the lattice of ankerite is well defined in the specialized literature as far as its thermal behaviour is concerned, and the mineral is a simple compound, I am not certain that the minerals I have

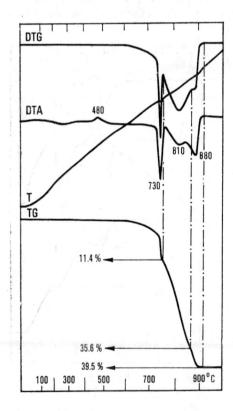

Figure 5.71 Thermal curves of a sample of an ankerite type mineral in which Mn^{2+} instead of Fe^{2+} was substituted for Mg^{2+} *(Popa and Todor, 1971).*

investigated may properly be called manganodolomites or rather *manganic ankerites* (Popa and Todor, 1971).

The mineral that I investigated has thermal curves similar to those of ankerite. The basic differences from the ankerites are that the residue remaining after complete decomposition of the carbonates is black, and the thermal effect of the decomposition of the manganese carbonate (the middle effect in the succession of the three endothermal effects) is more extensive, while the transition point from the decomposition of the manganese carbonate to that of the calcium carbonate is less well-marked (Figure 5.71).

I cannot conclude my discussion on this group of triple carbonates without mentioning a mineral or a mixture of minerals whose genesis is not yet clarified. This mineral is not mentioned in the mineralogical literature, but it frequently occurs native. It has been found at Işalniţa in Oltenia and Radoşca, in the Banat. This mineral is a very finely crystallized isomorphous association of magnesite and ankerite, and in most cases iron oxides could be identified in the mass of the samples, imparting a reddish colour to them.

Thermal curves (Figure 5.72) show, in the first place, an important endothermal effect caused by the thermal decomposition of magnesite, which is fully completed at about 650 °C. This effect is followed by the sequence of three endothermal effects specific to the resolution of ankerite.

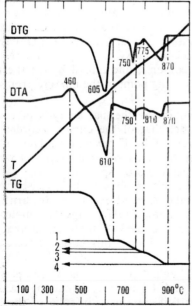

Figure 5.72 Thermal curves of a sample of mineral collected at Işalniţa, Romania, containing magnesite, ankerite, and iron oxides.

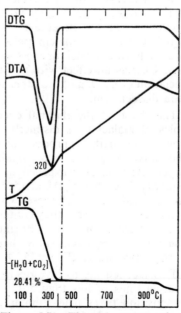

Figure 5.73 Thermal curves of a sample of malachite.

5.7.4 Group of Carbonates containing Structural Hydroxyls

To this group belong the main carbonates of copper: malachite, $Cu_2(CO_3)(OH)_2$, and azurite, $Cu_3(CO_3)_2(OH)_2$, as well as the compounds in which the cations are represented by Zn^{2+} and Pb^{2+}.

The characteristic behaviour of these carbonates on heating is their decomposition at low temperatures, with the total removal of hydroxyls and then of the carbon dioxide. This behaviour causes some specific endothermal effects, to appear on the thermal curves, corresponding to the percentage decomposition of the compound.

Malachite, $Cu_2(CO_3)(OH)_2$. Characteristic of the behaviour of these carbonates on heating is the endothermal effect they produce at temperatures ranging from 200 to 500 °C. This effect is associated with a loss of mass, as a result of the removal of a molecule of water and of a molecule of carbon dioxide. If the temperature is raised above 950 °C, then the thermal curves again record an endothermal effect. This is also associated with a loss of mass, as a result of the thermal dissociation of the CuO, produced from the decomposition, into Cu_2O, with the release of an atom of oxygen.

When carrying out a thermal analysis of copper carbonates and quantitative determinations are desired, it is not advisable to let the operating temperature exceed 800—900 °C. This is because the product resulting after the thermal dissociation of the CuO has no stable composition, as it is a mixture of CuO and Cu_2O, having no well-defined composition. In some cases, the DTA curve has recorded the resolution of CuO as an effect with two thermal maximums, one caused by the thermal dissociation of CuO, and the other due to the melting point of the mixture produced by the dissociation.

The shape of the thermal curves recorded in the thermal analysis of native samples of malachite is distinctly different from that of the curves recorded on samples of an artificial product, at a heating rate of 10 °C per minute. Thus, none of the native samples show a boundary between the range of temperatures at which the hydroxyl groups are expelled and that in which the decomposition of the carbonate takes place, whereas the artificial samples exhibit an obvious difference between the temperatures at which these two processes take place. Moreover, all the artificial samples have shown that they contain a larger amount of OH groups than indicated by the formula of malachite. Further, the curves recorded on the thermal analysis of the artificial products show that the decomposition of this basic carbonate is effected in two stages (Figure 5.74).

This fact led me to investigate the thermal behaviour of the native compounds at heating rates of less than 5 °C per minute, and I have found that the thermal decomposition takes place similarly to the artificial products, in spite of the fact that large thermal effects are obtained.

This justifies my conclusion that the difference in the behaviour on heating of the artificial products against the native ones, at high heating rates, is due to the

Figure 5.74   Thermal curves of an artificial sample of malachite.

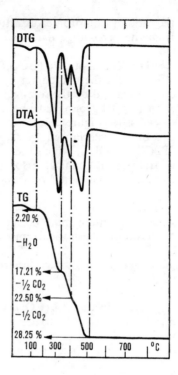

different degree of crystallization of the two classes of products. The thermal reactions occurring in the case of the artificial products are as follows:

$$Cu_2(CO_3)(OH)_2 \longrightarrow CuCO_3 + CuO + H_2O$$
$$2\,CuCO_3 \longrightarrow Cu_2OCO_3 + CO_2$$
$$Cu_2OCO_3 \longrightarrow 2CuO + CO_2$$

Azurite, $Cu_3(CO_3)_2(OH)_2$. Both native and artificial azurite behave similarly to malachite, the difference being that the percentage of OH groups expelled is smaller and the amount of CO_2 lost is larger. This difference causes an increase of the decomposition temperature by about 50 °C.

The percentage composition of samples from copper deposits may vary to a large extent as a result of isomorphous crystallizations with other carbonates. Basic copper carbonates will, however, undergo thermal transformations at comparatively lower temperatures than the other carbonates, so that they can readily be determined when they occur in associations. The only shortcoming which is involved in the determination of basic copper carbonates is the presence in some samples of zinc and lead carbonates, with which copper is isomorphous in the lattice. The most frequently encountered isomorphous mixture is "rhosassite", whose chemical formula is: $(Cu, Zn)_n(CO_3)_m(OH)_2$ — where $n = 2$ or 3 and $m = 1$ or 2. This mineral gives thermal curves that are identical to those of the pure basic copper carbonates, and the ratio of isomorphic substitution of zinc for copper cannot be determined, except from the percentage data of chemical analysis.

Hydrocerussite, $Pb_3(CO_3)_2(OH)_2$. This mineral shows a marked endothermal effect on the thermal curves, lying at temperatures ranging from 220 to 320 °C. This effect is caused by the removal of the OH groups from the lattice of hydrocerussite. After the OH groups have been expelled, the anhydrous carbonate behaves similarly to cerussite (Figure 5.75).

In the specialized literature, hydrocerussite is generally given the formula $2PbCO_3.Pb(OH)_2$, which indicates that the mineral in question is an isomorphously crystallized mechanical association of lead carbonate and lead hydroxide. Since, from a thermal point of view, the compound gives thermal effects successively appearing, and the ratio which expresses the loss of mass corresponding to the removal of OH groups and CO_2 is constant, in my opinion the chemical formula would be written more correctly as $Pb_3(CO_3)_2(OH)_2$.

Owing to the gradual removal of OH groups from the lattice of hydrocerussite, and also to the decomposition of the carbonate, which occurs in two stages with a corresponding to a loss of mass, hydrocerussite can be determined quantitatively by means of thermal analysis.

Hydrozincite, $Zn_5(CO_3)_2(OH_6)$. Thermal analyses performed by Beck (1950) and Cocco (1951) on hydrozincite refer only to the DTA curves. The observations made by these two investigators differ with regard to the stages of the thermal decomposition. Cocco shows that the DTA curves obtained indicated a single

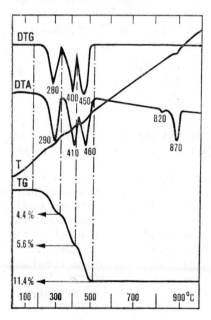

Figure 5.75   Thermal curves of a sample of hydrocerussite.

exothermal effect, hence that the product decomposes in a single stage, while Beck inferred the existence of three stages of decomposition.

I obtained thermal curves with three thermal effects: an endothermal effect attended by a loss of mass, corresponding to the removal of OH groups from zinc hydroxide, at temperatures ranging from 200 to 320 °C; a second endothermal effect, immediately following the first, which is due to the removal of a molecule of water from the OH groups bonded in the lattice of the basic zinc carbonate proper; and a third endothermal effect which is caused by the decomposition of the anhydrous zinc carbonate. Unlike the lead carbonate produced from hydrocerussite, the anhydrous zinc carbonate produced from hydrozincite fails to decompose in two stages.

Summing up, the reactions which occur when hydrozincite is heated, can be written as follows:

$$Zn_3(CO_3)_2(OH)_2 \cdot 2Zn(OH)_2 \longrightarrow Zn_3(CO_3)_2(OH)_2 + 2ZnO + 2H_2O$$
$$Zn_3(CO_3)_2(OH)_2 \longrightarrow 2ZnCO_3 + ZnO + H_2O$$
$$2ZnCO_3 \longrightarrow 2ZnO + 2CO_2$$

To conclude, the carbonates which contain OH groups are suitable for quantitative determination, owing to the losses of mass occurring at a comparatively low temperature as compared to other carbonates. Some difficulty, however, arises with regard to the strict marking of the limits between the losses of OH and CO_2 groups. Very good results are nevertheless obtained, if the percentage of CO_2 is determined by another method. By deducting the percentage of CO_2 (as determined by another method) from the total loss of mass obtained by thermal methods, we can accurately estimate the percentage of water produced by the removal of OH groups present in the lattice of the mineral in question.

5.7.5 Hydrated Magnesium Carbonates Group

From the data of Beck (1950) and from those of Tzvetkov *et al.* (1964), the natural hydrated magnesium carbonates, except anhydrous magnesite, are crystallized with n molecules of water, and include at the same time OH groups in their molecule. The above-mentioned researchers show that a large number of these minerals are to be found in nature. In what follows I shall present data concerning the thermal analysis of artinite and hydromagnesite only, because these are the most frequently encountered members of the group.

Artinite, $Mg_2(CO_3)(OH)_2.3H_2O$. This native carbonate has been investigated only by means of differential thermal analysis by Beck (1950) and Tzvetkov, Valskina, and Piloian (1964). These authors obtained different DTA curves even though chemical analyses have shown that they were all dealing with the same mineral. It follows that the differences between the thermal effects recorded by them are due only to the difference in the experimental conditions in which they performed their analyses. From the curves obtained by these researchers, it is difficult to give a quantitative explanation for the thermal processes which have taken place, even if the curves are interpreted separately.

From the thermal curves that I have obtained (Figure 5.76), it follows that artinite at first expels the three molecules of water in a single stage. This dehydration is marked on the thermal curves by an endothermic effect found at temperatures ranging from 150 to 280 °C. On further heating, one more water molecule (resulting from the two OH groups) is expelled. Its removal is marked by an endothermic effect which is hardly perceptible on the DTA curve, but is well-marked on the DTG curve, which shows that the removal of OH groups occurs at a high rate.

The decomposition of the remaining anhydrous magnesium carbonate is a process which takes place immediately and is marked by a third endothermic effect.

After the dehydration and decomposition effects have been completed, a slight exothermic effect appears on the DTA curve, as a result of a polymorphic transformation of MgO which, after decomposition, is in an amorphous condition.

Hydromagnesite, $Mg_5(CO_3)_4(OH)_2 \cdot 4H_2O$. In handbooks of mineralogy, two formulae are given for this compound, one corresponding to the mineral crystallized with three molecules of water, $Mg_4(CO_3)_3(OH)_2 \cdot 3H_2O$, and another corresponding to the mineral crystallized with four molecules of water, $Mg_5(CO_3)_4(OH)_2 \cdot 4H_2O$.

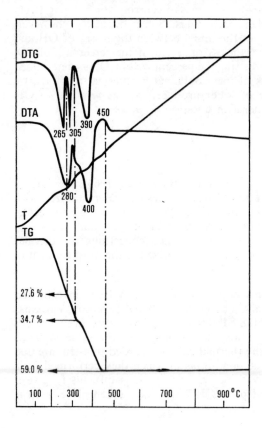

Figure 5.76   Thermal curves of artinite
(Popa and Todor, 1971).

According to Tzvetkov *et al.* (1964), the constitution of the compound is not yet exactly defined, because the percentage chemical analyses and the differential thermal curves have failed to provide conclusive evidence. I have found that this carbonate crystallizes with four molecules of water. I have come to this conclusion because the combined thermal curves have indicated variations of mass for H_2O, OH, and CO_2 corresponding to this compound (Figure 4.8).

At temperatures ranging from 210 to 395 °C, hydromagnesite undergoes its first thermal transformation, namely decomposition, as a result of which the four molecules of water are expelled. Following immediately upon dehydration there appears the second thermal effect at temperatures ranging from 395 to 460 °C, conclusively recorded as an endothermic effect on the TG and DTG curves only. The DTA curve, unlike the TG and DTG curves, indicates a yield of heat, the shape of the curve having a tendency towards an exothermic effect. This second effect corresponds to the removal of a CO_2 molecule, as a result of which the compound also undergoes a structural reorganization. Further, a third thermal effect follows, and this is due to the simultaneous removal of a molecule of water resulting from the OH groups, and of a molecule of CO_2. These are expelled at temperatures ranging from 460 to 515 °C.

Unlike TG and DTG curves, which show, that each thermal effect is attended by a marked loss of mass, the DTA curve shows an exothermic effect at a range of temperatures between 385 and 460 °C, which is due to a yield of heat as a result of the structural reorganization. It is probably this fact which led the above-mentioned authors, whose studies of this compound were performed only by means of the method of differential thermal analysis, to draw contradictory conclusions as to the composition of hydromagnesite.

After this sequence of three thermal effects follows another endothermic effect recorded on all thermal curves, much broader in aspect than the preceding ones and with a shape of curve indicating a double effect, in the temperature range from 515 — 545 — 640 °C. This effect corresponds to two CO_2 molecules being expelled. Finally, the residue is constant in weight and consists of MgO.

The reactions which take place with increasing temperature in the case of hydromagnesite may be represented as follows:

$$Mg_5(CO_3)_4(OH)_2 \cdot 4H_2O \longrightarrow Mg_5(CO_3)_4(OH)_2 + 4H_2O$$

$$Mg_5(CO_3)_4(OH)_2 \longrightarrow 2MgCO_3 + 3MgO + 2CO_2 + H_2O$$

$$2MgCO_3 \longrightarrow 2MgO + 2CO_2$$

5.8 SILICATES

This class includes a large number of known minerals whose basic structural unity is the silicon and oxygen tetrahedron, that is, the anionic group $[SiO_4]$ in which the Si^{4+} ion is always found tetrahedrally surrounded by four O^{2-} ions. The bonds between silicon and oxygen are strong, covalent, oriented ones. The distance between the silicon and oxygen ions is about 1.6 Å, and that between two neighbouring oxygen atoms is about 2.6 Å; this structure gives a great stability to the silicates.

Isomorphous substitution is very common and varied in the silicates. Melts and solutions out of which the silicate minerals crystallized contained many kinds of ions, so that similar cations had an opportunity of entering the lattice at random. For this reason, few of the silicates have the ideal composition of simple chemical compounds. Substitution of one cation for another in the lattice is determined more by the volume of the cation than by the valency. Naturally, when an ion with a certain valency is replaced by ions with a different valency, another modification must occur in the lattice to preserve electrical neutrality. Thus the properties are also modified, including their behaviour on heating.

Silicates may be classified in several ways, but two of these, namely on the basis of the chemical composition and their anionic structure are the most commonly used. None of the classifications used in mineralogy will be reproduced here, because it is very difficult to describe the thermal behaviour of silicates as a function of these classifications. We will divide the silicates into five groups according to their thermal behaviour for the purposes of this discussion.

5.8.1 Anhydrous Silicates

This group includes some of the compounds which derive from the $(SiO_4)^{4-}$ anion and metal cations, but only such compounds as do not hold hydroxyl groups of water molecules in their molecule. On heating, these compounds, either native or artificial, undergo physical transformations only. A common feature to all of them is that transformations caused by temperature, and melting in particular, take place at very high temperatures, which are difficult to produce in the instrumental installations currently used for thermal analyses. This is the reason why such compounds have not been studied much by thermal methods of analysis. The thermal behaviour of those native compounds which have been more extensively studied by thermal methods will be described in the following.

MAGNESIUM SILICATES, $MgO.SiO_2$. Two minerals are known within the framework of this system whose thermal effects lie at very high temperatures. These are forsterite and enstatite.

Forsterite, Mg_2SiO_4. Forsterite shows an endothermic effect on the DTA curve as a result of melting at 1890 °C.

Enstatite, $MgSiO_3$. Enstatite shows two endothermic effects on the DTA curve, one of low intensity situated at 1140 °C, due to a polymorphous transformation, and a second one, of high intensity due to melting of the mineral at 1557 °C.

CALCIUM SILICATES, $CaO.SiO_2$. Many compounds which can be obtained artificially also belong to this system, but here only two minerals frequently encountered in nature, rankinite and wollastonite, will be mentioned.

Rankinite, $3CaO.2SiO$. Rankinite shows a single endothermic effect on the DTA curve as a result of its melting at 1464 °C.

Wollastonite, CaSiO$_2$. Wollastonite shows two endothermic effects on the DTA curve, one caused by a polymorphous transformation which takes place at 1160 °C, and a second, as a result of the melting point, which occurs at 1540 °C.

FERROUS SILICATE, FeO.SiO$_2$.

Fayalite, Fe$_2$SiO$_3$. Fayalite is the only representative of this system which occurs native. On heating, this compound yields a single effect on the DTA curve at 1205 °C as a result of a melting and decomposition process in which Fe^{2+} is oxidized to Fe^{3+}, and oxidation which is partially marked also on DTG and TG curves by a slight increase in mass.

MANGANESE SILICATES, MnO.SiO$_2$. Two representatives of this system occur native, tefroite and rhodonite.

Tefroite, MnSiO$_2$ Tefroite shows a marked endothermic effect on the DTA curve as a result of its melting point at 1323 °C.

Rhodonite, MnSiO$_3$. Rhodonite shows only one endothermic effect on the DTA curve at 1215 °C, as a result of the melting of the silicate.

ZINC SILICATES, ZnO. SiO$_2$. Only one representative is encountered native within the framework of this system: willemite.

Willemite, Zn$_2$SiO$_4$. Willemite shows a single endothermic effect as a result of its melting at 1512 °C.

ZIRCONIUM SILICATE, ZrO$_2$.SiO$_2$. The native mineral representative of this systems named *zircon*, and its chemical formula is ZrSiO$_4$. This compound shows two endothermic effects on the DTA curve. The first effect is due to a polymorphous transformation which takes place at 680 °C, and the second effect is a result of the melting point at 1150 °C.

ALUMINIUM SILICATES, Al$_2$O$_3$.SiO$_2$. The native representatives of this system are *mullite* and the three allotropic states of one and the same mineral: *disten-andalusite-sillimanite.*

Mullite, 3Al$_2$O$_3$·2SiO$_2$. This mineral at high temperatures undergoes a dissociation of the type

$$3Al_2O_3 . 2SiO_2 \xrightleftharpoons{1810\ °C} 2Al_2O_3 + Al_2O_3.2SiO_2 \text{ (molten)},$$

as a result of which differential thermal analysis records an endothermic effect at 1810 °C. As a mineral it has been found native, but it frequently appears in the thermal reactions of other aluminosilicates, for example in porcelains and fine clays.

DISTEN, ANDALUSITE, AND SILLIMANITE. These compounds have the same chemical composition, but show structural differences. These differences are in the ways in which the aluminium ions are co-ordinated in the lattice.

On heating, sillimanite, andalusite, and disten decompose into mullite and free SiO_2 before melting. This decomposition proceeds differently which each of the three minerals. Differential thermal analysis records these processes as exothermic effects on the DTA curve (Figure 5.77) with different intensities and at various temperatures.

Sillimanite, Al(AlSiO$_5$), is the most difficult to decompose, temperatures of 1600 °C sometimes being necessary, when the transformation occurs throughout the whole mass of the crystals, and the newly formed mullite crystals are disposed parallel to the orientation of the initial sillimanite crystal.

Andalusite, Al$_2$(SiO$_4$)O, begins to change into mullite at 1400 °C and the reaction becomes intense at 1550 °C. The transformation takes place at the surface of the initial crystal, and the orientation of the needle-shaped mullite crystals is parallel to that of the initial andalusite crystal.

Disten, Al$_2$O(SiO$_4$), begins to decompose at 1200 °C, and the exothermic reaction becomes intense at 1300 °C. The mullite has a fibrous appearance, and the transformation takes place at the surface of the original disten crystal. The newly formed needle-shaped mullite crystals are orientated perpendicular to the surface of the disten crystal, which means that the decomposition is attended by an appreciable increase in volume.

Recent studies have shown that sillimanite, andalusite, and disten are in fact polymorphous high pressure states of the same mineral compound (Solacolu, 1968).

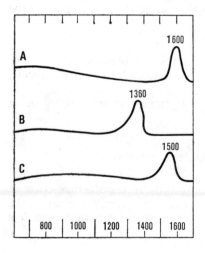

Figure 5.77 DTA curves of aluminium aluminosi-licates: *A*, sillimanite; *B*, disten; *C*, andalusit *(after Greig, 1925)*.

5.8.2 Mixed Anhydrous Crystals

This group includes the great majority of anhydrous native silicates. The number of minerals which can be classified into this group is extremely large. In the following, only a few of the most representative minerals will be mentioned as regard their behaviour on thermal analysis.

Olivine, (Mg, Fe)SiO_4. On heating, this mineral yields thermal curves with two small effects, indicating a polymorphous transformation at about 200 °C and another at 690 °C. The thermal effect specific to this mineral is that of the melting point which, however, varies within wide temperature limits. This temperature variation is closely connected with the ratio of forsterite to fayalite because, as it was seen, the melting point of forsterite is 1890 °C, and that of fayalite is 1205 °C; hence, the melting point of olivine may be found between these two values.

Feldspars, Me (AlSi$_3$O$_8$), where Me=Li, Na, K, Ca, etc. Out of all the mineral silicates, feldspars are the most widespread in the earth's crust, forming 50 per cent of its mass. This class of minerals was studied by the methods of thermal analysis by Kohler (1969) and by Kohler and Wieden (1954). The DTA curves obtained on these minerals show an endothermic effect in the temperature range between 700 and 900 °C, as a result of a polymorphous transformation which has taken place in the mass of the compounds.

Spodumene, LiAl(Si$_2$O$_6$). When subjected to differential thermal analysis, spodumene yields curves showing two effects. There is medium temperature effect at 500 °C, indicating a polymorphous transformation of the type $\beta \rightleftarrows \alpha$, as a result of which the compound passes from the monoclinic system into the tetragonal one. The second effect is a high temperature effect at 1420 °C, which indicates melting of the compound.

Eucrytite, LiAlSiO$_4$. This compound shows two effects on the differential thermal analysis curve, one at 972 °C caused by the polymorphous transformation of the compound (when it passes from the trigonal form into the hexagonal form), and another caused by the melting point at 1400 °C.

Albite, Na(AlSi$_3$O$_8$). Albite or sodium feldspar, appears, according to Solacolu (1968) in two polymorphous states, a low temperature one and a high temperature one, but thermal curves fail to present a conclusive effect marking the passage from one state into another. The only thermal transformation conclusively recorded on the DTA curve is the endothermic effect caused by melting at 1118 °C.

Nephelite, NaAlSiO$_4$. Nephelite shows two polymorphous states, *cornegieite*, the high temperature form in triclinic crystals, and *nepheline* the low temperature form in hexagonal crystals. The passage of cornegieite into nepheline is recorded on the DTA curve as a slight thermal effect, taking place at the temperature of 1254 °C. Another effect is recorded in the DTA curve at 1525 °C. This is due to the melting of the compound.

Nepheline and albite form a discontinuous isomorphic series which also shows a polymorphous transformation on the DTA curve in the temperature range from 1255 to 1280 °C. The thermal effect caused by melting has no fixed point because melting takes place at temperatures depending on the ratio of nepheline to albite. The melting point is included between the melting points of the two minerals.

Jadeite, NaAlSi$_2$O$_6$. Jadeite decomposes at 800 °C, passing into nepheline. This decomposition is marked on the DTA curve by a slight exothermic effect, after which, with rising temperature, the compund behaves like nepheline.

Orthose, K(AlSi$_3$O$_8$). Orthose decomposes at 1170 °C, when it passes into leucite and melt. The decomposition is recorded on the DTA curve by an endothermic effect.

Leucite, K(AlSi$_2$O$_8$). Leucite shows an effect on the DTA curve due to a polymorphous transformation of the type $\beta \rightleftarrows \alpha$ at 620 °C. The β form crystallizes in the tetragonal system, and the α form crystallizes in the cubic system. Melting of this mineral takes place at 1680 °C.

5.8.3   Silicates Containing Structural OH Groups

Minerals classified into this group contain OH groups in their molecule, in addition to the simple or complex $(SiO_4)^{4-}$ anion, together with the related metal cations. On heating, these compounds undergo both physical and chemical processes. The thermal curves record both the effects which are attended by loss of mass and the effects where there is no loss of mass.

A feature of the behaviour of these minerals on heating is the fact that after the removal of OH groups they will, in most cases, undergo structural reorganization. This transformation is recorded on thermal curves much better than in the case of anhydrous silicates. Owing to the loss in mass as a result of the removal of OH groups, these minerals allow quantitative determinations, but, of course, only if the mineral always contains a constant amount of hydroxyl groups. The number of minerals from the silicate groups which contain OH groups in their molecule is great. A description will be given in the following of the principal minerals most frequently encountered.

5.8.3.1   Serpentines group

Included under this name are all phyllitic minerals of the magnesium hydrosilicates type whose general formula is $Mg_6(Si_4O_{10})(OH)_8$. Varieties of these minerals are encountered in many cases in which other metal cations, such as Ni^{2+}, Fe^{+2}, Fe^{3+}, Al^{3+}, and even Cr^{3+}, are substituted isomorphously.

More recent investigations have shown that isomorphous substitutions may also take place in the tetrahedral layer, when Si^{4+} is replaced by trivalent ions. In this case an increase in the positive charges takes place in the tetrahedral layer and to compensate for these positive charges other trivalent ions will have to be substituted for the bivalent ions from the octahedral layer. From the minerals formed in this way, studies were made of the ferrous form, cronstedite, whose ideal formula is $(Fe_4^{2+}Fe_2^{3+})(Si_2Fe_2^{3+})O_{10}(OH)_8$, and of the aluminous form, amesite, with the formula $[(Mg, Fe_4^{2+})Al_2](Si_2Al_2)O_{10}(OH)_8$. These two minerals in fact represent the final terms of a series of more or less substituted minerals (Mackenzie, 1957).

These minerals are frequently contaminated with free iron oxides, which makes their optical identification rather difficult. Quite a number of attempts have been made to establish the number of minerals belonging to the serpentines group, but so far no one has succeeded. As to the results obtained by thermal methods, two main subgroups may be distinguished which are situated at two extremes, namely the antigorite group and the chrysotile group. A large number of serpentine minerals may be ranged between these two groups, generated on the one hand by isomorphous substitutions of cations in their lattice, and on the other hand by the association of minerals between these two groups which may occur in different proportions. In spite of these mineral variations, minerals classified in this range have the same structural scheme; they also exhibit a certain unity in their behaviour on heating.

On the basis of thermal curves obtained by the method of differential thermal analysis, Caillère (1936) pointed out that both antigorite, and chrysotile appear in two forms (α and β), and the α form behaves differently from the β form on heating. Further studies have shown that only thermal methods can be used to identify the α or β form of the minerals which make up this group.

The structure of these minerals is compact and their outer surface does not permit the absorption of large amounts of water. As a result, the hygroscopic moisture of these minerals is low, causing only a slight endothermic effect to appear on thermal curves at temperatures below 150 °C. Thermal effects characteristic of these minerals are however those caused by the removal of hydroxyl groups, and these are attended by a loss of mass. These thermal effects are generally identical in form and magnitude, but the temperature of the effect is slightly lower for ferriferous minerals, increasing with nickeliferous ones, to reach a maximum with the magnesian minerals. In some serpentines, exothermic effects will appear after the endothermic effects as a result of high temperature structural reorganization. The peak temperatures for these effects generally vary with the degree of crystallization of the sample. A brief description of the thermal behaviour of the principal minerals which make up this group will be given in the following.

α-Antigorite. This mineral yields a marked endothermic effect on heating. The effect is attended by a loss of mass corresponding to the amount of hydroxyl groups present in the lattice of the mineral. Removal of hydroxyl groups takes place in a temperature range from 750 to 800 °C, when the crystal lattice of the mineral collapses altogether. Immediately after the all hydroxyl groups have been removed, the dehydroxylated mineral undergoes a structural reorganization. This reorganization is marked only on the DTA curve in the form of a well-marked exothermic effect situated between 800 and 840 °C (Figure 5.78).

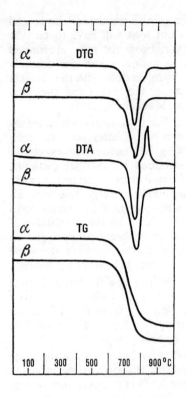

Figure 5.78 Thermal curves of α and β-antigorite.

β-Antigorite. The thermal behaviour of this mineral in respect of the removal of hydroxyl groups from its structure is wholly similar to that of α-antigorite, and it takes place in the same temperature range.

The fundamental difference of its behaviour on heating compared with α-antigorite is that after the dehydroxylation has taken place the remaining product will not undergo any other structural reorganization. Hence, in this case no exo-thermic effect appears on the DTA curve, a fact on which the identification of the two minerals is based (Figure 5.78).

α-Chrysotile. Thermal curves obtained in the case of α-chrysotile are also similar to those of α-antigorite, including both the thermal effect caused by dehydroxylation and that caused by the structural reorganization. Differences, however, appear in respect of the temperatures at which these effects take place. Thus, the endothermic effect caused by the removal of OH groups, attended by a loss of mass, takes place between 650 and 750 °C, hence at temperatures about 100 °C lower than in the case of α-antigorite. Nevertheless, the thermal effect caused by the structural reorganization appears at the same temperature as in the case of α-antigorite. Hence the only essential difference recorded on thermal curves between the two forms of antigorite is the temperature of the dehydroxylation effect. In the case of α-antigorite there is

Figure 5.79 Thermal curves of α and β chrysotile

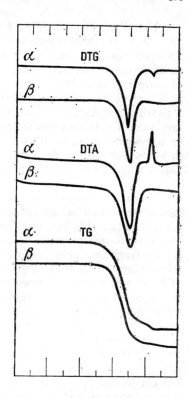

no flat horizontal portion on the DTA curve between the endothermic and the exothermic effect, whereas in the case of chrysotile this flat portion exists and extends over about 100 °C (Figure 5.79).

In all four minerals mentioned from the group of serpentines, the percentage loss of mass after dehydration is 12.9, provided no isomorphous substitutions have taken place in their lattice. Where isomorphous substitutions occur, the loss of mass diminishes as a function of the nature and the amount of the substituting ions. The thermal effects and the temperatures at which these thermal effects take place at a heating rate of 10 °C per minute are given in Table 5.1.

Table 5.1 **Temperatures at which thermal effects occur for Antigorite and Chrysotile**

	Endothermic effect for the α and β form	Exothermic effect for the α form
Antigorite	750—800 °C	800—840 °C
Chrysotile	650—750 °C	800—830 °C

Native associations formed between the serpentine minerals discussed overleaf yield thermal effects which are a combination of the effects of minerals involved. This fact has led a number of researchers to suggest that the group of serpentine minerals might consists of a much larger number of minerals than the two types of antigorite and chrysotile.

Native associations of serpentine minerals may be rather homogeneous or somewhat disperse. It is very difficult to assign names to these associations as if they were wholly independent minerals. In my opinion, these associations may not be considered as independent minerals, but only as mixtures of α and β-antigorite, or α and β-chrysotile. Kräutner (1968) considered these associations as independent minerals and his observations will be reported in the following.

Picrolite. Curves obtained in the thermal analysis of this mineral are a combination of the thermal effects of a mixture of β-chrysotile and α-antigorite. The DTA curve shows an endothermic effect with two more or less well-marked thermal maxima. The first maximum, situated at about 700 °C, indicates the removal of hydroxyl groups from the β-chrysotile lattice, and the second maximum, which lies at a temperature 50 to 80 °C higher than the previous one, is caused by the removal of hydroxyls from the lattice of α-antigorite. This broad endothermic effect with two thermal maxima is immediately followed by an exothermic effect due to the structural reorganization of the α form. The fact that the exothermic effect is smaller both in extent and intensity shows that an association of the α form and β form of both minerals is involved. Data from the literature does not make it clear whether the association involved is a mixture of β-chrysotile with α-antigorite, or a mixture of β-antigorite with α-chrysotile. However, on the basis of DTG and TG curves which indicate the variations in mass, it is possible to infer with a certain degree of precision the percentage ratio between the α form and the β form. Figure 5.80 illustrates the thermal curves obtained on such a mineral.

Picrosimine. According to data from the literature and from the differential thermal analysis of Kräutner (1958), this mineral would be a β-antigorite which expels hydroxyl groups in two steps. A larger amount of hydroxyl groups is removed at first, and this is recorded on the thermal curves by an endothermic effect at temperatures from 700 to 800 °C. The remaining hydroxyls are then removed. This is recorded on the thermal curves by an endothermic effect at a temperature about 50—60 °C higher than the first effect (Figure 5.81).

In my opinion the latter effect was not generated by a serpentine mineral, but by another mineral, perhaps by vermiculite which can be found as a contaminant in the mass of certain antigoritic serpentines of the β type. Moreover, with these types of minerals there is usually an endothermic effect in the temperature range from 100 to 200 °C which is more intense than is generally obtained for serpentine minerals; this effect is caused by the expulsion of the water adsorbed from the vermiculite lattice.

Marmolite. Differential thermal analysis curves from which the presence of this type of mineral was identified have two strong thermal effects, an endothermic

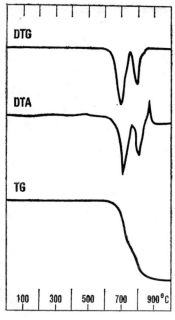

Figure 5.80 Thermal curves of picrolite.

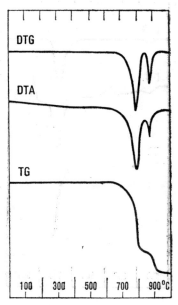

Figure 5.81 Thermal curves o picrosimine.

effect situated between 650 and 750 °C, and an exothermic effect lying at about 800 °C, the same as in α-chrysotile. There is also a slight endothermic effect at 110 °C and a slight exothermic effect at about 350 °C. It was found that these two effects vary in intensity with different samples (Figure 5.82). As a matter of fact, this mineral is just an α-chrysotile whose crystal mass includes free iron oxides and which exhibits a certain degree of decay.

In conclusion, let it be emphasised that the temperature limits shown above should not be considered as fixed, but rather as the more frequently encountered values. The thermal effects at low temperatures, that is below $+190$ °C, are due to a loss of hygroscopic moisture and appear only with samples which show a certain degree of decay or which may sometimes be contaminated with materials of a colloidal nature. Temperature variations of the thermal effects may also be influenced by the degree of crystallization of the samples or by the degree of isomorphous substitution, and hence are closely connected to the chemical composition. Variation of the chemical constitution, such as the substitution of Ni^{2+} for Mg^{2+} or Fe^{2+}, causes a notable change in the temperature of the maxima of the thermal effects, decreasing from Mg^{2+} towards Fe^{2+}. It should be borne in mind that in the case of ferriferous serpentines, the shape of the thermal curves may vary within very broad limits, depending on the experimental conditions. It will be affected in particular by the admission of oxygen into the installation,

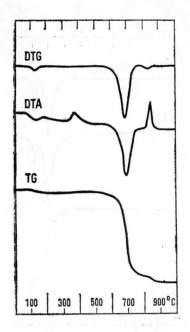

Figure 5.82 Thermal curves of marmolite.

which brings about an oxidation of ferrous iron. Certain organic contaminants also have an important bearing on the form of the thermal effects. They usually mask the thermal effects because oxidation of the organic matter produces exothermic effects which overlap with the endothermic effects of the minerals under investigation.

Associations of serpentine minerals which yield thermal curves different from those of simple serpentine minerals must be considered only as isomorphously crystallized mixtures of the α and β forms of the two groups of minerals. Hence, these two minerals, α and β-antigorite and α and β-chrysotile may be considered as two extremes which may form intermediate associations varying in all directions.

5.8.3.2   Amphiboles group

It is a peculiarity of amphiboles that double chains of silicon and oxygen tetrahedrons of the form $[Si_4O_{11}]^{6-}$ participate in their lattice. In this case an oxygen ion remains free, and this enters into the composition of the monovalent anion $(OH)^-$, leading to the formation of very stable compounds which theoretically contain two OH groups in their molecule.

According to Wittels (1951 and 1952), the thermal curves which are obtained when these minerals are heated show an endothermic effect between 925 and 1125 °C, specific to the loss of the OH group. As a result of the removal of these hydroxyl groups, the crystal structure is broken up and the thermal effect   is attended by a loss of mass equivalent to the amount of OH groups present in the lattice of the mineral under investigation.

With amphibole compounds of the magnesium type, before the dehydroxylation effect thermal curves show endothermic effects due to polymorphous transformations, whereas with ferriferous amphiboles thermal curves show endothermic effects due to the oxidation of bivalent iron.

Tremolite, $Ca_2Mg_5Si_8O_{22}(OH)_2$. The thermal effect specific to this mineral is given by the removal of hydroxyls from the structure of the mineral, a removal which in the case of the pure mineral is attended by a loss of mass of 2.8 per cent. According to data from the literature, the temperature of this endothermic effect varies greatly. Thus, some authors maintain that this endothermic effect is situated in the range of temperatures from 590 to 640 °C, whereas others contend that the effect lies in the temperature range from 990 to 1070 °C and that two further slight endothermic effects would appear on the DTA curve between 300 and 370 °C or between 370 and 420 °C, as well as an exothermic effect around 1070 °C.

It is difficult to decide from the data given in the literature, whether the dehydroxylation takes place in one step only or in two steps. Using the method of differential thermal analysis. Treiber, (1967) investigated various tremolite samples from carbonates collected at a place in Romania called Izvorul Oltului. In order to avoid the interference caused by carbonates, the tremolite crystals were cleaned mechanically at the surface to remove such carbonates. The thermal curves obtained showed two endothermic effects, one at 800 °C and one at 1050 °C. Assuming that the first effect is due to calcium carbonate, larger amounts of the sample were tested and it was found that the endothermic effect at 800 °C had increased both in intensity and in temperature. This fact led Treiber to conclude that the first effect between 800 and 880 °C was due to calcium carbonate impurities and not to tremolite. Moreover, when he treated the sample with dilute hydrochloric acid, removing the carbonates completely, and then analysed the tremolite again, he obtained only one endothermic effect at about 1050 °C (Figure 5.83).

Actinolite, $Ca_2(Mg, Fe)_5Si_8O_{22}(OH)_2$. This mineral is very similar to tremolite. The resemblance results from its chemical formula, in which Mg^{2+} is only partially replaced by Fe^{2+}. This substitution to a certain extent has repercussions on the behaviour of the mineral on heating, as a result of the oxidation of Fe^{2+} to Fe^{3+}.

The endothermic effect caused by the removal of OH groups, as in the case of tremolite, appears in two temperature ranges from 780 to 980 °C, and from 950 to 1015 °C. Many authors suggest that (owing to the presence of iron in the lattice) this effect ought to appear at a much lower temperature than in the case of tremolite, and after this effect has appeared an exothermic effect should also appear as a result of the oxidation of the bivalent iron. However, since actinolite has not been investigated by complex thermal methods (which on the DTG and TG curves could more conclusively show the effect caused by oxidation), we cannot prove or disprove this theory.

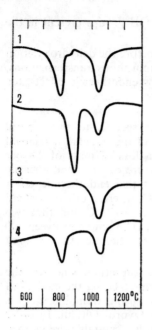

Figure 5.83   DTA curves of tremolite *(after Treiber, 1967):*
1, sample treated wih HCl; *2,* untreated tremolite from the same sample;
3, ground sample treated afterwards with HCl; *4,* artificial mixture of tremolite
(75 per cent) with calcite (25 per cent).

Hornblende, $Ca_2Na(Mg,Fe)_4(Al,Fe)[(Si,Al)_4O_{11}](OH)_2$. The chemical composition of hornblendes is highly varied, because the ratio of magnesium to bivalent iron on the one hand, and the ratio of aluminium to trivalent iron on the other hand are also variable to a large extent. This fact explains why the results obtained on various samples by the method of differential thermal analysis are not in agreement. For example, some analyses have shown that the hydroxyl groups are expelled from 800 to 1175 °C, but there were cases when dehydroxylations have taken place at much lower temperatures, even as low as 450 to 520 °C. Hence, it is very difficult to indicate a specific dehydroxylation temperature of this mineral.

Anthophyllite, $(Mg,Fe)_7Si_8O_{22}(OH)_2$. From percentage chemical analyses on various samples of anthophyllite, it appears that there exists a whole series of isomorphous associations of ferro-magnesium compounds, but so far no pure magnesium or pure ferriferous compounds have been found.

On heating, anthophyllite undergoes a polymorphous transformation at temperatures around 400 °C, when the rhombic form passes into a monoclinic form. With rising temperatures in the range from 825 to 875 °C, the bivalent iron passes into trivalent iron, which causes a slight endothermic effect to appear on the thermal curves. The endothermic effect produced by the removal of OH groups appears at high temperatures, around 1020 °C, and as a result anthophyllite passes into enstatite. This means that together with the loss of OH groups at high temperatures a transformation also takes place of the double tetrahedron chains into simple tetrahedron chains.

5.8.3.3   Epidote group

This group includes silicate minerals consisting of anionic radicals in the form of chains. As a matter of fact, epidote minerals are a sort of calcium aluminosilicate hydroxyl groups in their structure. In some cases, a partial substitution of iron for aluminium has taken place as well.

Epidote, $Ca_2(Al,Fe)_3Si_3O_{12}(OH)$. With this mineral, the only thermal effect perceptible on the curves is an endothermic effect which takes place at high temperatures as a result of the removal of the hydroxyl group. It was found that some samples expel OH groups in stages. Removal of the hydroxyl group begins at 910 °C, and as it proceeds two interruptions appear on the DTA curve, one at 938 °C and another at 837 °C. The maximum of the thermal effect of hydroxyl removal is at 1018 °C (Figure 5.84 A).

Authors who have pointed out these steps could not offer an explanation for them. Nevertheless, it is thought that they are caused by the presence of zoizite in some of the samples.

Zoizite, $Ca_2(Al,Fe)_3Si_3O_{12}(OH)$. The thermal curves of zoizite (Figure 5.84 B) show that the hydroxyl group begins to be expelled at 940 °C, the maximum of the thermal effect being at 1000 °C.

Prehnite, $Ca_2Al_2Si_3O_{10}(OH)_2$. On heating, the two hydroxyl groups of prehnite are removed in two steps. The endothermic effect recorded on the DTA curve (Figure 5.84 C) is broader than with the previous minerals, having a double shape of curve with two thermal maxima, one at 790 °C, and another at 870 °C. With some of the samples analysed, a slight trend towards an exothermic reaction appeared on the DTA curve at about 975 °C after the endothermic effect at 870 °C. This exothermic reaction is probably due to the recrystallization of Fe_2O_3 which is frequently present in this mineral.

Pectolite, $NaCa_2Si_3O_8OH$. The OH group of this mineral is readily removed. The endothermic effect begins at 745 °C, reaches a maximum at 780 °C, and ends at about 845 °C. The thermal effect produced by melting of this product appears at temperatures around 1000 °C and is represented by a broad endothermic effect.

Anauxite, $Al_2Si_3O_7(OH)_4$. On thermal curves this aluminosilicate shows two thermal effects. The first is an endothermic effect caused by the expulsion of hydroxyl groups in the temperature range from 585 to 610 °C, and the second is an exothermic effect caused by a structural reorganization in the temperature range from 975 to 1010 °C.

Dioptasite. For this compound, specialised handbooks give several formulae, which indicate that the OH groups should, in fact, be considered to consist of water molecules and not of hydroxyls. Thermal analyses, however, do not confirm this assumption.

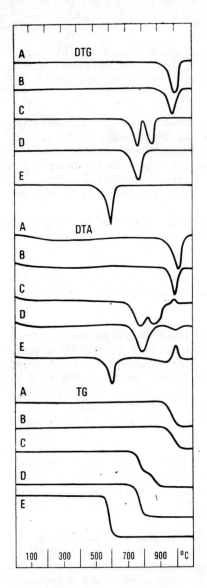

Figure 5.84 Thermal curves of the minerals from the epidote group: *A*, epidote; *B*, zoizite; *C*, prehnite; *D*, pectolite; *E*, anauxite.

Figure 5.85 Thermal curves of dioptasite (sample from Africa).

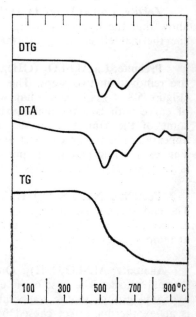

Samples which I have analysed in the form of very pure bluish-green crystals from Africa have shown that this mineral shows a marked loss of mass beginning at 450 °C and continuing through the whole range up to 800 °C. This loss of mass is marked on thermal curves (Figure 5.85) by a broad endothermic effect which has two thermal maxima, the first at temperatures around 540 °C showing a high intensity, and the second at temperatures around 630 °C of slight intensity. This fact proves that the mineral holds in its structure OH groups and not molecules of water of crystallization, because if it had crystallized with water molecules, those would have been expelled at a much lower temperature.

After dehydroxylation, with further rising temperatures dioptasite undergoes transformations which appear on the DTA curve in the form of two slight endo-exothermic effects in the temperature range from 830 to 860 °C. I consider these effects to be due to a reaction between copper oxide and silica.

5.8.3.4 Tourmaline group

Minerals from this group are highly varied as regards their composition, owing to the frequent isomorphous substitutions which take place in their structure. Because of this, they behave differently on heating. According to Kurylenko (1950), these minerals expel most of their hydroxyl groups at low temperatures, around 150 °C, but with some varieties the removal takes place between 430 and 480 °C and even at 770 °C. The thermal effect specific to these minerals is an endothermic effect which appears from 950 to 970 °C, and is caused by the removal of boron from the crystal system in the form of B_2O_3.

From Kurylenko's data, it follow that these minerals show a sequence of four endothermic effects on the thermal curves (Figure 5.86): the first and the last are intensive, the other two are of a very low intensity and all four are attended by losses in mass.

5.8.3.5 Micas and Similar Minerals group

The chemical composition of the minerals from the micas group is variable, owing to the frequent substitution of some cations for others. From a chemical viewpoint, these minerals form a distinct group from that of the aluminosilicates of the fluosilicate type. All minerals of this type are stable on heating until a temperature is reached which causes the hydroxyls to be removed. Depending on the mineral in which they are founs, these hydroxyls are expelled in various temperature ranges, so that minerals from the micas group can readily be identified by the methods of thermal analysis.

Muscovite, $K_2Al_4(Si_6Al_2)O_{20}(OH)_4$. The chemical formula of muscovite is a purely theoretical one, because owing to isomorphous substitutions, much more complicated chemical formulae are obtained. Thus alkaline or alkaline earth cations are substituted for potassium on the one hand, and aluminium from the octahedral layer is also replaced on the other hand. In nature, there are frequent cases when muscovite undergoes a series of transformations due to physical or chemical alterations whereby so-called *hydromicas*, which are in fact associations of various hydrated micas, are produced.

In thermal analyses, the curves obtained with different types of undecayed muscovites are similar (Figure 5.87 A). According to Grim and Rowland (1942

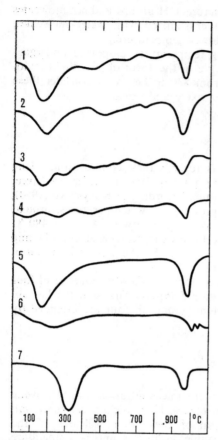

Figure 5.86   DTA curves of tourmalines
(after Kurylenko, 1950) :

1, black tourmaline from Switzerland; *2*, black
tourmaline from Brazil; *3*, black tourmaline from
Madagascar; *4*, decayed black tourmaline from
Madagascar; *5*, colourless tourmaline from the
isle of Elba; *6*, tourmaline rich in magnesium from
Czechoslovakia; *7*, red tourmaline from the USA.

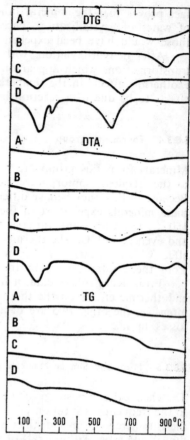

Figure 5.87   Thermal curves of minerals from the mica group: *A*, muscovite; *B*, broadly crystallized muscovite; *C*, hydromuscovite;
D, hydrated hydromuscovite.

and 1944), the expulsion of hydroxyl groups takes place between 750 and 950 °C,
which causes a broad endothermic effect to appear on the thermal curves. This
expulsion is attended by a loss in mass. As a rule, the maximum of this thermal
effect is situated at temperatures around 850 °C, the loss in mass being proportional
to the amount of water removed. The water originated in the hydroxyl groups.

Depending on the degree of decay, other thermal effects appear on the thermal
curves of muscovite. Thus, when the decay occurred only on the surface of the
crystals, then another effect appears on the thermal curves at about 550 °C, as a

result of the hydration of muscovite which passes into hydromuscovite (Figure 5.87 B). In these cases, the thermal effects, both that at 550 °C and that at 850 °C, are highly variable in intensity, depending on the degree of decay of the mineral. When the intensity of endothermic effect at 550 °C is the greater, then the effect at 850 °C produced by the undecayed muscovite is hardly perceptible. When the 850 °C effect disappears completely, we are dealing with an intensely decayed mica, called *hydromica*. Hydromicas are deficient in potassium, but they contain adsorbed water in excess. As a matter of fact, they are a stage in the conversion of micas into clays, a process which also leads to an increase of the silicon content.

The thermal curves (Figure 5.87 C) of hydrated micas are wholly similar to those of illites, presenting an endothermic effect from 100 to 200 °C as a result of the removal of the adsorbed water, an effect which is of lesser intensity than that of illite proper. Hydroxyl groups are expelled as in the case of illites from 450 to 650 °C, and with rising temperatures a slight exothermic effect will appear at about 860 °C as a result of a structural reorganization.

Sericite. The nature of this mineral from the group of the micas is greatly disputed. Some authors maintain that it is an intensely decayed mica, but not yet completely changed into clay, hence, something intermediate between hydromica and illite. Other authors (Mackenzie, 1957) assume that sericite is white mica with a high content of finely granulated silica, formed by the decay of feldspars in a mesothermal and hydrothermal low temperature metamorphism. From a thermal viewpoint, it is not possible to make a distinction on the basis of the thermal effects recorded on the curves, between hydromica and this type of mineral.

In my opinion, sericite can be considered to be a hydromica with an advanced degree of hydration, something between hydromica and illite, but closer to illite. As a matter of fact, the thermal curves of this mineral are similar both to those of an hydromica (Figure 5.87 C) and to those of illite (Figure 5.100).

Margarite, $CaAl_2(Al_2Si_2)O_{10}(OH)_2$. On heating, this mineral, of the brittle type of minerals, behaves similarly to muscovite, with the difference that the removal of hydroxyl groups takes place at a much higher temperature and in a much narrower temperature range. Thus, the thermal curves obtained on heating margarite (Figure 5.88) show a horrizontal segment up to about 925 °C, when a markerd endothermic effect appears, attended by a loss in mass corresponding to the amount of OH groups expelled.

Biotite, $K(Mg,Fe,Al)_{2-3}(Si_3Al)O_{10}(OH)_2$. The OH group of this mineral can be replaced by fluorine in proportion up to 4.23 per cent. Thermal curves (Figure 5.89) show that OH groups are expelled at temperatures higher than 900 °C, in some cases at 1050 °C. This temperature variation depends on the proportion of isomorphous substitution in the structure of biotite.

Glauconite. This mineral is an hydrated iron and magnesium aluminosilicate with a composition varying within fairly broad limits. Thermal curves of this mineral closely resemble those of hydromicas and illite, so great care must be exercised in the interpretation of these curves. Glauconite generally presents three

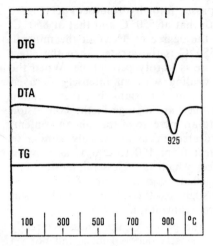

Figure 5.88   Thermal curves of margarite.

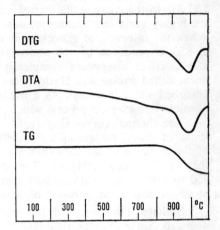

Figure 5.89   Thermal curves of biotite.

endothermic effects (Figure 5.90), the first two being attended by losses in mass. As to the temperature range, the first effect is situated between 100 and 200 °C, being caused by the removal of adsorbed water. The second effect occurring between 550 and 625 °C is of lesser extent than the first and is caused by the removal of hydroxyl groups from the lattice of the mineral. The third effect is of very slight intensity and is situated above 900 °C, being caused by a structural reorganization. Although the thermal curves of glauconite closely resemble those of illite, there are, nervertheless, two elements which can be used to distinguish these two minerals on the thermal curves, namely the maximum of the thermal effect caused by the removal of the hydroxyl groups lies at temperatures about 50 °C higher than in the case of illite, and the third effect is followed in the case of illite by a small exothermic effect, whereas with glauconite this effect is much less obvious.

5.8.3.6 Talcum and Pyrophyllite Group

This group is represented by two similar minerals with specific physical properties. The difference between these two minerals consists only in the fact that Mg^{2+} cations with the coordination number 6, fill all the voides between the two plane hexagonal lattices of $[Si_4O_{10}]$ in the structure of talcum, whereas Al^{3+} cations only fill two thirds of these places in the structure of pyrophyllite. Because of this difference, the hydroxyl groups from their structures are expelled in different temperature ranges. Considering the similarity of many of the physical properties of these two minerals, pyrophyllite is frequently mistaken for talcum and conversely. Hence, the thermal methods are indispensable to their identification and determination, especially when they are found in association.

Pyrophyllite, $Al_2(Si_4O_{10})(OH)_2$. Thermal curves of pyrophyllite (Figure 5.91) obtained by different authors show a broad endothermic effect situated from 650 to 800 °C, attended by a loss in mass as a result of the removal of OH groups. The broadness of the effect, as well as the temperature of the thermal maximum, vary depending on the degree of crystallization of the mineral and also on the amount of pyrophyllite present in the sample analysed. With very many samples a slight endothermic effect appears at 773 °C as a result of the polymorphous transformation of quartz present in the association with pyrophyllite. When pyrophyllite is heated at temperatures higher than 1000 °C, an exothermic effect appears owing to the formation of mullite. This effect is most frequently situated at 1200 °C.

Talcum, $Mg_3(Si_4O_{10})(OH)_2$. The thermal curves of this mineral (Figure 5.92) show a flat horizontal segment up to about 850—900 °C, when they begin to show an endothermic effect attended by a loss of mass as a result of the removal of hydroxyl groups. The maximum of this thermal effect usually lies at about 1000 °C.

Since talcum is frequently encountered as a product of the hydrothermal transformation of ultrabasic rocks rich in magnesium, it is usually associated with magnesium carbonates and sometimes also with calcium carbonates. The presence of these compounds is made obvious through their decomposition effects which take place, as we have already seen, at temperatures lower than the dehydroxylation temperature of talcum.

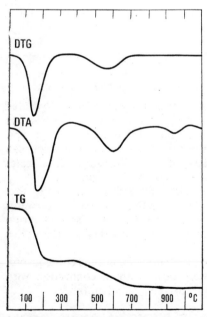

Figure 5.90 Thermal curves of
glauconite.

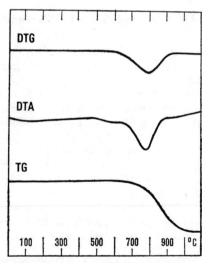

Figure 5.91 Thermal curves of
pyrophyllite.

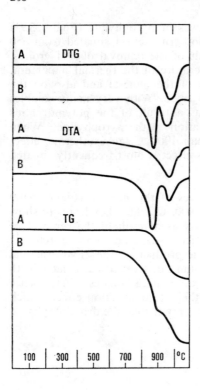

Figure 5.92   Thermal curves of talcum: *A*, simple mineral talcum from Cerişor — Hunedoara (Romania); *B*, talcum with calcite from Cerişor — Hunedoara (Romania).

5.8.4   Hydrated Silicates (Zeolites)

This group includes a large number of minerals essentially consisting of hydrated aluminosilicates. From the viewpoint of their composition, these minerals are subdivided into two groups: (1) silicates in whose formula there are no OH groups, but which have in their crystal structure a number of water molecules which can be considered, with certain reservation, as water of crystallization; (2) silicates which have OH groups and neutral water molecules in their structure.

These two forms of silicates are completely different. Silicates from the first group, also called the *zeolites group*, hold an almost definite number of water molecules bound in the crystal lattice. With the silicates from the second group the amount of water may vary because this water is only adsorbed in the lattice of the mineral.

In the following I shall be concerned only with minerals from the zeolite group, because the minerals from the second group were dealt with in connection with certain groups of silicates of little interest owing to their small number.

Zeolites group. Although the total number of elements which enter into the composition of these compounds is not great, there exists an extremely large number of mineral species which differ from one another not so much by their water content as by the ratio between cations, so that they often cannot be expressed by simple chemical formulae.

On heating, these compounds expel water at temperatures from 80 to 400 °C. The removal of water takes place continuously, being recorded on the curve by a broad thermal effect, and it is attended by a loss in mass corresponding to the water content expelled from the system. If the zeolitic water is removed at a low heating rate and the temperature is not allowed to increase above the final point of dehydration, then if the minerals are subjected to rehydration, they can reabsorb the same amount of water as they expelled. This water may also be replaced by molecules of other compounds such as hydrogen sulphide, alcohols, ammonia, etc., while the crystal medium preserves its homogeneity.

However, contrary to what was stated above, the water content of zeolite can be variable, depending directly on the outside conditions, that is, on the temperature and vapour pressure of the surroundings. If both the temperature and the vapour

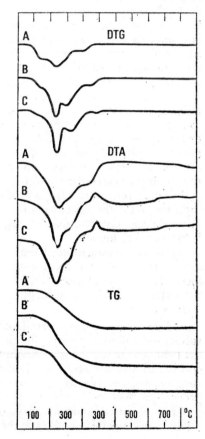

Figure 5.93 Thermal curves of three zeolite samples: A, white pearly zeolite; B, pink zeolite; C, red zeolite.

pressure are kept constant, each compound will then have a fixed number of water molecules. This water differs from the water of crystallization proper in that it is expelled under the action of thermal energy, namely not in steps (as for example in the case of sulphates), but gradually and slowly in a broad range of temperatures. However, I have noticed certain temperature steps in the removal of this water when I have used heating rates below 5 °C per minute. These steps are readily noticeable on the DTG curve (Figure 5.93).

In spite of the fact that this group of minerals has not been investigated sufficiently by thermal methods of analysis, it can nevertheless be assumed that at temperatures higher than 1000 °C other thermal effects are also obtained, for example polymorphous transformations and melting.

5.8.5 Clays and Similar Minerals

Argillaceous minerals are hydrated aluminium silicates which derive from the $(Si_2O_5)^{2-}$ anion. In general they have a well-defined crystal structure, but with frequent isomorphous substitutions in the lattice. The formation of these minerals is connected with the chemical decay of the rocks, but they cannot be considered as chemical deposits, because they do not precipitate from solutions. Owing to the isomorphous substitutions, no real formula can be assigned to the argillaceous minerals, save a purely theoretical one.

In general, by argillaceous minerals one most frequently understands polydispersed and polymineral rocks. However, this term is a misnomer, because as a general term it can be assigned to clays. Clay may be a simple mineral rock or a polymineral aggregate. As a rule, clays are contaminated with nonargillaceous minerals, organic remains, inorganic substances, organic substances, adsorbed cations, and more or less readily soluble salts. The stratified mixed forms from the hydromicas-montmorillonite, chlorite-vermiculite, and probably kaolinite-hydromicas series are also widespread in clays. These stratified mixed forms together with the isomorphous substitutions cause broad variations in the mineralogical composition of argillaceous minerals, and for implicity different behaviour on heating.

For the investigation of the mineral components of argillaceous rocks a large range of methods are used, both chemical and physical or instrumental. These methods depend on X-ray diffraction, on their behaviour when heated, on optical properties, on infrared absorption spectre, colour reactions, percentage chemical analyses, etc.

If the argillaceous material subjected to analysis consists of a single mineral species, — kaolinite, montmorillonite, vermiculite, etc., — in most cases, only one of the methods mentioned is sufficient for its identification. If the argillaceous material consists of an association of argillaceous minerals, possibly contaminated with other components, the investigation becomes more difficult and analysis by several procedures will be necessary for identification and determination.

For a better understanding of the thermal processes generated by each argillaceous mineral I shall try in the following to give certain structural explanations.

It is known that some of the minerals included in this group may also appear in nonargillaceous deposits. They are treated in this section on the consideration that they behave analogously on heating.

5.8.5.1 General Considerations on the Thermal Behaviour of Clays

It is necessary to state from the outset that certain alien mineral components present in argillaceous minerals may play a dominant part in determining the thermal effects which appear on heating. Indeed, small amounts of certain elements, such as, for instance, alkalies, may affect the temperature steps of the thermal effects, an influence which also occurs, to a lesser extent, in other minerals. It is known that at temperatures of 100–200 °C the volume of certain argillaceous minerals shrinks as a result of the loss of water which causes a dimensional change. In the case of expandable argillaceous minerals, temperatures of the order of 100–300 °C cause a loss of the swelling capacity of the mineral when it is subjected to renewed hydration. These changes are due to a complete loss of the water from between the layers. It is also known that the temperature at which the swelling capacity is irrevocably lost depends on the nature of the adsorbed cation. In the case of montmorillonite, for example, the loss of water takes place in the temperature ranges 105–225 °C, 300–390 °C, and 390–490 °C, when the adsorbed cations are lithium, calcium, or sodium, respectively.

At temperatures from 200 to 300 °C begins the oxidation of certain organic materials which are present in argillaceous minerals. The degree of oxidation depends on the nature of the organic material, on the amount of oxygen available in the furnace, and on the readiness with which this can penetrate into the mass of the argillaceous material in order to promote the oxidation. In general, the degree of oxidation increases with rising temperatures. It is well known that the oxidation of the organic material requires some time, which perceptibly affects the thermal curves; hence it should be removed before the mineral is analysed.

Another difficulty in the interpretation of thermal curves is caused by sulphides which are present in many clays. Pyrite is found most frequently. Oxidation of the sulphides begins from 400 to 500 °C in the presence of oxygen, when an intensely exothermic reaction takes place. When oxygen is not available in sufficient amounts in the instrumental installation, the oxidation of the sulphides may be very much delayed. Subsequently, sulphur set free from the sulphides, in the form of sulphur oxides may react with the cations of the argillaceous minerals which have become available by the partial break down of the lattice structure of some of the argillaceous minerals as a result of the removal of the OH groups, a process which takes place at temperatures immediately above the oxidation temperature of the sulphides. The nature of the resulting compounds is not well known, but their presence both on the thermal curves and in the residue is indicated by the appearance of certain sham thermal effects, and of black deposits in the residue. Starting sometimes even below 500 °C, and continuing in other cases up to 900 °C, hydroxyl groups are removed from the lattice of argillaceous minerals. The temperature range in which the hydroxyls are lost depends, for the most part, on the nature of the mineral, as well as on the dimensions of the particles. A reduction of particle dimensions below 2 mμ, in conditions in which the mineral is feebly crystallized, brings about a lowering of the temperature range in which the removal of the hydroxyls takes place, and the loss of mass is caused to take place in a broader temperature range.

The reaction for the removal of hydroxyls in ordinary experimental conditions at first sight requires only the application of a programme of constant temperature increase in unit time. Unlike oxidation reactions, the removal of hydroxyl groups does not depend on the presence of oxygen or of other products of oxidation set free as heating proceeds; it depends only on the readiness with which the water vapours formed in the system are expelled.

In some cases, if heating of the product is stopped after the hydroxyl groups have been removed, the argillaceous mineral may again attach the hydroxyl and restore the initial structure. Grim and Kulbick (1957) have studied such rehydrations and drawn the conclusion that if the removal of the hydroxyls is attended by an unimportant structural change, then the rehydration and restoration of the initial structure will occur readily under ordinary pressure and temperature conditions. When the removal of the hydroxyls is followed by important structural changes, then the rehydration and restoration of the structure take place more slowly, and moderate pressure and temperature rises are necessary.

With rising temperatures, after the removal of the hydroxyle first appears, nucleation begins. If the temperature is allowed to rise slowly, a perfect growth of the structural units of the new configuration takes place. The emergence of a new crystal configuration is sometimes attended by the release of a considerable amount of thermal energy, indicated on differential thermal analysis curves by a marked exothermic effect manifested in a narrow temperature range. If the sample were to be analysed by means of X-ray diffraction at the temperature of the maximum point of the exothermic effect, the analysis might not indicate the new crystal configuration which causes this exothermic reaction, because the new structural units may be too small or too imperfect to yield a diffraction of appreciable intensity.

It follows from the above, that thermal methods of analysis are apt to indicate much better the formation of new high temperature stages than X-ray diffraction, which had for a long time been considered as the only method permitting an identification of the products resulting from the burning of clays.

5.8.5.2 Separation of Clays for Analysis

Before attempting a detailed description of the thermal processes specific to each mineral entering into the composition of clays, it is necessary to give a brief description of the method by which clays are separated with a view to their analysis. Since it is known that any argillaceous mineral contains particles of less than 0.002 mm, 50 per cent of which are smaller than 0.001 mm, thermal analyses must be carried out only on these particles. Their separation is generally made by sedimentation in water. If the separation aims also at a quantitative separation by fractions, it is called *granulometric analysis*. The physical basis of the granulometric analysis by the sedimentation method is the difference in the falling rate of the particles of different sizes contained in an argillaceous material uniformly dispersed in a liquid medium. In the following I shall deal only with the separation of the fractions required for analyses by thermal methods, and not for granulometric analyses proper, which is described in detail in various standards.

The first step for separating the fraction required for the thermal analysis is the preparation of the sample. The sample is dried in air at the ambient temperature for 2—3 days. After drying, the sample is ground in a procelain mortar, by gently pressing with the pestle so as to avoid crushing the mineral particles against the walls of the mortar. A rubber coated pestle is recommended for this purpose. The ground sample is passed through a sieve with 2 mm apertures, and the residue which has remained on the sieve is rejected. In order to disperse the particles of argillaceous minerals in water, it is necessary first to destroy any organic matter present and to decompose the carbonates. About 5 g of the sifted sample is taken in a tall beaker of 400 ml capacity and treated with 25 ml hydrogen peroxide (6 volume per cent) and the beaker is covered with a watch glass. The beaker is placed on a water bath or on an asbestos gauze over a small flame and stirred occasionally. When oxygen release ceases, the operation is repeated until the oxidation is complete, a point recognized by the discolouration of the sample. The presence of an excess of carbonate prevents the oxidation of the organic matter. Hence it is necessary, where there is an excess of carbonate, prior to carrying out the oxidation to decompose the carbonates by cautiously adding a solution of dilute (2N) acetic acid, avoiding as far as possible a large excess of acid. After cooling the contents of the beaker are transferred into a sedimentation cylinder of 30 cm in height, with a capacity of about 1200 ml. The solution is made up to 1000 ml with distilled water. The cylinder is covered with a rubber stopper and shaken manually for about 10 minutes. The cylinder solution is then allowed to rest for seven hours on a table or on a bracket free of vibrations. Then, by means of a glass tube bent in a U shape at one end, the supernatant suspension is siphoned off, introducing the tube to a depth of 10 cm measured from the upper level of the liquid downwards. This operation is repeated several times, until there is enough separated clay in the siphoned liquid.

The suspension in the collecting vessel is separated by filtration and washed 3—4 times with distilled water. It is then allowed to dry at room temperature. The dry clay after being finely ground in an agate mortar is ready for analysis.

Table 5.2 shows the falling rates of argillaceous particles of 0.002 mm in diameter.

5.8.5.3 Minerals from the Allophane Group

Argillaceous minerals from this group are amorphous, a fact which is proved by X-ray diffraction. Allophanes are, in fact, typical solid pseudosolutions with a vitreous or pitch-like gloss, and they are frequently transparent. Their chemical composition varies, according to data from the literature, for example: Al_2O_3 23.5—41.6 per cent; SiO_2 21.4—39.1 per cent; H_2O 39.0—43.9 per cent. They often

Table 5.2 **Falling rates of argillaceous particles of 0.002 mm in diameter**

Temperature °C	Falling rate cm s^{-1}	Faling time of particles in a column of 10 cm in height	
15	0.0003065	9 h	13 min
16	0.0003145	8	50
17	0.0003226	8	36
18	0.0003311	8	23
19	0.0003394	8	11
20	0.0003479	8	00
21	0.0003567	7	47
22	0.0003652	7	36
23	0.0003742	7	25
24	0.0003833	7	15
25	0.0003922	7	05

contain a series of other components in small amounts, including Fe^{3+}, Mg^{2+}, H^+, Na^+, Cu^{2+}, Zn^{2+}, CO_3^{2-}, SO_4^{2-}, etc.

Nevertheless, an organized crystal structure is not completely missing from these minerals. Rather, the arrangement of the tetrahedron and octahedron units is not sufficiently regular to permit good X-ray diffraction and the individual units, even if they are well-ordered, are too small to produce diffraction effects.

The thermal curves of the principal mineral, allophane, show a marked endothermal effect between 100 and 200 °C, attended by a substantial loss of mass. This effect is caused by the removal of the water retained by allophane, as in the case of colloidal silica. Although the endothermic effect on the DTA curve, situated between 100 and 200 °C shows an abundant removal of water, the DTG and TG curves illustrate the fact that the sample continues to expel a small amount of water up to temperatures from 350 to 400 °C. With rising temperatures, the thermal curves fail to indicate a variation of mass up to temperatures above 900 °C, when the DTA curve shows a transformation recorded as an exothermic effect, analogous to feebly crystallized kaolinite, with the difference being that the thermal effect is of lesser intensity.

The physical properties of allophane generally resemble those of halloysite and of montmorillonite, and they are difficult to investigate. Allophane may sometimes show good dispersion in water, with very small particles, but it sometimes fails to disperse. In argillaceous materials containing allophane, sulphates or phosphates are usually present in proportions of up to 5 per cent. These will cause supplementary endothermic effects to appear on thermal curves as a result of their decomposition.

5.8.5.4   Minerals from the Kaolinite Group

A crystal structure of kaolin was proposed by Pauling in 1903. He sketched the structure of the elementary crystallization cell. Like Pauling suggested, kaolin consists of a single plane of silicon tetrahedrons and of a plane of aluminium octahedrons so arranged that one silicon tetrahedron and one of the bonds of the octahedron plane form a mutual bond. All types of silicon tetrahedrons are turned in the same direction, towards the centre of the unit formed by the silicon tetrahedrons and the aluminium octahedrons.

The structural theoretical formula of kaolinite is $Al_2(Si_2O_5)(OH)_4$. The mineral has the following chemical composition: SiO_2 46.54 per cent; Al_2O_3 39.50 per cent; H_2O 13.95 per cent.

Analyses of a large number of simple mineral samples of kaolinite have shown that there are few cases in which isomorphous substitutions have taken place in the lattice. In these few cases, Fe and Ti were substituted for Al. Three polymorphous modifications of one and the same mineral belong to this group: kaolinite, dikite, and nakrite. A fourth mineral, anauxite, which has not been well investigated, was included in this group, although it holds in its structure an excess of silicon ions.

All these minerals which from a chemical viewpoint can be considered identical, yield thermal curves that are to a certain extent different, thus enabling their identification.

Kaolinite was formed at low temperatures, dikite in hydrothermal waters at medium temperatures, and nakrite at high temperatures, by hydrothermal and pneumotolithic processes. These genesis conditions cause the differences which appear on the thermal curves. When they are well-crystallized, these minerals present a horizontal section on the thermal curves up to about 400 °C, except when they contain water as moisture, which is removed up to 110 °C and causes on the thermal curves an endothermic effect attended by a loss of mass. When the minerals are feebly crystallized, at 100 to 200 °C the thermal curves show an endothermic effect attended by a loss in mass due to the removal of the water which had been retained between the leaflets. This retention of water by feebly crystallized kaolinites can be attributed to a slight increase of the space between the leaflets parallel to the c — axis which occurs in these cases.

The removal of the hydroxyls takes place from 450 to 700 °C, the temperature varying from one type of kaolinite to another, and this variation can be explained by a variation of the size of the particles (as it was seen in Chapter 2, the dehydration temperature decreases with decreasing particle size). But, this variation may also be caused by the degree of crystallization, because more feebly crystallized kaolinite loses hydroxyls more readily than the well-crystallized one.

For dikite and nakrite the dehydration temperature is somewhat higher. Peak temperatures of the thermal effects of the three minerals are for kaolinite from 550 to 600 °C, for dikite from 600 to 650 °C, and for nakrite of almost 700 °C. With increasing temperatures, in the range 900—1000 °C, on the DTA curve there appears a marked endothermic effect due to a structural reorganization. This exothermic effect is also different in shape and temperature for well-crystallized varieties as compared to the more feebly crystallized ones. When kaolinite is feebly crystallized, the exothermic effect is less intense, taking place in a broader temperature range; if a perpendicular were to be dropped from the peak of the effect to the base line in the thermal curve, the two segments would not be equal, unlike the well-crystallized kaolinites in which the two segments of the exothermic effect are equal.

With regard to the new structural organization which yields the exothermic effect, some investigators assign it to the formation of γ-Al_2O_3, others consider that when amorphous, pure alumina is heated γ-Al_2O_3 arises, and this will crystallize in a broad temperature range and at a lower temperature, while others still assume this thermal process to be caused by the formation of mullite.

In general, all investigators are agreed that at temperatures of about 1200 °C some aluminas of the γ form which could be present in dehydrated kaolinite disappear, and the phases formed are mullite and crystobalite, both in well-crystallized kaolinites and in feebly crystallized ones.

The intensity of the exothermic effect of kaolinite from 900 to 1000 °C is also affected by the presence of some elements in the form of impurities, even in very small amounts. Parmelee and Rodriguez (1942) have shown that zinc, lithium, magnesium, iron, manganese, cerium, and molybdenum sensibly accelerate the formation of mullite from kaolinite, whereas barium and calcium cause only an insignificant acceleration, whilst potassium and tin retard the formation of this compound. Particularly interesting is the conclusion reached by Wahl (1958) who specifies that a part of the mullites which he calls "primary mullites" were formed at a temperature of 975 °C as a result of the exothermic process and that the ordinary mullite which he calls "secondary mullite" is formed at temperature around 1200 °C. He maintained that primary mullite is formed in appreciable amounts by heating the well-crystallized kaolinite, whilst more loosely organized kaolinite develops very little primary mullite. He also showed that magnesium, iron, lead, barium, and calcium, when present in small amounts in the form of traces, intensely promote the formation of mullite. On the other hand, alkali ions retard its formation. Figure 5.94 illustrates the thermal curves of the three minerals in an idealized form.

5.8.5.5   Minerals from the Halloysite Group

From the theoretical viewpoint, there are two forms of halloysite whose chemical formulae are: $Al_2(Si_2O_5)(OH)_4$ and $Al_2(Si_2O_5) . (OH)_4 . 2H_2O$. But this group includes a great number of mineral species and varieties with a fairly complex composition, owing to the isomorphic replacement of Al^{3+} with other metal cations.

The two purely aluminous varieties will be described in the following, because all the mineral species of this group have common physical properties and behave similarly on heating.

Minerals of the halloysite group are formed of successive layers of silicon tetrahedrons and aluminium octahedrons of the same structural composition as the composition of kaolinite.

The more hydrated forms are made up of kaolinite layers separated from one another by a single layer of water molecules. The hydrated forms have a tendency to pass into less hydrated forms at the temperature of the surroundings, losing some of the water adsorbed. According to Brindley, Robinson, and Goodyear (1948), a partial dehydration of halloysite begins at temperatures from 60 to 75 °C, but for the dehydration to be total temperatures up to 400 °C are required. The water between the layers can be replaced by other molecules, a fact which causes variations

Figure 5.94 Thermal curves of the minerals of the kaolinite group: *A*, kaolinite; *B*, dikite; *C*, nakrite.

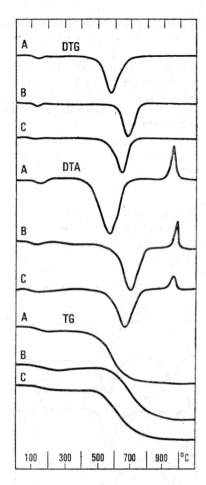

in the direction of the *c*-axis of the mineral. The hydrated form with two molecules of water, $Al_2(Si_2O_5)(OH)_4 . 2H_2O$, is developed in structural units of tubular form; on dehydration this structure begins to break up.

There are a series of names for halloysite forms mostly connected with the degree of hydration. Nevertheless, the names of *metahalloysite* for the feebly hydrated form, and halloysite proper or *endellite* for the more hydrated forms (Grim, 1962) have become more general in recent times. The thermal curves of halloysite differ from those of kaolinite only by the presence of a marked endothermic effect in the temperature range from 100 to 200 °C, as a result of the removal of the adsorbed water between the layers.

Hydroxyl groups are removed at temperatures above 450 °C. 55 kcal per mole of water are required for this removal. After this water is removed, there remains a structure which in certain respects is similar to that of metakaolinite. According to Roy (1955), the *metakaolinite* stage persists only up to temperatures about 670 to 700 °C, when γ-Al_2O_3 is developed simultaneously, and persists up to about 950 °C, when it fades away with the emergence of the mullite nucleation. Hence hydroxyls are expelled at temperatures similar to those specific for feebly crystallized kaolinite, and the endothermic effect recorded on the curves is generally asymmetrical, being wider towards lower temperatures and narrower on the side of higher temperatures.

The thermal transformations of halloysite caused by the new structural organization which takes place at high temperatures are similar to those of feebly crystallized kaolinite. There is, however, less certainty in respect of the nature of the high temperature processes in halloysite than in kaolinite, because the results obtained on halloysite samples are less conclusive than for kaolinite. All halloysite samples show a tendency to break up at higher temperatures, so that the residue remaining in the reaction crucible shows a series of cracks. Figure 5.95 illustrates the thermal curves of halloysite and metahalloysite.

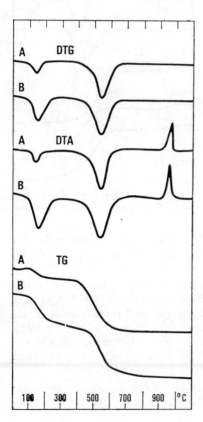

Figure 5.95 Thermal curves of the two forms of halloysite: *A*, metahalloysite; *B*, ordinary halloysite.

5.8.5.6 Minerals from the Montmorillonite Group

In the large class of argillaceous minerals with a 2:1 type lattice, one may distinguish two large groups: the montmorillonite group and the hydrated micas. 2:1 type lattices are those in which the structural cell consists of two layers of tetrahedrons, $(SiO)^{4-}$, arranged in hexagonal rings and these two layers are connected through the agency of a layer of $AlO_4(OH)_2$ octahedrons having common peaks with those of the tetrahedrons. Owing to the isomorphous substitutions which are very frequently encountered in these minerals, on one hand, and to the extremely small crystal particles emerging, on the other hand, their identification is very difficult. Good results were obtained in their investigation recently by means of studies carried out by several procedures including X-ray diffraction, combined thermal methods, infrared spectra, chemical analyses, etc.

Montmorillonite. This name has ben assigned to the argillaceous mineral whose theoretical formula is $Al_2(Si_4O_{10})(OH)_2$, which holds adsorbed between its layers a comparatively high content of water molecules. The theoretical composition of this mineral, excluding the water adsorbed between the layers, is as follows: SiO_2 66.7 per cent; Al_2O_3 28.3 per cent; H_2O from hydroxyl groups 5.0 per cent.

The structure most frequently ascribed to montmorillonite minerals is analogous to that of pyrophyllite, from which it differs only in the distribution of the constituent ions and through the superposition of the multiple leaflets. Hence montmorillonite is formed of planes of two silicon tetrahedrons and a central plane with aluminium octahedrons.

The unvarying feature of the structure of montmorillonite is that water and other polar molecules of an organic nature can enter between the unit layers, causing a displacement in the lattice in the direction of the c-axis. This interpenetration between layers is different from that of halloysite, because in the interstratifications with polar molecules between the planes, thick layers of polar molecules can develop, whereas in halloysite only one layer of polar molecules can arise. Dimensions of the c-axis of montmorillonite are not fixed; they vary from 9.6 Å, when there are no polar molecules between the layers, up to about 15 Å, when there are polar molecules between the layers.

Cations adsorbed between the layers which are arranged one on top of the other in the direction of the c-axis can be exchanged with one another. For example, Na can be exchanged with K^+, Rb^+, Ca^{2+}, Sr^{2+}, etc., and conversely. This substitution depends on the dimensions of the interstratifications and on the radius of the cation. The thickness of the layers with water between the structural units depends on the nature of the adsorbed cation and on the pressure of the water vapours in the respective surroundings. Under the moisture and temperature conditions of the ordinary surroundings, sodium montmorillonite (in which sodium is the adsorbed ion) has one water molecule in the intermediate spaces, and the dimension of the space in the direction of the c-axis is about 12.5 Å. If a calcium ion is adsorbed between the layers of montmorillonite, then there will be two water molecules between these layers, and the dimension of the space in the direction of the c-axis will be about 15.5 Å (Grim, 1962). The property of retaining different amounts of water, depending on the adsorbed cation, is reversible if the structure of montmorillonite is not completely destroyed by the motion of the polar molecules between the layers upon heating.

As can be seens, montmorillonites always differ from the theoretical formula, because of the substitution of aluminium and probably also of silicon, in the lattice. In the tetrahedral plane, the substitution is limited up to about 15 per cent, whereas in the octahedral plane it may extend to completion, giving rise to a great variety of mineral species classified in this group.

This diversification of the minerals from the montmorillonite group, as it is to be expected, causes a great variety of the thermal effects and especially affects the temperatures at which the thermal effects occur.

In the following, I shall describe in detail the thermal behaviour of montmorillonite proper, and of several other members of the group.

Grim and Kulbick (1957 and 1961) carried out differential thermal analysis of these minerals. They show that on the basis of thermal curves one can distinguish two kinds of dioctahedral montmorillonites, the "Cheto" type montmorillonite and the "Wyoming" type montmorillonite. These types were also confirmed by high-temperature X-ray diffraction studies. Thus, in the "Cheto" type montmorillonite, after heating the sample to 1000 °C, β-quartz, cristoballite, and cordierite appear in the X-ray diagrams, whereas in the "Wyoming" type mullite and cristoballite, but no β-quartz, will appear.

There are three thermal processes specific to minerals of the montmorillonite group. The first is a marked endothermic effect which appears between 100 and 250 °C and is attended by a substantial loss of mass as a result of the removal of absorbed water. The dehydration is a reversible process, if the temperature has not been raised above 250 °C. Hence, on renewed hydration, the mineral again absorbs water and expels it in the same form on subsequent heating. The amount of water released depends on the relative humidity and the nature of the exchange cations in the mineral. Therefore, neither by its form nor by its size can this endothermic effect serve as a precise identification feature of minerals from this group. After a large series of experiments the conclusion was reached that the hydration energy of the exchange cation affects the form of the thermal effect. Barshad (1950) shows that the form of the first effect varies, depending on the nature of the exchange cation, as follows. In the case in which the predominating exchange cations are Ca^{2+}, Mg^{2+}, and Ba^{2+}, this effect appears with a double or even treble shape of curve, and in the case in which these exchange cations are Na^+, K^+, H^+, Li^+, and NH_4^+, then the thermal effect is simple and of small extent (Figure 5.96). (When the exchange cation is NH_4^+, the thermal curves also show a slight endothermic effect around 400 °C, which probably originates from the evolution of NH_3). According to the form of this effect, if the other effects which appear on the thermal curves indicate the presence of montmorillonite, conclusions can be drawn as to the valency of the exchangeable cation.

The second effect, specific to the temperature range of each mineral in this group is also endothermic; it is attended by a loss of mass, as a result of the removal of the hydroxyl groups from the lattice of the mineral in the form of water vapour. In the case of montmorillonite proper, this thermal effect is usually situated from

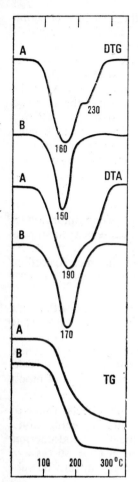

Figure 5.96 Comparison of the thermal effects of the dehydration of montmorillonites: *A*, saturated with bivalent ions; *B*, saturated with monovalent ions.

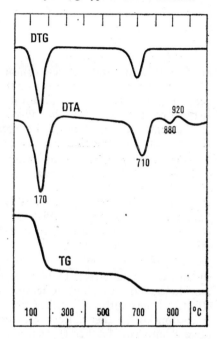

Figure 5.97 Thermal curves of Wyoming type montmorillonite.

670 to 710 °C. The form of DTA curves gives no indication as to the amount of hydroxyl groups released in the temperature range in which the respective effect is situated.

According to some researchers, no further loss of hydroxyls takes place at 900 °C, whilst others maintain that at 900 °C some hydroxyl groups which had not been fully removed would continue to be released. In addition, it was assumed that the marked thermal effect indicates the release of the hydroxyl groups contained in the octahedral layer, whereas the hydroxyl groups arising from the tetrahedral layer would be expelled gradually up to a temperature of 900 °C. After investigating Wyoming type montmorillonite samples, I have found that hydroxyl groups are removed for the most part at 700 °C, and after this effect a very slight loss of mass takes place (Figure 5.97).

The isomorphic substitution which has taken place in the structure of montmorillonite exerts a very great influence on the thermal effect caused by the removal of hydroxyl groups, and particularly on the peak temperature of this effect. In general, the Al-OH single bond is stronger than the Fe-OH single bond; on the other hand, the Mg-OH single bond is much more resistant than the Al-OH single bond. Hence, with "nontronitic" type minerals in which Fe was substituted for Al in the octahedral co-ordination, the thermal effect produced by the removal of the hydroxyl groups is situated at the lowest temperatures, namely from 400 to 550 °C, whereas when aluminium from the octahedral co-ordination was fully replaced with magnesium (a "saponitic" type mineral), the thermal effect caused by the removal of hydroxyls groups is situated from 800 to 900 °C. The thermal effects caused by the removal of hydroxyls from all minerals in this group are between these two temperature ranges, regardless of the nature and extent of the isomorphous substitution.

With rising temperatures, two thermal effects specific to this mineral appear above 800 °C and these effects can be used to establish the type of montmorillonite. These effects are recorded only on the DTA curves; hence the cause of their appearance is a structural reorganization which is not attended by mass variations. As to the form, the first effect is endothermic, and the second exothermic. According to the temperature difference between these two effects, it is possible to establish the type of montmorillonite (Lucas and Tranth, 1965).

On heating, Cheto type montmorillonite yields thermal curves with three endothermal effects whose peaks are at 150, 700, and 850 °C and an exothermic effect situated at about 1000 °C. The first two effects are attended by a loss of mass; they are therefore recorded also by DTG and TG curves. The temperature difference between the endothermic effect at 850 °C and the exothermic effect at 1000 °C is about 150 °C; such a temperature difference is specific only to this type of montmorillonite (Figure 5.98 A).

Wyoming type montmorillonite also has three endothermic effects, followed by an exothermic effect. Unlike the Cheto type montmorillonite, Wyoming montmorillonite fails to show a temperature interval between the third endothermic effect and the exothermic effect because the two effects occur in close succession. According to the thermal curves, this type of montmorillonite can in turn be subdivided into two further types.

The first type of montmorillonite yields a first endothermic effect from 130 to 170 °C, a second around temperatures of 700 °C, and the last endothermic effect immediately followed by the exothermic effect at temperatures of about 900 °C with a maximum temperature interval between them of 30 °C. In the second type of montmorillonite, the second endothermic effect occurs at lower temperatures, situated at about 570 °C. Hence the differences recorded between the two varieties of Wyoming type montmorillonites refer only to the temperatures at which OH groups are removed (Figure 5.98 B and C).

A third type of montmorillonite, called an *intermediate montmorillonite*, can also be defined by the shape and temperature of the thermal effects. The last endothermal effect in this type is more prominent than in the previous cases, and it is followed by an exothermic effect whose intensity is much smaller than in the previous

Figure 5.98 DTA curves of the four types of montmorillonites identified by Lucas and Tranth (1965): *A*, Cheto type; *B*, Wyoming type I; *C*, Wyoming type II; *D*, intermediate type.

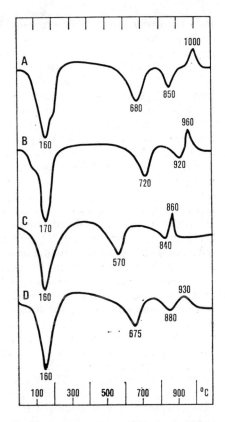

cases. The temperature interval between the two effects is of about 60 °C, therefore intermediate to the two types (Figure 5.98 *D*).

Chemical analyses carried out on montmorillonites from the first two groups have shown a difference in the isomorphous replacement of the octahedra. Thus, in the Cheto type montmorillonite, 25—35 per cent of the aluminium found in octahedral co-ordination was replaced by magnesium, whilst in the Wyoming type, aluminium was replaced to the extent of only 5—10 per cent. The situation is the other way round in respect of iron, which occurs more abundantly in the octahedral co-ordination of the Wyoming type montmorillonite (about 15 per cent) than in the Cheto type montmorillonite (about 5 per cent). Investigations of the cation exchange capacity have also shown differences between these two types. In the case of Cheto type montmorillonites, the cation exchange capacity is between 114 and 133 milliequivalents for a 100 g sample, whereas for the Wyoming type montmorillonite the exchange capacity is between 89 and 111 milliequivalents.

Grim and Kulbicki (1961) consider that the differences between Wyoming type montmorillonites and the Cheto type are mainly structural rather than chemical. Thus, the crystallization of quartz from the silica produced at high temperatures in

the Cheto type montmorillonite would be due to the presence of reversed tetrahedrons. Nevertheless, up to the present it was neither possible to prove nor to
disprove the existence of any reversed tetrahedrons.

Investigations have shown that the structure of montmorillonite is far from
ordered. This fact was checked by Glaeser and Mering (1958), who have shown
that the negative charges resulting from isomorphous replacements would respond
to static equilibria. This means that the forces emerging are not ordered, but turned
towards each other, in a random structure (Mering, 1964). It is therefore to be
assumed that heating at high temperatures must enhance the breaking up of such
a structure. Thus, the third endothermic effect recorded on the DTA curve at a
temperature of about 900 °C corresponds to a consumption of thermal energy which
is required to bring about the transformation of ordered anhydrous montmorillonite
into a disordered anhydrous material. Hence the endothermic effect at about 900 °C
can be interpreted in the sense that it is caused by the passage of the lattice from
an ordered to a disordered condition. The absorbed heat energy is required to
break up the bond existing between various componets. The emergence, after this
effect, of quartz or of cristobalite or of both minerals simultaneously implies that the
bonds in the montmorillonite lattice are totally or partially broken.

It may therefore be assumed that beginning at 900 °C montmorillonite partly
or wholly loses its old structure and that the thermal effects at higher temperatures
will essentially depend on the total chemical composition of the mineral. At these
temperatures, the oxides formed which can react together are: SiO_2, Al_2O_3, MgO
(FeO, Fe_2O_3), the first two of which predominate in the case of montmorillonite.
The other oxides are found in too small amounts to react directly with silica or
alumina, so that they will behave only as admixtures, a fact which has importance
for the ceramics industry. This reaction of the oxides in the solid state is indicated
on the DTA curve by an exothermic effect, which shows that the constituents of
montmorillonite are reorganized in a lower state of energy than the previous one.
It has been seen from the above that the exothermic effects of the two types of
montmorillonites are not identical as to temperature and size. In the case of the
Cheto type montmorillonite where a larger amount of crystallized mineral is formed
by structural reorganization, energy is released in smaller amounts and its exothermic
effect will be smaller, whereas in the case of the Wyoming type montmorillonite
the opposite argument applies.

In conclusion, from Grim and Kulbicki (1957 and 1961) and Lucas and Trauth
(1965), it follows that montmorillonites differ only because of the structural reorganization brought about by solid state reactions which take place at high temperatures.

An important part in the structural reorganization at high temperatures is
played by the presence of Mg and Fe on the binary system SiO_2-Al_2O_3. This fact
has led to the classification of montmorillonite into three types. The first type is
the Cheto type montmorillonite in which the second predominating element in
the octahedral structure, after aluminium, is magnesium. Depending on the magnesium contents one may distinguish: (a) purely aluminous and magnesium
montmorillonites in which the ratio MgO/Fe_2O_3 tends towards infinity and (b)
aluminous, magnesian, and ferriferous montmorillonites in which the Mg content
is greater than the Fe content, the ratio MgO/Fe_2O_3 being greater than 2.

The second type is the Wyoming type montmorillonite in which the second predominating element in the octahedral structure, after aluminium, is iron. Depending on the iron content one may distinguish: (a) purely aluminous and ferric montmorillonites, in which the ratio Fe_2O_3/MgO tends towards infinity; and (b) aluminous, ferric, and magnesian montmorillonites in which the ratio MgO/Fe_2O_3 is smaller than 0.9.

The third type is the intermediate montmorillonite in which the iron and magnesium contents are more or less equal, that is, MgO/Fe_2O_3 is greater than 0.9 but smaller than 2.

As we have seen above, isomorphous substitutions in the lattice of minerals from the montmorillonites group exert a notable influence on the thermal effect, particularly on the temperatures at which the minerals undergo dehydroxylation. In the following I shall briefly present the other minerals classified in this group.

Nontronite. With this mineral the first endothermic effect caused by the removal of the water adsorbed is wholly similar to that of montmorillonite. The second endothermic effect caused by the removal of hydroxyl groups appears at a temperature about 150 °C lower than in a genuine montmorillonite, the removal of the hydroxyls starting at temperatures of about 400 °C. The third endothermic effect appears, as in montmorillonites, at about 900 °C, but in most cases this effect is not specific. The exothermic effect is less marked than with montmorillonite.

Beidelite. The thermal curves of this mineral are analogous to those of montmorillonite, the only difference being that the endothermic effect caused by the removal of the hydroxyl groups is situated at a lower temperature than that of montmorillonite, but higher than that of nontronite.

Saponite. This argillaceous mineral loses the hydroxyl groups at much higher temperatures than the other minerals from this series. The endothermic effect caused by the dehydroxylation of this magnesian montmorillonite appears in the temperature range from 800 to 900 °C. The high temperature at which this effect appears, as well as the high MgO content against that of SiO_2 and Al_2O_3 cause the other two exothermic effects for the breaking up and the reorganization of the lattice specific to these groups of minerals to be non-existent or very slight. Figure 5.99 illustrates the thermal curves of saponite.

5.8.5.7 Minerals from the Illite Group

Illite minerals are similar to hydrated micas, with a lattice of the 2:1 type. Specific to illite is the substitution of Al^{3+} for Si^{4+} in the tetrahedral co-ordination. This substitution gives rise to an excess of negative charges which is balanced in the lattice with K^+ ions.

Illite, the principal mineral of the group, has an identical structure with that of muscovite mica, from which it differs only by the fact that in illite one quarter of

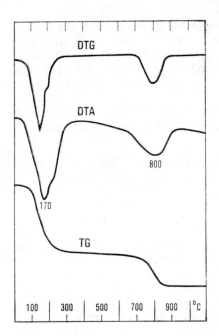

Figure 5.99 Thermal curves of saponite.

the silicon atoms have been replaced by aluminium, and the number of potassium ions is proportionally greater than in muscovite mica. The basic structural unit of illite is a layer consisting of two planes of silicon tetrahedrons having a central plane of aluminium octahedrons. The peaks of all the tetrahedrons in each plane with silicon are oriented towards the centre of the unit and are combined with the planes of aluminium octahedrons in a single layer with the replacement of the hydroxyls with oxygen. From a theoretical point of view, the structural unit is the same as that of the montmorillonite, with the difference being that some Si^{4+} atoms are replaced with Al^{3+} ions, and the excess of charges are balanced with K^+ ions. The potassium ions which balance the charges are placed between the cross-linking leaflets in the dodecahedral co-ordination, dividing their charges between the adjoining leafllets which they bind together. The bond between the cross-linking leaflets is strong enough to preclude the penetration of water molecules between them, which explains why on the thermal curves at temperatures below $300\,°C$ these minerals do not show substantial mass losses like montmorillonite.

As is known, the theoretical formula of muscovite mica is $(Si_6Al_2)(Al_4)$ $O_{20}(OH)_4K_2$.

Hydrated micas, in whose group illite is also included, differ from muscovite mica in several ways. In the first place, hydrated micas have less silicon replaced with aluminium. In the well-crystallized simple mineral, mica, aluminium was substituted for silicon in the ratio of 4 : 1, whereas in hydrated micas this substitution ratio is of about 6 : 1. In the second place, as a consequence of these substitutions, the ratio SiO_2/Al_2O_3 is reduced and thus the excess of negative charges is reduced from two units per elementary cell to about 1.3. This fact explains why the potassium ions from between the leaflets of the hydrated micas are partially replaced with other cations, for example Ca^{2+}, Mg^{2+}, H^+, etc.

It is very difficult to give a real formula of illite. Nevertheless, scientists are agreed that the following formulae would be the closest to the truth: $(Si_{8-y}Al_y)(Al_4Fe_4 Mg_{4-6})O_{20}(OH)_4K_y$.

It follows from this formula that illite shows great variation in respect of the chemical composition. If, for example, the amount of K_2O for muscovite is of 8.8 per cent, with illite minerals this value may decrease several times down to 2—3 per cent, and the amount of adsorbed water would increase by about 8—9 per cent.

It is considered that, as K^+ is progressively replaced with another cation or with water, in the course of normal degradation with time, weathering would bring about, under certain conditions, a distortion of the lattice with the possible formation of montmorillonites. Nevertheless, these hydrated micas have also been called "degraded illites" (Grim, 1962), and it is not to be expected that they should have all the properties of montmorillonite in which, as could be seen, the deficit of charges is smaller, and the substitutions which have caused this deficit of charges occurred more in the octahedral co-ordination of the structure than in the tretrahedral one.

The thermal curves obtained on such minerals resemble, as do also the crystal lattices, those of biotite or muscovite micas.

Muscovite, as we have seen, shows a slow loss of mass due to dehydration up to 800 °C, whereas biotite shows a more marked loss of mass up to 400 °C, followed by an almost horizontal shape of curve up to 800 °C, when a sudden loss of mass begins, owing to the removal of the hydroxyls, at 850 to 1000 °C.

The thermal effects of illites are similar to those of muscovites in some cases and to those of montmorillonites in others, depending on the degree of crystallization. At low temperatures, below 250 °C, illites show an endothermic effect due to the removal of the adsorbed water. This effect is less intense than that obtained in the case of montmorillonite, indicating a loss of mass of not more than 6—7 per cent. The loss of the hydroxyls in the lattice of the illites begins at about 400 °C and may continue up to about 900 °C. In the tetrahedral co-ordinates, the removal of the hydroxyls takes place gradually and over a broad temperature interval, whereas the hydroxyls from the dioctahedral co-ordination are removed rapidly, over a narrow temperature interval, 450—550 °C. This shows that the dehydroxylation of hydromicas is very closely connected with the dimensions of the particles and with the duration of the heating time.

As compared to kaolinite and halloysite, the dehydroxylation of illites is slow and gradual, the endothermic effect obtained being much broader and more reduced in height. Grim and Brandley (1940) have shown that the loss of the hydroxyls from the dioctahedral groups is not attended by a disturbance of the structure and that in this case the structure of the illites is not destroyed up to a temperature of 850 °C. This is wholly in accord with Roy (1949) observations on muscovite, namely that the dehydroxylation of muscovite fails to indicate any structural change up to a temperature of 940 °C. Likewise, when hydroxyls are only partially removed, this process is attended by an insignificant expansion in the lattice in the direction of the c — axis and not by the full breaking up of the lattice. According to Grim and Brandley, the thermal processes caused by the removal of the adsorbed water and of the hydroxyls are reversible, because illite heated at 800 °C and then left for a longer time may adsorb water from the surroundings, which means that no breaking up of the crystal lattice has taken place up to this temperature.

The third temperature effect caused by structural reorganizations also exists in the case of illites. Thus, at temperatures around 900 °C there appears a slight endothermic effect which indicates the breaking up of the crystal lattice. In many cases, as with montmorillonite, this third endothermic effect is followed by an exothermic effect which can be explained by the formation of spinel. Thus, Grim and Brandley have noticed the formation of spinel in all cases where illite was heated at 850 °C, and in much greater amounts when illite was heated at about 1200 °C.

In nature, illite and montmorillonite frequently form structures with interpolated layers, associated structures, etc. Such is the argillaceous mineral from Sárospatok (Hungary), which was at some time considered world-wide as a standard illite sample. Subsequent researches conducted on this mineral, however, have shown that it is formed from lamellae whose nucleus consists of illite, but in which the surface of the lamella was changed into montmorillonite, a process which has been confirmed using chemical analyses and X-ray diffraction. These analyses have indicated the presence of illite, whereas the cation exchange capacity corresponds to montmorillonite.

On the thermal curves, this associated illite-montmorillonite structure may comparatively readily be recognized in the temperature range in which the removal of hydroxyl groups takes place. Two endothermic effects appear in this temperature range attended by a loss of mass. The first effect is due to the removal of the hydroxyl groups from the illite lattice, and the second is due to the removal of the hydroxyl groups from the montmorillonite lattice. The problem is somewhat more complicated when the argillaceous mineral of montmorillonite type is a nontronite, because in this case the effects of the removal of the OH groups overlap.

In a series of samples coming especially from sediments of marine origin, I have observed the presence of illite as well as kaolinite. In this case, the two minerals can no longer be identified by the temperature range specific to the removal of the OH groups, because the thermal effects of the removal of these groups occur at approximately the same temperature. The presence of kaolinite is marked on the thermal curves by the exothermic effect at high temperatures specific to this mineral, and the presence of illite is marked on the thermal curves by the presence of the endothermic effect specific to the removal of the adsorbed water.

Figure 5.100 illustrates comparatively the DTA curves of the illite minerals and of muscovites.

In concluding this discussion of the illite group, it should be mentioned that most specialized handbooks include sericite in this group, because sericite, as was already shown, is an intermediate mineral between micas and illites. It was included in the micas group, because it presents some thermal features which are closer to the micas than to the illites.

Figure 5.100 DTA curves of some minerals from the illite-muscovite group *(after Mackenzie, 1957)*: *A,* muscovite; *B,* sericite; *C,* broadly crystallized muscovite; *D,* muscovite; *E,* muscovite; *F,* sericite; *G,* sericite; *H,* sericite; *I,* illite; *J,* illite; *K,* illite.

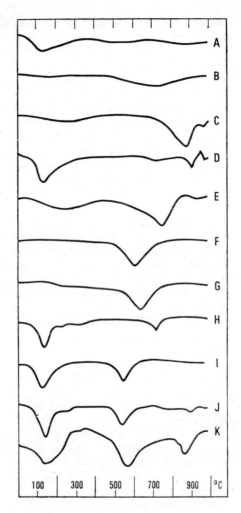

5.8.5.8 Minerals of the Chlorite Group

Minerals included in this group are similar in many respects to the micas, crystallizing however in the monoclinic system. The structure of true chlorites consists of a succession of layers of the type of tri-octahedral mica with magnesium hydroxyde and brucite layers. These layers are continuous in the direction of the *a*-and *b*-axes, and are arranged one on top of the other in the direction of the *c*-axis, which permits a cleavage in this direction.

Layers of the mica type have the theoretical formula $(Mg, Fe)_6(Si, Al)_8 O_{20}(OH)_4$, and those of the brucite type have the formula $(Mg, Al)_6 (OH)_{12}$. This association of mica type with brucite type layers gives great stability, because of the negative charges resulting from an isomorphous replacement of Si^{4+} by the trivalent ions from the brucite layer. In this case, numerous elements may take equivalent positions in the crystal lattice. Thus, Al^{3+} may be replaced isomorphously with Fe^{3+} and Cr^{3+}, and in much smaller amount Mg^{2+} may be replaced isomorphously with Fe^{2+}, Ni^{2+} and Ti^{4+}. In spite of substitutions of this kind, the electrical neutrality of the elementary crystallization cell is preserved. The degree of substitution varies from one mineral to another, both quantitatively and in respect of the type of substituted ions. Therefore, there is a whole series of minerals. Depending on the chemical composition they were given various names, differing from one another only by the manner and extent of the substitution.

Minerals from the chlorite group are very widely distributed in nature. All varieties of chlorite coming from various rocks, other than argillaceous ones, are well crystallized in the form of green-coloured aggregates with a scaly or lamellar appearance. Those coming from clays are feebly organized structurally, having a finely granular appearance. In this case it is not possible to determine minerals of these types because brucite type layers are more poorly organized from a crystallographic point of view, and their arrangement in successive mica-brucite type layers is less regular than with minerals originating in other rocks.

In connection with these minerals it is important to bear in mind the fact that the thickness of the layer consisting of a mica type plane and a brucite type plane is of 14 Å, exactly twice the thickness of the caolinite layer, which makes a differentiation of these two minerals on the basis of X-ray diffraction extremely difficult (Grim, 1962).

Chlorites from argillaceous minerals always appear in association with other argillaceous minerals, rendering their investigation more laborious. Indeed, it is hard to establish if some properties of these minerals are a consequence of certain arrangements of the associated layers or a consequence of the chlorite minerals themselves.

As to the chlorites arising from various rocks other than argillaceous ones, it is possible to distinguish several types of minerals whose names and chemical composition are listed in Table 5.3.

Although from data listed in the table overleaf it follows that chlorite minerals exhibit a great variety in composition, they nevertheless give thermal curves which to a certain extent are specific to each separate mineral. Most thermal curves obtained on these minerals show a first very strongly marked endothermic effect at temperature around 600 °C. This is attended by a loss of mass. The first effect is followed by another endothermic and very strongly marked effect at temperatures around 800 °C. This too is attended by a loss of mass. Both thermal effects are caused by the dehydroxylation of the mineral on heating, the first effect corresponding to the dehydroxylation of the brucite type layer, and the second effect to that of the mica type layer. On further heating, at temperatures of about 900 °C, an exothermic effect of highly variable magnitude appears on the thermal curves.

Although this succession of thermal effects is highly typical of a broad range of chlorite type minerals, it may nevertheless frequently happen that the thermal effect should appear doubled on the curves in the form of secondary peaks, as is

Table 5.3 Chemical composition of some mineral species of the chlorite type according to Betehtin (1953)[1] and Mackenzie (1957)[2]

Mineral	Percentage of:					
	MgO	FeO	Fe_2C_3	Al_2O_3	SiO_2	H_2O
Penninite [1]	17.4—35.9	0.7—17.4	00.0— 5.7	13.8—21.3	29.8—33.7	11.5—14.6
Clinochlorite [1]	17.0—34.5	1.8—12.2	0.0— 3.0	13.1—17.6	28.3—33.9	11.7—14.2
Chamosite [1]	impurities	34.3—42.3	0.0— 6.0	13.0—20.1	22.8—29.0	10.0—13.0
Thuringite [1]	impurities	19.8—39.3	7.2—31.7	15.6—21.1	19.4—28.8	4.6—13.2
Beralite [2]	2.35	43.01	0.67	21.40	22.27	10.10
Sheridonite [2]	30.96	1.24	0.20	27.68	27.12	12.92
Ripidolite [2]	19.85	18.73	1.90	20.85	26.50	11.65
Leuchtenbergite [2]	31.11	4.85	2.00	18.28	31.18	12.52

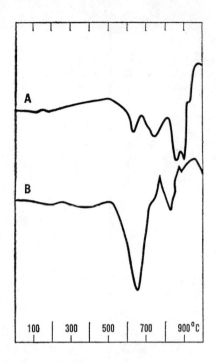

Figure 5.101   DTA curves of the two types of chlorite: A, leuchtenbergite; B, ripidolite.

the case of leuchtenbergite (Figure 5.101 A). Likewise, some minerals from this group are dehydroxylated in a single temperature range, presenting a single endothermic effect, for example, ripidolite (Figure 5.101 B).

In general, it is very difficult to establish the type of chlorite by the method of differential thermal analysis. However, let it be mentioned that the thermal curves obtained on a broad range of chlorite samples either well crystallized or feebly crystallized (the so-called pseudochlorites), presented an endothermic effect at low temperatures from 100 to 250 °C, attended by a loss of mass caused by the removal of the adsorbed water. In connection with the exothermic effect at 900 °C, when the mineral undergoes a structural reorganization Orcel and Caillère (1938) and Ali and Bridley (1948) hold the view that by this reorganization olivine is formed in the case of magnesian chlorites, whereas Nelson (1953) advanced the opinion that spinel is formed. On heating ferriferous chlorites behave differently from magnesian chlorites, but the causes of this difference have not been elucidated as yet. It is considered that the different behaviour of ferriferous chlorites is caused by the presence of the ferrous iron, which oxidises passing into ferric iron. The oxidation of Fe^{2+} to Fe^{3+} takes place with an increase in mass, making for a very marked and broad exothermic effect recorded on the DTA curve, owing to overlapping of the two thermal processes, the new structural organization and the oxidation of ferrous iron.

The differences appearing on the thermal curves with chlorite minerals are due on the one hand to the dimensions of the particles, and on the other hand to the highly varied chemical composition.

When iron is the predominating cation which was substituted for magnesium in the brucite layer, the temperature of the endothermic effect caused by the dehydroxylation of the brucite type layer drops below 500 °C, whereas when no isomorphous substitutions have taken place in the brucite layer, leaving magnesium as the predominating cation, the temperature of the endothermic effect rises towards 600 °C.

The temperature of the second endothermic effect corresponding to the dehydroxylation of the mica type layer is also variable. In the case of this effect, the temperature variation is caused by the degree of substitution of silicon from the tetrahedral planes of the mica type lattice. The smaller the proportion of silicon substituted, i.e., the closer this layer approaches a mica type lattice, the higher is the temperature of the effect, and the more the degree of substitution for silicon, the lower will drop the temperature of the effect. Thus penninite and clinochlorite, which are chlorite minerals with a higher silicon content, have a dehydroxylation effect of the mica type layer situated at temperatures of 800—810 °C, whereas thuringite, in which iron was substituted for silicon, is dehydroxylated at a lower temperature.

The maximum temperature of the exothermic effect is difficult to correlate with the composition of the mineral which has generated it, because, as has already been shown, this temperature depends on the ferrous iron content.

In summing up, it can be stated that, in general, the thermal curves obtained by heating chlorite type minerals shows a first comparatively broad endothermic effect in the temperature range from 450 to 660 °C, followed by a second effect, also endothermic, of lesser extent, from 700 to 800 °C, and then by an exothermic effect situated at a temperature of 900 °C.

In most cases, the thermal curves obtained for thuringite and ripidolite have shown only two thermal effects, a broad endothermic effect situated at about 550 °C, and an exothermic effect which for ripidolite in situated at 750 °C and for thuringite at 950 °C.

The thermal curves obtained on pseudochlorite also show two endothermic effects, the first of which is situated at a lower temperature than with well-crystallized chlorites, but is smaller in extent than the second. In the case of pseudochlorite it should be noted that the exothermic effect caused by the new structural organization is much broader than for well-crystallized chlorites.

For a better distinction of chlorites from pseudochlorites, Deb (1950) has initiated a procedure based on an acid treatment. First, a thermal determination of the sample as such is carried out; then a certain amount from the initial sample is taken and treated with acid. This treatment almost completely dissolves the brucite type layer. After the treated sample is washed with water and dried at the temperature of the surroundings, it is again subjected to the thermal analysis. The thermal curves which are obtained with the sample which has not been treated and with that treated with acid are compared. If the sample subjected to analysis

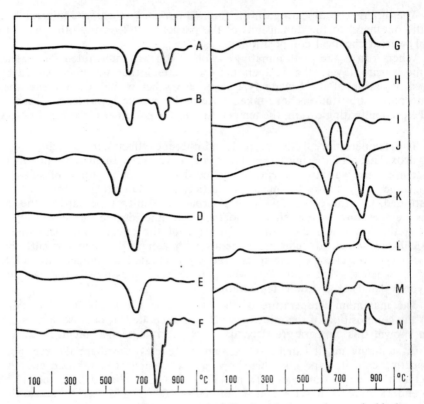

Figure 5.102 DTA curves of well-crystallized chlorites, of pseudochlorites, as well as of coarsely and finely ground chlorites *(after Orcel, 1930, and Sabatier, 1950): A,* sheridonite; *B,* grochanite; *C,* turingite; *D,* pseudochlorite-clinochlorite; *E,* clinochlorite; *F,* chlorite; *G, H, I, J,* chlorite materials with large granules; *K, L, M, N,* the same samples *(G, H, I, J)* finely ground.

contains a mineral of the ordinary chlorite type, then the three thermal effects specific to chlorite minerals will appear both in the first and in the second case. If the sample subjected to analysis consists of pseudochlorites, then the two series of curves are no longer identical. With the treated sample the first thermal effect will fail to appear, because it would have been caused by the dehydroxylation of the brucite layer which was in this case removed by the treatment with acid, whereas with the sample which was not treated with acid the endothermic effect appears on the curves.

In general, the identification of chlorite type minerals on the basis of thermal analyses is possible only for well-crystallized minerals; in the other cases, it may at most be said that a chlorite is involved. For comparison, Figure 5.102 illustrates the thermal curves of certain well-crystallized chlorite type minerals, as well as of some pseudochlorites.

5.8.5.9 Minerals from the Vermiculite Group

The best chemical data on vermiculite were provided by Gruner (1934), who, on the basis of X-ray diffraction studies, selected several samples which may be considered true vermiculites. The chemical formula of vermiculite, established from the average of the analyses carried out by Gruner, is:

$$0.02 \ Ca \ 0.65Mg(Mg_{4.56}, \ Fe^{2+}_{0.08}, \ Ni_{0.32}, \ Al_{0.42}, \ Fe^{3+}_{0.62})(Si_{5.66}, \ Al_{2.34}) \ O_{20} \ (OH)_4 \cdot 8.76 \ H_2O.$$

In native conditions, most vermiculites seem to be saturated with replaceable Mg^{2+}, but vermiculites are encountered in which the replaceable ion may be different. Interstratified cations from the vermiculite lattice may readily be replaced by other cations as with the other argillaceous minerals.

The thermal behaviour of vermiculites is closely connected with the cation with which it is saturated, so that the thermal transformations take place in different temperature ranges according to the cation. In order to make the discussion of the behaviour of vermiculites on heating easier for the reader, the thermal effects will be presented over three intervals of temperature.

Low temperature thermal effects up to 350 °C. Since in the great majority of cases, vermiculites are saturated with Mg^{2+} ions, the description will refer in the first place to vermiculites saturated with Mg^{2+}.

In ordinary vermiculites saturated with Mg^{2+}, the silicate layers are separated from the double layers of water molecules which contain the exchangeable cation. The analyses of the structure of vermiculites saturated with Mg^{2+} have proved that there are 24 water molecule places per cell unit. Data of the chemical analyses carried out with a view to determining the cationic exchange have shown that the ratio of the exchangeable cation to the water molecules does not differ too much from this value. Expulsion of the water adsorbed between the layers causes a low temperature endothermic effect which has three thermal maxima, two of which are intensely masked (Figure 5.103 *A*). Detailed data concerning the number of water molecules present in vermiculite as a function of the exchangeable cation, and on the processes which take place on heating, confirmed for each stage by X-ray diffraction, can be found in Mackenzie's (1957) book, *The Differential Thermal Investigation of Clays.*

It is assumed that the step-wise dehydration vermiculites saturated with Mg^{2+} ions is caused by the existence of three different energy levels with which the interstratified water molecules are retained, energy levels which depend on the distance between the Mg^{2+} cation and the water molecules. Thus, the first water molecules to be removed are the water molecules which are not in direct contact with the cation, next the water molecules which are in close vicinity to the cation, but which nevertheless have no direct contact with it, are removed and the last to be removed are the water molecules which form a cover around the cation.

The above observations are absolutely valid for the whole range of vermiculites when they are fully saturated with Mg^{2+} ions. In the case where the cation which saturates the vermiculites lattice is some other ion but Mg^{2+}, the endothermic effect caused by dehydration will have another shape of curve (Figure 5.103), but

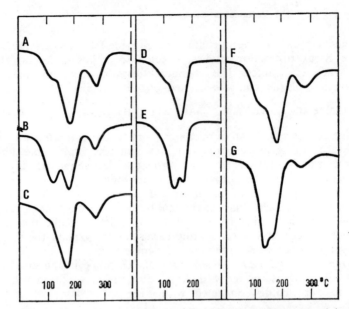

Figure 5.103 DTA curves of the endothermic effect caused by the dehydration of some vermiculites as a function of the exchangeable cation *(after Mackenzie, 1957)*: *A, B, C,* vermiculite saturated with Mg^{2+} in various proportions; *D, E,* vermiculite saturated with Na^+ in various proportions; *F, G,* saponite saturated with Mg^{2+}.

no precise interpretation of the way in which dehydration takes place can be made because of lack of sufficient structural information concerning the stages which appears in the course of the dehydration process.

From the thermal curves illustrated in Figure 5.104 obtained on a vermiculite in which the cation which saturates the lattice was Mg^{2+}, Ca^{2+}, Sr^{2+}, Ba^{2+}, Li^+ and Na^+, it is possible to infer that the removal of water molecules occurs as a direct function of the cations. The temperatures of the thermal maxima decreases in the following order, $Mg^{2+} > Ca^{2+} > Ba^{2+} > Na^+$. To a certain extent this fact also reflects the hydration energy of the interstratified cation as well as the different content of interstratified water molecules. Nevertheless, as has already been shown, the degree of grinding and of crystallization, and the settling degree of the sample in the reaction groove can distort the shape of the thermal effect.

Thermal effects in the temperature range from 350 to 700 °C. In this temperature range, almost all vermiculites show a horizontal segment on the thermal curves, as a result of the fact that in this temperature range the mineral is stable. Nevertheless, it is thought that at these temperatures the mineral would still expel the remaining water which had not been removed up to 350 °C and which represents about six per cent of the total amount of interstratified water. The removal of this

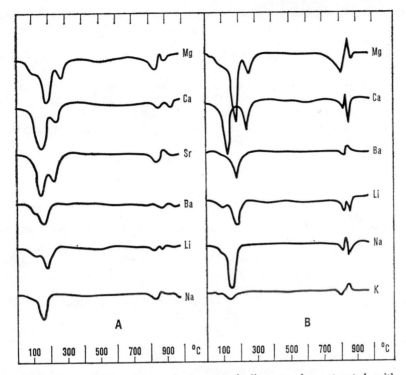

Figure 5.104 DTA curves of two vermiculite samples saturated with different cations *(after Mackenzie, 1957): A.* West Chester vermiculite; *B.* Macbon County vermiculite.

water appears on the thermal curves in the form of an endothermic effect in this temperature range.

The fact that this endothermic effect extends over such a temperature interval, and is inconclusive, is due, to a certain extent, to its overlapping with the exothermic effect caused by the oxidation of the bivalent iron present in almost all vermiculites to tervalent iron.

Thermal effects at temperatures above 700 °C. Segments of the thermal curves of vermiculites at temperatures above 700 °C seem to indicate two endothermic effects separated by an exothermic effect. This sequence of thermal effects is situated from 800 to 900 °C, the temperatures of the thermal maxima depending largely on the nature of the interstratified cation. In fact, this is the temperature range in which the removal of the hydroxyl groups takes place, as a result of which vermiculite passes into enstatite, $Mg_2(Si_2O_6)$.

According to Sabatier (1952), in certain situations the formation of enstatite is attended by a marked exothermic effect, for example when enstatite recrystallizes from amorphous gels, but other authors, for example Brandley and Grim (1951), contest the existence of exothermic effects in the formation of enstatite.

The most specific behaviour of vermiculite on heating is that it increases its volume. Essentially, under the pressure of the molecular water which arises by the removal of the OH groups and which is changed into vapour, on heating the various crystal individuals will rapidly swell and break apart parallel to the c-axis, and this to such an extent that they form vermicular filaments or columns. The volume increase of the vermiculite may reach up to 25 times its initial volume. Hence, when this mineral is subjected to thermal analysis the reaction groove must only partially be filled with the material.

5.8.5.10   Associated Stratified Argillaceous Minerals

Many argillaceous minerals may be composed of several minerals which may be associated in various ratios.

The association may consist of particles of argillaceous minerals in which there is no preferential geometrical orientation of one particle against other particles close to it. Other types of associations are the interstratifications of argillaceous minerals in which each individual layer is made up of only one layer or of several layers of one mineral. These structures of associated layers, also called mixed layer structures, are the consequence of the fact that the layers of different argillaceous minerals are similar, being composed of layers of silicon tetrahedrons and inner bundles of octahedral layers of oxygen and hydroxyl groups. Structures of associated stratified minerals are just as stable as those composed of a single type of layers specific to a simple mineral.

Associated stratified mineral structures are of two types, those with regular interstratification and those with irregular interstratification.

The regular interstratification may consist of an arrangement along the c-axis in the form of regular repetitions of the various layers. A typical example of regular stratification is that of chlorite type minerals which are composed of a regular sequence of mica and brucite layers.

The irregular interstratification is an associated stratification in which there is no uniform distribution of the layers. The association may be formed of two or more types of layers of a mineral with random alternations of different layers from another mineral.

Associated stratified minerals have an inherent variability, and they cannot, therefore, be given a specific name: they can be considered as associations of the layers of the minerals included. The study of associated stratified minerals by conventional analytical methods is difficult (chemical analyses, microscopical observations, etc.) and therefore the literature contains many references to associations of argillaceous minerals and it is almost certain that in many cases such minerals are associations of stratified minerals. X-ray diffraction studies have revealed the presence of associated stratified mineral structures, permitting in some cases the establishment of the nature and the abundance of the units which make up these minerals. Thermal analysis also has established the presence of certain associated stratified mineral structures.

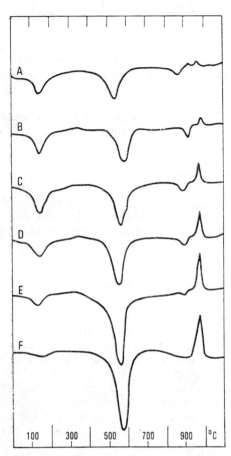

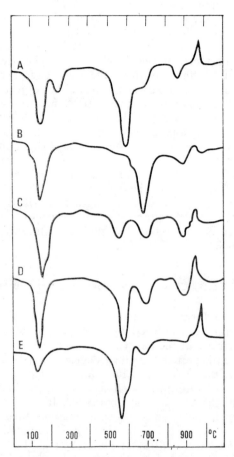

Figure 5.105 DTA curves of an illite and kaolinite mixture *(according to Grim and Rowland, 1942)*: *A*, illite 95 per cent and kaolinite 5 per cent; *B*, illite 90 per cent and kaolinite 10 per cent; *C*, illite 75 per cent and kaolinite 25 per cent; *D*, illite 50 per cent and kaolinite 50 per cent; *E*, illite 25 per cent and kaolinite 75 per cent; *F*, illite 10 per cent and kaolinite 90 per cent.

Figure 5.106 DTA curves of some mixtures of argillaceous minerals *(after Grim and Rowland, 1942 and Grim, 1953)*: *A*, montmorillonite saturated with calcium 50 per cent and kaolinite 50 per cent; *B*, montmorillonite saturated with Na 75 per cent and illite 25 per cent; *C*, montmorillonite saturated with Na 25 per cent and illite 75 per cent; *D*, kaolinite, montmorillonite saturated with Na and illite in proportion of 1:1:1; *E*, kaolinite, montmorillonite saturated with Na and illite in proportion of 3 : 1 : 1.

Grim and Rowland (1942) have investigated artificial mixtures in various proportions of these minerals and have found the following. In the case of the mixture of kaolinite and illite, the determination of these two minerals on the basis of the thermal curves is difficult (Figure 5.105). The first effect of illite may be misleading, because from this effect one may assume also the existence of a substance of the fireclay type. The second endothermic effect of illite and that of kaolinite overlap. The third endothermic effect and the exothermic effect for illite appear separately from the large exothermic effect of kaolinite, but on the illite curve alone, these effects are less conspicuous.

A mixture of kaolinite and montmorillonite can be determined much more readily, especially when the montmorillonite is saturated with calcium, because with both minerals the specific effects appear more prominently. The determination is more difficult if in addition to montmorillonite there is also illite, although the effect of illite at 600 °C and that of montmorillonite at 700 °C indicate the presence of these two minerals.

In the case of a mixture consisting of kaolinite, illite, and montmorillonite the determination of the presence of illite is not possible, because the first effect of illite is masked by that of montmorillonite, and the second effect of illite is masked by that of kaolinite.

5.8.5.11 General Conclusions on Thermal Behaviour of Argillaceous Minerals

The form and intensity of the thermal curves obtained on argillaceous minerals are much affected by the amorphous cover, by the disordered structures at the surface of the particles (the so-called Beilby layers), by the dimensional differences of the particles, by their degree of crystallinity and by the isomorphous substitutions in the crystal structure. As a consequence, a good quantitative determination of the concentration of argillaceous minerals in a given native sample by means of thermal methods is almost impossible. It was noticed that even pure kaolinite, obtained from well-studied deposits, presents thermal effects whose maxima vary by 100 to 176 °C or by 23 to 43 cal/g for the endothermic reaction at 600 °C and for the exothermic effect at about 980 °C. For other minerals, quantitative results may be obtained if the samples analysed were formed under the same natural conditions and only if the minerals show a similar chemical composition which are very rarely encountered in nature.

These conclusions were reached as a result of extended experiments and on the basis of analyses in which experimental errors were eliminated by strictly observing the experimental parameters outlined in Chapter 2. Some of these observations have been presented earlier in the discussion. Their enumeration is nevertheless necessary because they are strictly connected with the argillaceous minerals.

Particle dimensions of the mineral investigated. Many researchers have found that the finer the particles of the sample, the lower is the temperature at which the transformation takes place, and the smaller is the area of the thermal effects.

For example, quartz in the form of very small crystals (chalcedony) shows on X-ray investigation a perfect crystal structure, and its DTA curve shows only a negligible effect due to the passage from the α to the β form, unlike well-crystallized quartz, in which this effect is much better marked.

Obviously, the smaller the dimension of the crystals, the smaller are the forces required by the transformations which go on inside them. Even an elementary qualitative identification may be impossible with many minerals, owing to differences in the temperature peak of the thermal effect may be shifted by up to 200 °C, and the intensity of the effect may be much diminished.

Another difficulty which appears in the thermal analysis of these minerals comes from the fact that with the decreasing dimensions of the particles, the relative influence of the so-called amorphous or glassy Beilby layer increases with a detrimental influence on the thermal curves. This layer has physico-chemical properties very different from those of the crystallized material. Thus, it was noticed that by grinding kaolin in a ball mill for a very long time, the specific endothermic effect at 600 °C was almost completely suppressed, a fact which was confirmed also by X-ray investigations which have shown that these samples have a feeble crystal orientation. Hence the conclusion was drawn that by long-lasting grinding permutoid or amphoteric amorphous materials of the $Al(OH)_3$ and H_4SiO_4 type are formed, which coat the mineral particles with a thin layer with totally different physico-chemical properties from those of the initial minerals.

Degree of crystallization of the mineral under investigation. As could be seen also in the case of minerals of the kaolinite-halloysite group, the degree of crystallization exerts a notable influence on the shape of the thermal curves. It can readily be understood that a mineral with a high degree of crystallization should require more thermal energy for its passage to a new state than a more feebly crystallized one. As a rule, thermal curves obtained in the analysis of samples with a feeble crystallization present a thermal effect with a much more abrupt slope towards the end of the effect than at its beginning, whereas well-crystallized samples show approximately equal slopes.

If the shape coefficient of the thermal effect recorded on the DTA curve is determined by the ratio tan α/tan β (where α is the first part of the effect, and β is the final part of the effect) kaolinite may easily be distinguished from halloysite. This is a result of the fact that if the two tangents are equal, their ratio will be equal to unity, and in this case kaolinite is involved, whereas if the ratio is different from unity, halloysite is involved. This shape coefficient of a thermal effect may be applied to most minerals in order to infer the degree of crystallization.

Consequently, owing to some imperfections of the crystals rather than to their dimensions, thermal curves may appear completely asymmetrical.

Ion substitutions in the crystal lattice of the investigated mineral. Substitution of another ion for aluminium, magnesium or silicon in the lattice of a mineral modifies the temperatures and the shape of the thermal effects. It is known that the presence of iron as a substituting element in the lattice of argillaceous minerals greatly depresses the temperature of the thermal effects and changes their intensity.

Temperatures of thermal transformations are affected also by the way in which certain ions, and especially the OH groups, are bound. Thus, OH groups show different ways of bonding for example in talc, antigorite, and brucite, so that the endothermic effects appear at different temperatures, depending on the strength of the bond.

In the case of argillaceous minerals whose structural cell is of the 2:1 type, the thermal curves obtained can differ with regard to the temperature range in which the removal of the adsorbed water takes place. This is due to the predominating constituent in the octahedral layer. If aluminium predominates in this layer, then the adsorbed water is removed at lower temperatures than when the predominating constituent is magnesium.

Role of exchangeable cations in the minerals investigated. A number of authors have shown that the presence of exchangeable cations in some argillaceous minerals affects the form, shape and amplitude of the low-temperature thermal effects. The best example, in this sense, is montmorillonite in which the thermal effect due to the removal of the adsorbed water is different depending on the nature of the exchangeable cation. Figure 5.107 shows the DTA curves of montmorillonite

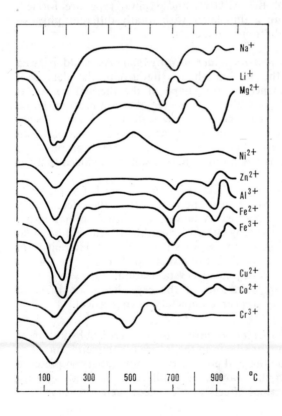

Figure 5.107   DTA curves of mont-morillonite saturated with various cations *(after Muksinov, Tadiev and Zakirov, 1968).*

saturated with various cations. These differences have been noticed also in the case of minerals of the vermiculite group, by Barschad (1948) and Arnes (1951). Both authors have shown that vermiculite minerals draw their leaflets closer when they are saturated with the cations K^+, NH_4^+, Rb^+, and Cs^+ and expel water molecules from between the strata when the mineral is saturated with Ca^{2+}, Mg^{2+} or Sr^{2+}.

Although it is thought that the activation energy made obvious by thermal curves is directly connected with the hydration of the exchange cation, it nevertheless depends also on the charge density between the layers. Thus, the cations which yield double thermal maxima in the case of vermiculite may give simple thermal maxima in the case of montmorillonites. Obviously, minerals which have a reduced cation exchange capacity, for example minerals from the kaolinite group, fail to manifest these influences on the thermal curves. When studying low temperature thermal effects one must not lose sight of the influences which the experimental conditions exert on them, because the reproducibility of the results is, to the highest degree, affected by experimental conditions at these low-temperatures.

When argillaceous minerals are investigated by thermal methods of analysis, experimental conditions are largely established depending on the nature of the investigation. In the case of research for the purpose of identifying the components which make up the sample analysed, it is imperative to strictly observe the experimental conditions, whereas for industrial purposes only the transformations which take place as a function of temperature will be followed up.

6

Applicability of Thermal Methods of Analysis for Investigating Complex Rocks

The study of simple minerals by thermal methods gives satisfactory results, but there is great difficulty in the interpretation of thermal curves in the case of complex rocks. This is due to the fact that some thermal effects, either of a physical or of a chemical nature, tend to exert a mutual influence particularly when their temperatures are not far apart. Certain specific thermal effects tend to be masked, leading to erroneous qualitative and quantitative interpretations.

Consequently, thermal analyses of complex rocks must be conducted according to a procedure adapted to the type of the rock analysed. A highly important fact in these cases is to establish right from the beginning the nature of the respective rock, as well as the group of minerals which must be identified. Although, at first sight, one might think that this is a very difficult thing to do, because each rock represents a case in itself, nevertheless, considering that rocks have arisen under specific conditions, according to well-defined laws, classifying them into specific types of rocks, they can be grouped very well by common procedures.

With complex rocks it is also necessary to make interpretations correlating the thermal data with analytical data obtained by other methods, especially with those derived from percentile chemical analyses. It is known that in any compound there is a close connection between the mineral components and the chemical composition. This connection is expressed by a number of chemical formulae equal to the number of minerals present in the association. As was shown in previous chapters, when only chemical data is used, the calculation may lead at most to a number of chemical compounds, without specifying what compound is involved. Using chemical data with that obtained by thermal methods, the composition of the respective compounds may be stated precisely, in most cases.

6.1 SALT ROCKS

Under this name are included rocks formed of chemically precipitated compounds produced by the bonding of halogens, and of the anion SO_4^{2+} with the cations Na^+, K^+, Mg^{2+}, and Ca^{2+}. For determining the composition of these rocks a procedure may be used which is based on the formulae quoted by Marcocevski and Petrow (1964), permitting the calculation from the data of the chemical analyses, the content of simple salts. From the scheme presented in Figure 6.1 it can be seen that by the combination of simple salts, a number of theoretically possible minerals may be reached. Although the number of minerals corresponding to each formula is large, in nature the association of minerals is much more limited. For example, according to the scheme, anhydrite and gypsum appear in all types of combinations, but in nature these minerals appear only at the periphery of salt deposits, and in the deposit they appear, at most, as impurities.

To illustrate these considerations, I shall show how chemical data are interpreted in correlation with those of thermal analyses for a sample coming from the Tazlău mine in Romania, whose chemical analysis is outlined in Table 6.1.

Table 6.1 **Percentage chemical composition expressed in grammes and milliequivalents of a sample coming from the Tazlău mine (Romania)**

	Content in %					
	SO_4^{2-}	Ca^{2+}	Mg^{2+}	K^+	Na^+	Cl^-
grammes	55.47	7.97	4.60	7.78	8.06	6.65
milliequivalents	1154.87	397.70	378.41	198.96	350.59	187.57

From the chemical data listed in Table 6.1 it follows that the type of mineralization which has generated this data is classified into the principal group *III*, subgroup *C* of the scheme in Figure 6.1, because the percentage contents of anions and cations, expressed in milliequivalents, corresponds to the following formula:

$$[\Sigma me_{SO_4^{2-}} - \Sigma me_{Ca^{2+}}] > [\Sigma me_{Mg^{2+}} + \Sigma me_{K^+}]$$

By calculating the content of simple salts from data listed in Table 6.1 by the procedure given below, the following salts will be arrived at: $CaSO_4$, $MgSO_4$, K_2SO_4, Na_2SO_4, and $NaCl$, but it is not possible to establish which are the mineral compounds.

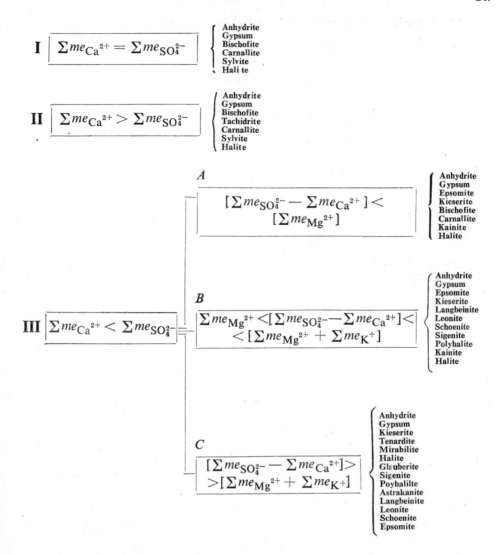

Figure 6.1 Scheme of the distribution of mineral compounds from salt deposits, derived from the ratio of the sum of milliequivalents[1] of the anion against the cations Ca^{2+}, Mg^{2+} and K^+. These sums of milliequivalents are calculated from the data of the percentile chemical analyses.

[1] Milliequivalent = Amount of anions or cations expressed in grammes, multiplied by 1000 and divided by the chemical equivalent. By chemical equivalent one understands the amount of an element, of a radical or of a compound which combines with or is substituted for an atom of hydrogen in the reaction considered. For elements, the chemical equivalent is given by the ratio between the atomic mass and the valency.

The following is an example of a calculation scheme:

1. $Ca^{2+} \dfrac{SO_4^{2-}}{Ca^{2+}} = 7.97 \times 2.3968 = 19.10 \ SO_{4(Ca)}^{2-}$

2. $Ca^{2+} + SO_{4(Ca)}^{2-} = 7.97 + 19.10 = 27.07 \ CaSO_4$

3. $Mg^{2+} \dfrac{SO_4^{2-}}{Mg^{2+}} = 4.60 \times 3.9512 = 18.17 \ SO_{4(Mg)}^{2-}$

4. $Mg_2^+ + SO_{4(Mg)}^{2-} = 4.60 + 18.17 = 22.77 \ MgSO_4$

5. $K^+ \dfrac{SO_4^{2-}}{2K^+} = 7.78 \times 1.2284 = 9.56 \ SO_{4(K)}^{2-}$

6. $K^+ + SO_{4(K)}^{2-} = 7.78 + 9.56 = 17.34 \ K_2SO_4$

7. $SO_{4(total)}^{2-} - [SO_{4(Ca)}^{2-} + SO_{4(Mg)}^{2-} + SO_{4(K)}^{2-}] = 8.64 \ SO_{4(Na)}^{2-}$

8. $SO_{4(Na)}^{2-} \dfrac{2Na^+}{SO_4^{2-}} = 8.64 \times 0.4787 = 4.13 \ Na_{(SO_4)}^+$

9. $SO_{4(Na)}^{2-} + Na_{(SO_4)}^+ = 8.64 + 4.13 = 12.77 \ Na_2SO_4$

10. $Na_{(total)}^+ - Na_{(SO_4)}^+ = 8.06 - 4.13 = 3.93 \ Na_{(Cl)}^+$

11. $Na^+ \dfrac{Cl^-}{Na^+} = 3.93 \times 1.5421 = 6.06 \ Cl_{(Na)}^-$

12. $Na_{(Cl)}^+ + Cl_{(Na)}^- = 3.93 + 6.06 = 9.99 \ NaCl$

(It will be noticed that the value calculated for the Cl^- ion is approximately equal to that determined chemically, 6.06 as compared to 6.65).

By closely examining the thermal curves obtained on the same sample (Figure 6.2) it will be noticed that from 150 to 300 °C we have two endothermic effects attended by a loss of mass which is the same both for the first and for the second effect. It follows that the mineral which has generated this loss of mass expels the water of crystallization in two steps, but each time in the same amount. By observing the previous scheme and data from the simple minerals, as well as chemical results of the simple salts, it can be seen that this mineral is astrakanite, $Na_2Mg(SO_4)_2.4H_2O$. With rising temperature another endothermic effect also appears at about 350 °C, likewise attended by a loss of mass. On the same grounds as before, the conclusion was arrived at that polyhalite, $K_2Ca_2Mg(SO_4)_4. 2H_2O$ is involved. DTG curves run smoothly , indicating no change, whereas the DTA curve shows a further endothermic effect caused by melting of the mixture.

By adding the loss of mass due to the removal of the water of crystallization with the components calculated from chemical data the following mineralogical composition of the sample analysed is arrived at: astrakanite 30 per cent, polyhalite 60 per cent, and halite 10 per cent.

Figure 6.2 Thermal curves of a sample of salts from the deposit at Tazlău (Romania).

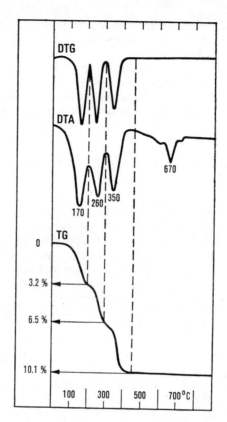

6.2 COMPLEX SULPHATE ROCKS

În general, alkaline and alkaline-earth sulphates, except gypsum, as well as the sulphates of heavy metals which are found in sedimentary rocks, are water soluble. The other minerals present besides the sulphates are practically insoluble. For sulphate rocks, a first thermal analysis giving the thermal effects both of the sulphates and of the other minerals. A second analysis is then carried out, this time on the sample from which the soluble sulphates had been completely removed by washing out with water. The thermal curves which are now obtained give indications as to the nature of the minerals present besides the sulphates. The thermal curves would also show the presence of gypsum. For quantitative determinations of the soluble sulphates, the procedure is as follows. A known amount of sample is dissolved in a known volume of water. From the resulting solution an aliquot is taken for chemical analyses, and the remainder is evaporated down to a small volume, after which it is allowed to rest at room temperature for recrystallization of the salts. A new thermal determination is now carried out on the recrystallized salts.

The thermal curves obtained on the raw sample, on the sample from which the sulphates were removed, as well as on the recrystallized salts, are processed together with the data of the percentile chemical analyses, and in this way a knowledge of the composition of the minerals marking up the rock will be obtained.

6.3 CARBONATE ROCKS

To the group of carbonate rocks belong calcars, marls, and dolomites. The determination of the composition of these rocks by thermal methods of analysis is comparatively simple because, as it was seen, carbonates decompose at well-defined temperatures, and the minerals with which they are found in association do not generally interfere with the effects, or if they do interfere then they can be removed much more readily than in other cases.

The easiest way is to analyse thermally the raw sample, and then the sample remaining after the removal of the carbonates by treatment with an acid, in most cases with dilute acetic or hydrochloric acid. For example, Figure 6.3 shows the thermal curves of a dolomitic marl; the curves from the upper part of the figure were produced by heating the raw sample, and the curves from the lower part of the figure were obtained by heating the sample after the carbonates had been removed.

The way in which the quantitative interpretations are made in these cases has been presented in one of my previous works (Todor, 1967) on the determination of calcite and dolomite in carbonate soil. Briefly, these interpretations start from the thermal curves obtained by the procedure described above.

If on the thermal curves obtained it is possible to determine precisely the loss of mass corresponding to the carbon dioxide released in the decomposition of carbonates under the action of the thermal energy, then the quantitative interpretation of the carbonate content will be made as shown at the end of Chapter 2.

In the case where on the thermal curves obtained on the raw sample it is not possible to make a precise distinction of the loss of mass due to carbon dioxide released from carbonates, because this effect overlaps the thermal effects of other minerals, then the carbon dioxide released from carbonates has to be determined by another analytical method. When from the thermal curves it follows that only one carbonate is present in the sample analysed, then the whole amount of carbon dioxide determined corresponds to this carbonate, and if from the thermal curves it follows that several carbonates are present in the sample, then determinations can be made with good results, establishing the total loss of mass by thermal methods, and determining the amount of carbon dioxide by another method. This operating procedure gives good results in the analysis both of carbonate soils, and of marls and complex carbonate rocks, where besides the type of the carbonate it is necessary to determine the associated minerals.

Figure 6.3 Thermal curves of a dolomitic marl obtained on the sample as such, and after it was treated with HCl for the removal of carbonates.

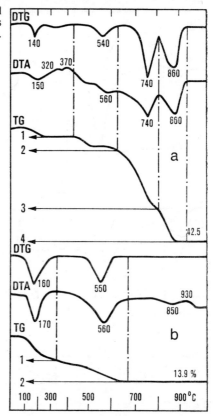

In concluding this description of the procedure for the determination of carbonates and of the associated minerals, some comments are presented on the action of the acid on these minerals. This is necessary, because in the specialised literature contradictory opinions are expressed as to whether the acid has an effect on the structure of argillaceous minerals or not. I have found that from the viewpoint of the results obtained by thermal methods, the attack with acids has no influence on the argillaceous minerals from the kaolinite, montmorillonite and illite groups. Figures 6.4 and 6.5 illustrate the thermal curves of kaolinite, and those of montmorillonite, both treated and not treated with a solution of dilutes hydrochloric acid. When the argillaceous minerals belong to the groups of chlorite and vermiculites, the acid attack has a notable influence.

In the other types of complex rocks, the operating procedure is analogous to that for simple compounds, and in some cases a procedure analogous to that related above may be applied. The starting point in each separate case is represented by the thermal curves obtained on the raw rock. In some cases, very good results

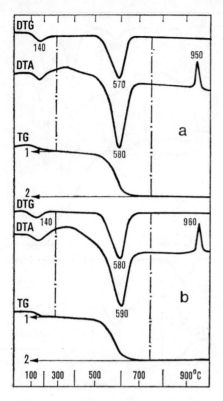

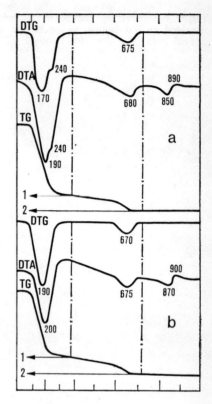

Figure 6.4   Thermal curves of a
           kaolinite sample:

a, not treated with acid; *b*, treated with HCl.

Figure 6.5 Thermal curves of a sample
     of montmorillonite   saturated   with
                     bivalent ions:

a, not treated with acid; *b*, treated with HCl.

were obtained by separating some fractions from the sample by different methods, for example by sedimentation in water or in other liquids with different densities, by magnetic separation or simply by manual separation by means of a pair of pincers or of a needle.

In concluding, it can be said that thermal methods of analysis have an almost unlimited sphere of application, for analysing minerals. Although their level of precision is below other kinds of chemical or physical analyses, some determinations and interpretations can be made only with their help.

REFERENCES

1. ARENS P. L., A study on the differential Thermal Analysis of Clays and Clay Minerals. *Wegeningen, Netherlands,* 1951.
2. BARSHAD J., Differential thermal analysis of vermiculite. *Amer. Min.,* **33,** 1948, 655.
3. BARSHAD J., Calibration of DTA apparatus. *Amer. Min.,* **37,** 1952, 667.
4. BARCHARDS J. H., Initial reaction rates from a DTA. *J. Inorg. Nuclear Chem.,* **12,** 1960, 252.
5. BECK C., Differential thermal analysis curves of carbonate minerals. *Amer. Min.,* **35,** 1950, №. 11—12.
6. BERG L. G. and EGUNOV V. P., Quantitative differential thermal analysis I (Mathematical problems of quantitative thermal analysis). *J. Thermal Anal.,* **1,** 1969, 5.
7. BERG L. G. and SAIBOVA M. T., Physico-chemical investigation of some crystal hydrates. *Uzbek. Chem. J.,* **6,** 1962, 54.
8. BETEHTIN G. A., Curs de Mineralogie (Lectures on Mineralogy.) *Editura tehnică, Bucharest (Technical Publishing House,* tr. from Russian, 1953).
9. BOERSMA S. L., Theory of differential thermal analysis and new methods of measurement and interpretation. *J. Am. Ceram. Soc.,* **38,** 1955, 281; *Ceram. Abstr.,* **17,** 170.
10. BRANDLEY W. F. and GRIM R. E., High-temperature effects of clay and related minerals. *Amer. Min.,* **36,** 1951, 182.
11. CAILLÈRE S. and POBEGUIE T., Contribution à l'étude des carbonates simples anhydres. *Bull. Soc. Franç. Minéral. et Cristallogr.,* **83,** 1960, No. 1.
12. CARTHEW A. R., Quantitative estimation of kaolinite by DTA. *Amer. Min.,* **40,** 1955, 107.
13. COCCO C., Carbonati basici di rame e zinco. *Period. Mineral. Roma,* **20,** 1951, No. 1.
14. COCCO C., Differential thermal analysis of some sulphate minerals. *Period. Mineral. Roma,* **21,** 1952, No. 1.
15. DEB B. C., Estimation and removal of free iron oxides. *J. Soil Sci.,* **1,** 1950, 212.
16. DUVAL C., Inorganic Thermogravimetric Analysis. *Elsevier Publishing Co.,* Amsterdam, 1963.
17. DUVAL C., L'évolution des méthodes thermoanalytiques depuis Le Châtelier jusqu'au 3e Congrès de l'ICTA. Nomenclature actuelle. *Chimie Analytique,* **54,** 1972, 132.
18. ERDEY L., PAULIK F. and PAULIK J., Differential thermogravimetry. *Nature,* **174,** 1954, 885.
19. ERDEY L., PAULIK F. and PAULIK J., Standardization of experimental conditions used for thermal analyses. *Anal. Chim. Acta,* **34,** 1966, No. 4, 419.
20. EYRAUD C. and GOTON R., Theoretical and experimental consideration in differential heat analysis. *Comp. rend.,* **240,** 1955, 423.
21. FAUST G. T., Huntite, $Mg_3Ca(CO_3)_4$, a new mineral. *Amer. Min.,* **38,** 1953, No. 1—2.
22. FÖDVARI V. M., The role of differential thermal analysis in mineralogy and geological prospecting. *Acta Geol. Tom. V, Fasc. 1, Budapest,* 1958.
23. FÖDVARI V. M. and KOBLENEZ V., Factors in the thermal decomposition of dolomite. *Acta Geol. Acta Sci. Hung.,* **3,** 1955, 15.
24. GLOESER R. and MERING J., Le rôle de la valence des cations échangeables dans l'héctorite. *C. R. Acad. Sci. Paris,* **246,** 1958, 1569.

25. GOD G. M., Thermochemical changes in alunite and alunite clays. *J. Am. Ceram. Soc.*, **33**, 1950, 208; *Ceram. Abstr.*, 145.
26. GRAF L. D., DTA of low-iron dolomites. *Amer. Min.*, **37**, 1952, 1.
27. GRIM R. E., Clay mineralogy. McGraw-Hill, London, 1953.
28. GRIM R. E., Applied clay mineralogy. McGraw-Hill, London, 1962.
29. GRIM R. E., Etude aux rayons X, des réactions des minéraux argileux à hautes températures. *Bull. Soc. Franç. Ceram.*, **36**, 1957, 21.
30. GRIM R. E. and KULBICK G., Montmorillonite: high-temperature reactions and classifications. *Amer. Min.*, **46**, 1961, 1239.
31. GRIM R. E. and ROWLAND R. A., DTA of clay minerals, etc. *Amer. Min.*, **27**, 1942, 746 and 801.
32. GRIMSHOW R. W. and ROBERTS A. L., The quantitative determination of some minerals in ceramic materials by thermal means. *Trans. Brit. Ceram. Soc.*, **52**, 1953, No. 1, 50.
33. GRUVER R. M., DTA of ceramic materials I and II. *J. Am. Ceram. Soc.*, **33**, 1950, 96 and 171.
34. GRUZ-ERDEY T. and SCHOY G., Theoretical Physical Chemistry. Technical Publishing House, Bucharest (transl. from Hungarian), 1957.
35. HOFFMANN U., KOCH G. and WEISS A., Saponites. *Ceram. Abstr.*, **131**, 1955.
36. HOROWITZ H. H. and METZGER G., The thermal dissociation of minerals. *Analyt. Chem.*, **31**, 1963, 1464.
37. IVANOVA V. P., Thermal diagrams of minerals. *Zapiskj vsesoiuz mineral obshcestva*, **90**, 1961, 50.
38. KERR P. F. and KULP J., Differential thermal analysis of siderite. *Amer. Min.*, **32**, 1947, No. 11—12.
39. KEYSER W. L., Differential thermobalance. *Nature*, **172**, 1953, 1364.
40. KISSINGER H. E., Reaction kinetics in differential thermal analysis. *Amer. Min.*, **32**, 1957, No. 11—12.
41. KOBLENNEZ V. and TOLNAY V., The thermal dissociation of ankerite. *Magyar Allami. Föld. Int. Evi. Jelentése*, 1957—1958.
42. KÖHLER A. and WEDEN P., DTA of felspars. *Neues Jb. Miner. Mh.*, 1954, 249.
43. KRÄUTNER M., Identification criteria of serpentine minerals by means of differential thermal analysis. *Stud. Cerc. Geol. Acad. RPR*, 1958, 281.
44. KULP J. L., KENT P. and KERR P. F., Thermal study of the Ca—Mg—Fe carbonate minerals. *Amer. Min.*, **36**, 1951, No. 9—10.
45. KURYLENKO C., DTA of tourmaline. *Bull. Soc. Franç. Miner.*, **73**, 1950, 49.
46. LUKASZEWSKI M. G. Differential thermal analysis. *Laboratory Practice*, **14**, 1965, No. 11, 1277; **14**, 1965, No. 12, 1399; **15**, 1966, No. 1—2, 82, 187; **15**, 1966, No. 3—4, 302 and 438; **15**, 1966, No. 5, 551; **15**, 1966, No. 7, 762; **15**, 1966; No. 7, 762; **15**, 1966, No. 8, 861.
47. LÓRÁNT B., Derivatographic investigation of the sulphates, separation of the water of crystallization, and thermal decomposition. *Z. Analyst. Chem.*, **3**, 1966, No. 219, 256.
48. LUCAS J., and TRANTH N., Study of the high-temperature behaviour of montmorillonite *Bull. Serv. Cart. Géologique de l'Alsace Lorraine*, **18**, 1965, 4.
49. MARCOCEVSKI I. V. and PETROV E. M., Salt Solutions and Salts Analysis Methods. Chimia Publ. House, Moskow—Leningrad, 1964.
50. MABEL H. W. der VON, Quantitative differential thermal analysis of clay and other minerals. *Amer. Min.*, **41**, 1956, No. 3—4.
51. MAULY R. L., DTA of certain phosphates. *Amer. Min.*, **35**, 1950, 108.
52. MACKENZIE R. C., The differential thermal investigation of clays. *Mineralogical Society*. London, 1957.
53. MACKENZIE R. C. and FARQUHARSON K. R., Standardization of DTA technique. *C. R. XIX Congr. Géol. Int. Alger*, **18**, 1952, 183.
54. MUKSINOV T. K., TADGIEV F. C. and ZAKIROV M. S., The study of the influence of exchange cations on the processes taking place in montmorillonite on heating. *Proceedings of symposium Alma-Ata Kaz. SSR*, 1968, 46.

55. MURGULESCU I. G. and SEGAL E., Kinetic study of heterogeneous reactions by means of thermogravimetric data. *St. Cerc. Chim.* Tom., **15**, 1967, No. 4, 261.

56. MURGULESCU I. G., FĂTU D. and SEGAL E., Contributions à l'étude cinétique des decompositions endothermiques dans des systèmes solide-gaz, à l'aide des données thermogravimétriques *J. Thermal Anal.*, **1**, 1969, 97.

57. MURRAY P., Structural variations of some kaolinites in relation to dehydrated halloysite. *Amer. Min.*, **39**, 1954, 93.

58. NGUYEN-BA-CHANH and BASTIDE J. P., Etude par microanalyse thermique differentielle du système NaCl-KCl. *J. Chim. Phy.* Tom., **65**, 1968, No. 7—8.

59. OSTROFF A. G. and SANDERSON R. T., Thermal stability of some metal sulphates. *J. Inorg. and Nuclear Chem.*, **9**, 1958, 45.

60. PARMELEE C. W. and RODRIGUEZ A. R., Catalytic mullitization of kaolinite. *J. Amer. Ceram. Soc.*, **25**, 1942, 1.

61. PAPIU C. V., Petrography of Sedimentary Rocks. Scientific Publishing House, Bucharest, 1960.

62. PAULIK F., PAULIK J. and ERDEY L., Die Derivatographie. *Z. Analyt. Chem.*, **3**, 1958, No. 4, 1 and 160.

63. PAULIK F., PAULIK J. and ERDEY L., Determination of the pyrites content of bauxites by thermal methods. *Anal. Chim. Acta*, **29**, 1963, No. 5, 381.

64. PILOJAN G. O., Introduction into the Theory of Thermal Analysis. Nauk. Publ. House, Moskow, 1964.

65. POPA GR. and TODOR N. D., Determination of the siderite and ankerite content by thermal analysis methods. *Revue Roum. de Chimie*, **15**, 1970, 589.

66. POPA GR. and TODOR N. D., Determination of manganocalcites and of manganodolomites by thermal methods. *Revista de chimie analitică*, **1**, 1971, 37.

67. POPA GR. and TODOR N. D., L'étude des alunites à l'aide des méthodes thermiques. *Revue Roum. de chimie*, **16**, 1971, 381.

68. POPA GR. and TODOR N. D., A study of the thermal transformation effects of magnesium carbonates with a view to their determination. *Third nat. anal. chem. conf.*, Braşov, (Roumania), 1971, Tome IV.

69. POPA GR. and TODOR N. D., Thermoanalytic determination of native copper and iron sulphates of the oxidized pyrites and chalcopyrites deposits. *A. R. cong. anal. chem.* Kyoto — Japan, 1972, 11.

70. REY M. and KOSTOMAROF V., Interpretation physico-chimique de l'analyse thermique differentielle. *Silicates Ind.*, **24**, 1959, 603.

71. ROY R. Decomposition and resynthesis of micas *J. Amer. Ceram. Soc.* **32**, 1942, 202.

72. SABATIER G., Determination of the heats of transformation by differential thermal analysis. *Bull. Soc. Fr. Miner.*, **77**, 1954, 953.

73. SAGORODSKIJ G. D., Koliciestvennoe opredelenie mineralov v porodah metodom termografii. *Ukrainskij chem. journ.* 1953, No. 2.

74. SOULE J. L., Quantitative interpretation of differential thermal analysis. *J. Phys. Radium.* **13**, 1952, 516.

75. SCHEAMLI W. and BECKER F., A comparison of the differential thermal analysis of some minerals and some soils in air and in vacuum. *Ceram. Abstr.*, 184, 1961.

76. SMOTHERS W. J. and YAO-CHIANG M. S., Handbook of Differential Thermal Analysis. Chemical Publ. Co. Inc., New York, 1966.

77. TIVODOR K., Derivatographic examination of bauxite minerals. *Geologie*, Berlin, 1964, No. 2.

78. TODOR N. D., Determination of mineralogic composition of soil carbonates by thermal methods. *Papers of National Soil Science Conf. Eforie* (Romania), 1967, No. 4A.

79. TODOR N. D., Physical Analysis Methods in Analytical Chemistry. (In Romanian). C.D.I.C.P., Bucureşti, 1970, Vol. 1.

80. TODOR N. D., Survey of thermal analysis methods and recommendations on data communication. (In Romanian). *Revista de chimie*, **24**, 1973, No. 10, 822.
81. TODOR N. D., Corrélation entre la réaction Meigen et les phénomènes thermiques pour la détermination des aragonites. *Colloque National de Spéologie "Emile Racovitza"*, Bucureşti — Cluj (Romania), 1971, 615.
82. TODOR N. D., Definition of the composition of oil bearing rocks by thermal methods after separation of the bituminous materials (In Romanian). *Third National Conference of Analytical Chemistry*, Braşov, 1971, Tome 4.
83. TOPOR D. N., Differential Thermal and Thermogravimetric Analysis of Minerals. Nedra Publ. House, Moskow, 1964.
84. TREIBER I., Processing of Mineralogic and Petrographic Materials. (In Romanian). Didactic and Pedagogical Publishing House, Bucharest, 1967.
85. WARNE S. J. and BAYLISS P., The differential thermal analysis of cerussite. *Amer. Min.*, **47**, 1962, No. 9—10.
86. WITTELS M., Structural changes in amphiboles I. *Amer. Min.*, **36**, 1951, 851.
87. WITTELS M., Structural changes in amphiboles II. *Amer. Min.*, **37**, 1952, 28.